BASIC STATISTICAL CONCEPTS

BASIC STATISTICAL CONCEPTS

Joe Kennedy Adams

Assistant Professor of Psychology
Bryn Mawr College

McGRAW-HILL BOOK COMPANY, INC.

New York   Toronto   London

1955

BASIC STATISTICAL CONCEPTS

Library of Congress Catalog Card Number 55-5681

THE MAPLE PRESS COMPANY, YORK, PA.

To Pauline

PREFACE

This book is intended primarily as a text for a one- or two-semester course for students who have had little or no previous calculus or statistics. It has two main purposes:

1. To develop some basic mathematico-logical concepts of statistics, particularly the logic of statistical inference.

2. To develop an understanding of the language used in mathematical statistics, including elementary calculus. It is assumed that understanding must include some facility in reading compact mathematical expressions and in applying mathematical theorems to empirical problems without extended explanations of what the theorems mean.

This approach is based on the premise that the college student, whether oriented toward applications or toward mathematics, can best spend his time and energy in a first course in statistics in mastering some of the abstract concepts, i.e., mathematical models, and some of the mathematical language of the field. Because of the stress on abstract definitions and mathematical models, applications have for the most part been subordinated; in many cases examples and exercises have deliberately been made trivial so as not to detract from the abstract structure. All data in this text are hypothetical, though many of them are characteristic of those actually obtained. Ideally, genuine data on genuine problems should be presented, and I admire the thoroughness with which some authors have done this, but on the other hand genuine data involve technicalities of special fields, especially since, to do justice to the data and to avoid overgeneralizations, the specific conditions under which actual data were obtained should be presented. It was thought worthwhile to avoid these technicalities; however, many of the types of problems to which statistical applications have been made are clearly indicated.

The sequence of the book is as follows: An attempt is made to get the student to build up a precise understanding of what is meant by "expected sampling distribution of a statistic" (later the word "expected" is dropped) at as early a stage as possible. It was believed that the best way to accomplish this was first to introduce combinatorial theorems and exercises, so that the student would be able to work out some simple sampling distributions for himself. The third chapter, on statistical inference, which is the most important one in the book, presents the concepts of expected sampling distribution, testing of hypotheses, confidence intervals, and power of a test *without introducing other than finite populations;* it seemed to the author that the student can best understand these concepts without having to be concerned with infinity, continuity, density, or the normal curve. In this feature the book was unique at the time of writing, but since that time another text incorporating essentially this same feature has been published.

Definitions which are often given only implicitly (e.g., population, distribution, discrete) are made explicit, and for this purpose I have utilized a common concept of mathematical logic, that of a class of ordered pairs. The introduction of this concept may appear slightly pedantic, but it seemed justified by its simplicity and precision.

No attempt is made to give the student an understanding of the problems involved in a rigorous empirical definition of "random sample"; errors in application do not lie at this level.

Not until the student has already been introduced to most of the concepts peculiar to statistics is the topic of continuous distributions introduced. At this point I have attempted to present the fundamental concepts of the calculus—limit, derivative, and integral. It is admittedly radical to take the position that these concepts can be learned by the student as an incidental part of a course in statistics; however, most teachers who are shocked at the idea of requiring their students to learn a little of the calculus seem to overlook the fact that most courses in calculus spend most of the course on *techniques* of differentiation and integration and on particular kinds of applications rather than on the fundamental concepts. Any student who has the intelligence necessary to understand the subtle concepts of statistical inference can certainly understand those of elementary calculus.

With the concepts and language of elementary calculus available it is then easy to present discussions of the normal, t, and χ^2 distributions. Regression and correlation are discussed in the context of bivariate distributions. Analysis of variance is introduced, but no attempt is made to go into the many complexities of this topic. The concluding chapter is a short one on nonparametric statistics.

Beginning with the chapter on normal distributions, it is necessary to state many theorems without proving them. I must apologize for the rather tiresome repetition of "we state without proof," but I wanted the student to be reasonably clear about what he is expected to take on faith. For those with a background in calculus many proofs are presented in the Appendix; for the convenience of teachers other proofs, given usually by Cramér, Hoel, Mood, or Wilks are referred to in footnotes.

The book becomes increasingly compact in the language used and often leaves out details which should be filled in by the student, who will find it essential to do a considerable number of the exercises as he reads the book.

In the last chapter there are almost no examples, and this chapter can perhaps be used as one test of whether the student has learned to understand simple mathematical language.

A brief development of elementary calculus and an introduction to mathematical statistics precedes the proofs in the Appendix. I doubt that those having no previous calculus will be able to follow the subsequent proofs on the basis of the Appendix alone, but this development may be helpful as a review and it may be useful to teachers with heterogeneous classes who want to supplement the body of the text. In particular, it may be desirable or even necessary to supplement the introduction to calculus given so briefly in Chap. 8.

It is with considerable humility that the author, who is not a mathematician, offers a text that has as its purpose the presentation of some basic mathematical concepts; it is hoped that it will be found reasonably adequate both by those nonmathematicians for whom it was primarily written and also by mathematicians interested in how well those outside their field understand it.

There are many to whom I am indebted. Among these are D. A. Grant, with whom I first studied statistics and who aroused my interest in the subject, Harold Gulliksen, and S. S. Wilks, with whom I did further study. Not being a mathematician, I have drawn considerably from other authors, particularly S. S. Wilks, Harald Cramér, A. M. Mood, and P. G. Hoel, and, in the calculus, Richard Courant. I hope that at no point I have stepped over the boundary of plagiarism, but in mathematics it is difficult to know just where that boundary is. Professor Wilks was kind enough to look over part of my manuscript and to make some helpful comments, pro and con my point of view. I am also indebted to Harold Freeman, who made numerous helpful criticisms and suggestions.

Grateful acknowledgment is made also to Catherine Thompson and Maxine Merrington, and to E. S. Pearson, editor of *Biometrika,* for permission to include Tables D.3 and D.5, which are abridged versions of tables published in *Biometrika.* I am indebted to Professor Sir Ronald A. Fisher, Cambridge, to Dr. Frank Yates, Rothamsted, and to Messrs. Oliver & Boyd, Ltd., Edinburgh, for permission to reprint Table D.4, which is an abridgment from their book, *Statistical tables for use in biological, agricultural, and medical research;* to A. M. Mood, for permission to reprint from his book, *Introduction to the theory of statistics,* the tables referred to above, which Professor Mood abridged; to W. J. Dixon and F. J. Massey, for permission to reprint Fig. 11.1.1 and Tables D.3, D.6, and D.7 from their book, *Introduction to statistical analysis;* to Frieda S. Swed and C. Eisenhart and to the editor of the *Annals of Mathematical Statistics* for permission to reprint Table D.7, which first appeared in the *Annals;* to J. P. Guilford, for permission to reprint Tables C.2, C.4, and C.5 from his book, *Fundamental statistics in psychology and education;* to Professor Sir Ronald A. Fisher and Messrs. Oliver & Boyd, Ltd., Edinburgh, for permission to reprint Table C.5, derived (by Guilford) from *Statistical methods for research workers;* to H. Sorenson for permission to reprint Table C.1 from *Statistics for students of psychology and education;* and to Frank Wilcoxon and the American Cyanamid Company for permission to reprint Table D.8 from *Some rapid approximate statistical procedures.*

My greatest debt is to my wife, Pauline Austin Adams, without whose tremendous aid and encouragement this manuscript might never have been completed.

JOE KENNEDY ADAMS

CONTENTS

PREFACE vii

CHAPTER 1. FINITE POPULATIONS AND THEIR DISTRIBUTIONS 1

  1.1. Problems dealt with by statistics 1
  1.2. Sets and values. 2
  1.3. Populations. 3
  1.4. Frequency functions of finite populations 5
  1.5. Cumulative distribution functions of finite populations 6
  1.6. Graphic methods of showing distributions 7
  1.7. Some simple problems involving distributions 7
  1.8. Some combinatorial considerations 11

CHAPTER 2. SAMPLING FROM A FINITE POPULATION 17

  2.1. Expected sampling distributions 17
  2.2. Random sampling 18
  2.3. Probability 21
  2.4. The calculus of probabilities 25

CHAPTER 3. STATISTICAL INFERENCE 30

  3.1. Expected sampling distributions yielded by different hypotheses . 30
  3.2. Testing hypotheses about the population 32
  3.3. Confidence intervals 36
  3.4. Power of a test. 37
  3.5. Increasing the power of a test by increasing the number of obser-
      vations 38
  3.6. A word of caution 41
  3.7. The logic of statistical inference 41
  3.8. Two types of error. 45
  3.9. Confidence intervals with one bound only 47

CHAPTER 4. PARAMETERS AND STATISTICS 50

  4.1. Definitions 50
  4.2. Measures of central tendency. 50
  4.3. Measures of variability 52
  4.4. Abbreviations 55
  4.5. Moments 57

4.6. Computation of moments. 57
4.7. Transformations of values for computational purposes 59
4.8. Grouping of data into class intervals 61

CHAPTER 5. HYPERGEOMETRIC AND BINOMIAL DISTRIBUTIONS 64

5.1. Hypergeometric distributions. 64
5.2. Moments of a hypergeometric distribution 64
5.3. Binomial distributions. 65
5.4. Moments of a binomial distribution. 67
5.5. Binomial as limit of hypergeometric. 70
5.6. Fitting a binomial to sample data 73

CHAPTER 6. POISSON DISTRIBUTIONS 75

6.1. A Poisson as an approximation to a binomial 75
6.2. Computation of a Poisson 78
6.3. Definition 78
6.4. Moments of a Poisson distribution 78
6.5. Poisson distributions as exact 80

CHAPTER 7. DISCRETE DISTRIBUTIONS 82

7.1. Definition 82
7.2. The logic of statistical inference for discrete distributions . . . 83

CHAPTER 8. CONTINUOUS DISTRIBUTIONS 84

8.1. Continuous populations 84
8.2. Proportion density. 84
8.3. Continuous distributions 88
8.4. Definite integrals 90
8.5. Indefinite integrals. 92
8.6. A physical model for distributions 94
8.7. Moments of continuous distributions 94

CHAPTER 9. NORMAL DISTRIBUTIONS 96

9.1. A normal distribution as an approximation to a binomial distribution 96
9.2. Definition of normal distributions 98
9.3. Moments of normal distributions 100
9.4. The special case $c\ (= \mu) = 0$ and $k\ (= \sigma) = 1$ 102
9.5. Tests of hypotheses and confidence intervals 105
9.6. The central-limit theorem. 110
9.7. Confidence interval for a mean of a nonnormal population . . . 113
9.8. Difference between two independent normally distributed variates . 116
9.9. Fitting a normal distribution to a sample 121

CHAPTER 10. CHI SQUARE. 123

10.1. Definition of chi square 123
10.2. Goodness of fit when the hypothetical distribution is completely
specified. 124
10.3. Goodness of fit when the hypothetical distribution is incompletely
specified. 130

10.4. Test of independence in a contingency table 133
10.5. Tests of homogeneity 138
10.6. Test for variance of a normal population 141

CHAPTER 11. "STUDENT'S" t DISTRIBUTIONS 143

11.1. Definition of t_n and the distribution of t_n 143
11.2. Testing hypotheses about population means and finding confidence
intervals with small samples from normal populations with unknown
variances 145
11.3. A criterion for the discarding of exceptional observations and the
testing of a difference between the mean of a subsample and the mean
of the sample 150

CHAPTER 12. BIVARIATE DISTRIBUTIONS 152

12.1. Definition and properties of bivariate distributions 152
12.2. Regression 157
12.3. Linear regression 162
12.4. The correlation ratio 168
12.5. The sampling distribution of r 170
12.6. The scatter plot 173
12.7. Computation of r 175

CHAPTER 13. F DISTRIBUTIONS AND THE ANALYSIS OF VARIANCE . . . 180

13.1. Definition of F 180
13.2. Distribution of F 180
13.3. The ratio of unbiased estimates of two population variances. . . 181
13.4. The special case $\sigma_1^2 = \sigma_2^2$ 182
13.5. The special case $\mu_1 = \mu_2$; $\sigma_1^2 = \sigma_2^2$ 183
13.6. The case of several groups 185
13.7. The partition of a sample into k groups 191
13.8. The double partition of a sample 194
13.9. Computation of sums of squares 201

CHAPTER 14. NONPARAMETRIC STATISTICS 204

14.1. Definition 204
14.2. The sign test 204
14.3. The run test 205
14.4. Tolerance limits 206
14.5. Order statistics 207
14.6. Confidence intervals for percentile points 208
14.7. Wilcoxon's matched-pairs signed-ranks test 209

REFERENCES 213

APPENDIX A. SOME HINTS ON HOW TO ASK QUESTIONS OF MATHEMATICAL
STATISTICIANS 217

APPENDIX B. MATHEMATICAL APPENDIX 219

B.1. Limit of a sequence 219
B.2. Limit of a series 220

B.3. Continuous functions 222
B.4. The definite integral 223
B.5. The derivative. 224
B.6. Primitive functions 230
B.7. Indefinite integrals 231
B.8. Fundamental theorem of the calculus 231
B.9. Distribution functions (continuous case) 232
B.10. Mathematical expectation 233
B.11. Power series 234
B.12. Moment-generating functions 235
B.13. Change of variable 236
B.14. Multiple integration 237
B.15. Joint distributions of random variables. 240
B.16. Expectation of sample moments about the origin. 242
B.17. Mean and variance of the sum of independent random variables . 243
B.18. The law of large numbers 243
B.19. Tchebysheff's inequality 244
B.20. Expectation of the sample variance. 245
B.21. Properties of normal distributions 245
B.22. Properties of chi-square distributions 249
B.23. The distribution of t_n 250
B.24. The distribution of $F_{m,n}$ 251
B.25. The linear mean regression line 252
B.26. Bivariate normal distributions 252

APPENDIX C.   MISCELLANEOUS TABLES 255

C.1. Squares and square roots of numbers from 1 to 1,000 256
C.2. Four-place common logarithms of numbers (base 10) 269
C.3. Natural logarithms (base e) 271
C.4. Trigonometric functions 272
C.5. Transformation of r to z (and ρ to ξ) 273
C.6. Derivatives. 274
C.7. Primitive functions (indefinite integrals) 275

APPENDIX D.   TABLES OF SAMPLING DISTRIBUTIONS 277

D.1. Ordinates of the normal density function with zero mean and unit
     variance 278
D.2. Cumulative normal distributions 279
D.3. Cumulative chi-square distributions 280
D.4. Cumulative t distributions 281
D.5. Cumulative F distributions 282
D.6. Critical values of r for sign test 284
D.7. Confidence limits for number of runs 285
D.8. Probabilities for Wilcoxon's matched-pairs signed-ranks test . . 288

GLOSSARY. 289

ANSWERS TO ODD-NUMBERED EXERCISES 290

INDEX. 299

BASIC STATISTICAL CONCEPTS

Chapter 1

FINITE POPULATIONS AND
THEIR DISTRIBUTIONS

1.1. Problems Dealt with by Statistics. Statistics deals with the following kinds of problems:

1. *The Descriptive Problem.* A set of observations or conceivable observations is often conceptually unwieldy; it is necessary to organize and condense such a set into an understandable and convenient form. This kind of problem ranges from very simple ones, such as that presented by a set of 1,000 intelligence-test scores from 1,000 different individuals under conditions as nearly constant as possible, to extremely complex problems, such as that presented by a set of 20 different measures on each of 1,000 different subjects, in a situation in which we are interested in the interrelations among the 20 measures.

2. *The Problem of Inference.* We may start with a set of well-defined conditions under which we can make observations and try to infer what observations we should expect under these conditions, or, on the other hand, we may start with a set of observations and wish to infer what the conditions were which led to that set of observations. For example, we may start with a group of people comprised of 7,000 Republicans and 10,000 non-Republicans and try to infer what to expect (approximately, that is, within certain limits) if we should draw a group of 100 people at random from this total group of 17,000; or, conversely, we may draw a group of 100 people at random from a total group of 17,000 of unknown composition, observe that 40 are Republicans, and try to infer the total number of Republicans (approximately, that is, within certain limits) in the group

1

of 17,000. These problems of inference, like the problems of description, range from a fairly simple level to a very complex level; however, even on the simple level the concepts involved are rather subtle and merit careful and prolonged study.

It is with the second kind of problem that we shall be primarily concerned; however, the two kinds of problems are by no means entirely separate from each other.

1.2. Sets and Values. Almost any object can be classified in many different ways. (The word "object" is used to refer not only to material objects but also to conceptual entities such as numbers and geometrical forms, and also to such entities as families, pairs of genes, specimens, bacterial colonies, insurance policies, perceptions, experimental procedures, sets or sequences of observations, etc.) For example, we can classify people according to age, sex, marital status, height, weight, race, color of eyes, score on a certain test, etc., and we can classify positive integers ("whole numbers") according to whether they are even or odd, whether they are greater than 10, whether they are divisible by 3, etc. We shall call the one and only one category into which we classify a certain member of a set the *value* of that member, with the understanding, of course, that it is the value only with respect to a given classification scheme. For example, if we are using age as the classification scheme, the value of a certain person may be twenty-five years; if we are using color of eyes, the value of the same person may be blue.

Definition. The *value* of a member of a set is the one and only one category into which that member is classified according to a given classification scheme.

Examples. **1.** If people in a given group are classified according to their heights, the value of John Stewart Jones may be 6 ft 1 in.; if people in the same group are classified according to their names, the value of John Stewart Jones is his name, "John Stewart Jones."

2. If positive integers in a given set are classified according to their sizes, the value of an integer is itself; if the integers are classified according to whether they are even or odd, the value of the number 3 is odd.

It is necessary to distinguish carefully between a *member* of a set and its *value*. The set obtained by tossing a six-sided die and that obtained by spinning a pointer that can land on any numeral from 1 through 6 cannot have the same members, though their members may have the same values.[1]

We shall use capital letters (with subscripts) to refer to members and small letters (with subscripts) to refer to values. For example, we may say, "Consider the set X_1, X_2, X_3, X_4, X_5 with values x_1, x_2, and x_3. Let the value of X_1 be x_1, the value of X_2 be x_3, the value of X_3 be x_2, the value of X_4 be x_1, and the value of X_5 be x_3."

A shorter way of saying the same thing is as follows: "Consider the set X_i, $i = 1, 2, \ldots, 5$. Let value $(X_1) = x_1$, value $(X_2) = x_3$, value $(X_3) = x_2$, value $(X_4) = x_1$, and value $(X_5) = x_3$."

By letting x be an abbreviation for "value" we can be even more brief, as follows: "Consider the set X_i, $i = 1, 2, \ldots, 5$. Let $x(X_1) = x_1$ (read 'Let the value of X_1 equal x_1'), $x(X_2) = x_3$, $x(X_3) = x_2$, $x(X_4) = x_1$, and $x(X_5) = x_3$."

1.3. Populations. When each member of a set has a value, the set is a *population* or *universe*. It is incorrect to call any set a "population" unless the principle of classification is specified, implicitly or explicitly; thus, it is incorrect to say "a population of books" or "a population of integers," but correct to say "a population of books classified according to author" or "a population of integers classified according to size."

It is convenient to think of each member as being *paired* with its value, the value being placed first in each pair. Thus a population of five people classified according to age could be the class of pairs (24, John Doe, Jr.), (23, Mary Doe), (47, John Doe), (46, Jane Doe), (1, John Doe III). These same people classified according to sex would be the *different* population (male, John Doe, Jr.), (female, Mary Doe), etc.

The population described at the end of Sec. 1.2 is the class of pairs (x_1, X_1), (x_3, X_2), (x_2, X_3), (x_1, X_4), (x_3, X_5).

---

[1] Strictly speaking, the numerals "1" and "6" should be enclosed in quotation marks in this sentence. In this text, however, numerals without quotes are used to refer either to numerals or to numbers, depending upon the context. Quotes have also been omitted (with some exceptions) when mentioning or defining various other symbols; this usage is consistent with that of most texts in mathematics, though not with those in mathematical logic, in which the use and mention of a symbol are carefully distinguished.

A class of pairs such that within each pair there is a definite order stipulated is called a *class of ordered pairs*. A class of ordered pairs such that if any two pairs have the same second member they also have the same first member is a *function*. As we stipulated that each member of a population (that is, the second member of a pair) has one and only one value (the first member of the pair), a population is a certain kind of function. Unfortunately the student has probably thought of a function as an *expression* such as $f(x) = x^2$ or $y = x^2$, or as the *rule* given by these expressions.[1] Note, however, that these expressions merely tell us what number to pair with a given number; for example, with 1 we pair 1, with 2 we pair 4, with 3 we pair 9, etc. In other words, these expressions give us a class of pairs, of which some members are (1,1), (4,2), and (9,3). The fact that we cannot list *all* the pairs is irrelevant at this point of our discussion; the point is that neither expressions, rules, nor graphs are functions; it is the class of ordered pairs that is the function.

Just as we would call the class of pairs given by $f(x) = x^2$ the *square* function, so we can call a population a *value* function.

Definition. A *population* or *universe* is a value function, that is, a class of ordered pairs such that the second member of each pair is a member of a set and the first member of the pair is the value of that member of the set.

Examples. 1. The population of 5 flips of a coin, each flip classified according to heads or tails as follows: (heads, first flip), (heads, second flip), (tails, third flip), (heads, fourth flip), (tails, fifth flip).

---

[1] Thus students are often bewildered when they encounter for the first time functions which cannot be defined by a simple equation, although such functions are extremely common in advanced mathematics. An example is: let $f(x) = x$ if x is a member of the sequence 1, $\frac{1}{2}$, $\frac{1}{3}$, . . . , $1/n$, . . . ; let $f(x) = 0$ otherwise. Students are sometimes also surprised to learn that any constant is a function of a variable, as it provides us with something—namely, itself—to pair with each value of the variable. Therefore, a statement that is true of functions in general is true of constants in particular. For example, if

$$E[f(x) + g(x)] = E[f(x)] + E[g(x)]$$

where f and g are any functions whatsoever, then in particular

$$E(x^2 - 4) = E(x^2) + E(-4)$$

as $g(x)$ in this case is the constant -4. We leave E undefined at this point.

2. The population of 1,000 students in a certain college, classified according to the numerical value of the IQ (as measured by the Stanford Binet): (118, Roberta Jones), (110, William Williams), etc.

EXERCISES

1.3.1. Which of the following classes of ordered pairs could *not* be a population?

a. $(4, X_1)$, $(1, X_2)$, $(1, X_3)$, $(2, X_4)$
b. $(4, X_1)$, $(1, X_2)$, $(2, X_2)$, $(5, X_3)$
c. (x_2, X_1), (x_4, X_2), (x_1, X_3), (x_2, X_4)
d. $(100, N.Q.)$, $(100, P.Z.)$, $(110, G.X.)$
e. $(2,5)$, $(2,6)$, $(3,7)$
f. $(2,5)$, $(3,5)$, $(4,6)$

1.3.2. Which of the following rules could *not* give a population, the members in each case being the first 100 positive integers (whole numbers)?

a. $x(X) = X - 2$
b. $x(X) = 0$ if X is even, 1 if X is odd
c. $x(X) = \pm\sqrt{X}$
d. $x(X) = \sqrt[3]{X}$
e. $x(X) =$ the positive square root of X
f. $x(X) = X$ if X is even, $X - 3$ if X is odd

1.3.3. Assuming that each of the following expressions refers to a population, distinguish between members and values in each case:

a. Diameters of 10,000 screws
b. Satisfactory and unsatisfactory performances in a training course
c. Red and white blood cells in 1 ml of blood
d. Durations of telephone conversations occurring between 11 A.M. and 12 noon in a large city
e. Several thousand radio tubes which have been inspected for defectives

1.4. Frequency Functions of Finite Populations.

Although each member of a population has one and only one value, it will not usually be the case that each value is assumed by only one member. The frequency function of a finite population is the way in which the members are distributed into the value categories. A precise definition is the following.

Definition. The frequency function (abbreviated fr.f.) of a finite population is the class of all ordered pairs such that the second member of each pair is a value and the first member is the (nonzero) proportion of the population having that value.[1]

---

[1] The term "relative frequency function" might be more appropriate, but "frequency function" is a standard term.

Examples. **1.** The frequency function of 300 tosses of a six-sided die of which 46 are 1's, 51 are 2's, 53 are 3's, 47 are 4's, 50 are 5's, and 53 are 6's is the class of pairs $(^{46}\!/_{300},1)$, $(^{51}\!/_{300},2)$, $(^{53}\!/_{300},3)$, $(^{47}\!/_{300},4)$, $(^{50}\!/_{300},5)$, $(^{53}\!/_{300},6)$.

2. The fr.f. of two tosses of a coin, both of which are heads, is the class (1, heads).

3. The fr.f of the population described at the end of Sec. 1.2 is the class $(^2\!/_5,x_1)$, $(^1\!/_5,x_2)$, $(^2\!/_5,x_3)$.

Just as we used $x(X)$ to abbreviate "the value of X" we shall use $f(x)$ as an abbreviation for "the proportion of the population having the value x." Thus the fr.f. given in Example 1 can be given by writing $f(1) = ^{46}\!/_{300}$; $f(2) = ^{51}\!/_{300}$; $f(3) = ^{53}\!/_{300}$; $f(4) = ^{47}\!/_{300}$; $f(5) = ^{50}\!/_{300}$; $f(6) = ^{53}\!/_{300}$. Similarly, the fr.f. given in Example 2 is given by $f(\text{heads}) = 1$.

1.5. Cumulative Distribution Functions of Finite Populations. When the values of a population can be arranged in an order, from lowest to highest, it is in many cases convenient to indicate for each value the proportion of the population having values less than or equal to that value. For example, the population whose fr.f. is given in Example 1 in Sec. 1.4 can be equally precisely described by the class of pairs $(^{46}\!/_{300},1)$, $(^{97}\!/_{300},2)$, $(^{150}\!/_{300},3)$, $(^{197}\!/_{300},4)$, $(^{247}\!/_{300},5)$, $(1,6)$. In other words, $^{46}\!/_{300}$ of the population has values less than or equal to 1 (and since 1 is the lowest value, this means that $^{46}\!/_{300}$ of the population has the value 1), $^{97}\!/_{300}$ has values less than or equal to 2, $^{150}\!/_{300}$ has values less than or equal to 3, etc. Obviously the proportion of the population having values less than or equal to the highest value is always 1.

Definition. The *cumulative distribution function* (abbreviated c.d.f., or simply F) of a finite population is the class of all ordered pairs such that the second member of each pair is a value and the first member is the proportion of the population having values less than or equal to the second member.

Example. If a fr.f. is $(^1\!/_8,^1\!/_2)$, $(^1\!/_4,1)$, $(^1\!/_2,2)$, $(^1\!/_8,3)$, then the c.d.f. for the same population is $(^1\!/_8,^1\!/_2)$, $(^3\!/_8,1)$, $(^7\!/_8,2)$, $(1,3)$.

We shall use $F(x)$ as an abbreviation for "the proportion of the population having values less than or equal to x." Thus, in the above example, $F(^1\!/_2) = ^1\!/_8$; $F(1) = ^3\!/_8$; etc.

If the values of a finite population are qualitative categories like schizophrenic, manic-depressive, paranoiac, etc., we can of course arrange the values in an *arbitrary* order and thus obtain a c.d.f.; with an arbitrary order, however, the c.d.f. would not be meaningful.

Cumulative distribution functions are sometimes called merely "distribution functions." We shall use the term "distribution," however, to refer either to a fr.f. or to a c.d.f. Thus "the distribution of a population" means the way in which the members are distributed into the value categories, given either by the fr.f. or by the c.d.f. It should be noted that the fr.f. is a function of the c.d.f., that is, once the c.d.f. is specified the fr.f. is also implicitly specified; conversely, once the fr.f. is specified and an order assigned, either implicitly or explicitly, to the values, the c.d.f. is also implicitly specified. If the values of a population are such that $x_1 < x_2 < x_3 < \cdots < x_k$, then

$$F(x_i) = f(x_1) + f(x_2) + \cdots + f(x_i)$$
$$f(x_i) = F(x_i) - F(x_{i-1})$$

1.6. Graphic Methods of Showing Distributions. Figure 1.6.1 shows some commonly used graphic methods of describing frequency functions and cumulative distribution functions.

1.7. Some Simple Problems Involving Distributions. Suppose we have two six-sided dice, one red and one blue. What is the distribution of the population comprised of all possible pairs of faces which can turn up if the two dice are tossed, each pair having as value the total number of dots appearing on the two dice? First let us list the possible pairs of faces, giving within each pair the number of dots on the red die first and the number of dots on the blue die second.

$$
\begin{array}{cccc}
(1,1) & (1,2) & \cdots & (1,6) \\
(2,1) & (2,2) & \cdots & (2,6) \\
\cdot & \cdot & \cdots & \cdot \\
\cdot & \cdot & \cdots & \cdot \\
\cdot & \cdot & \cdots & \cdot \\
(6,1) & (6,2) & \cdots & (6,6)
\end{array}
$$

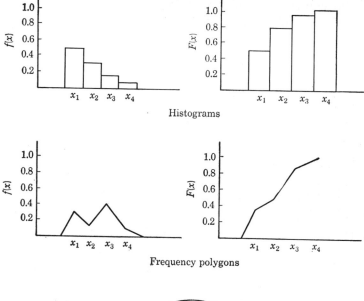

Histograms

Frequency polygons

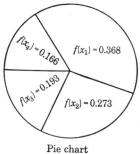

Pie chart

FIG. 1.6.1. Graphic methods of showing distributions.

The population has 36 members. Since value $(1,1) = 2$, value $(1,2) = 3$, etc., the population itself is the class of pairs

$$[2, (1,1)] \quad [3, (1,2)] \quad . \ . \ . \quad [7, (1,6)]$$
$$[3, (2,1)] \quad [4, (2,2)] \quad . \ . \ . \quad [8, (2,6)]$$
$$\cdot \qquad\qquad \cdot \qquad\qquad . \ . \ . \qquad \cdot$$
$$\cdot \qquad\qquad \cdot \qquad\qquad . \ . \ . \qquad \cdot$$
$$\cdot \qquad\qquad \cdot \qquad\qquad . \ . \ . \qquad \cdot$$
$$[7, (6,1)] \quad [8, (6,2)] \quad . \ . \ . \quad [12, (6,6)]$$

The fr.f. is therefore the class of pairs $(\frac{1}{36},2)$, $(\frac{2}{36},3)$, etc., given more conveniently by the following table (also given is the c.d.f.):

x	$f(x)$	$F(x)$	x	$f(x)$	$F(x)$
2	$\frac{1}{36}$	$\frac{1}{36}$	8	$\frac{5}{36}$	$\frac{13}{18}$
3	$\frac{2}{36}$	$\frac{1}{12}$	9	$\frac{4}{36}$	$\frac{5}{6}$
4	$\frac{3}{36}$	$\frac{1}{6}$	10	$\frac{3}{36}$	$\frac{11}{12}$
5	$\frac{4}{36}$	$\frac{5}{18}$	11	$\frac{2}{36}$	$\frac{35}{36}$
6	$\frac{5}{36}$	$\frac{5}{12}$	12	$\frac{1}{36}$	1
7	$\frac{6}{36}$	$\frac{7}{12}$			

The student should note that, although there is only one combination of numerals which gives the value 3 and one combination of numerals which gives the value 2, nevertheless $f(3)$ is greater than $f(2)$ because we can obtain a 2 and a 1 in two ways and a 1 and a 1 in only one way. Considerable care must be exercised in the enumeration of the ways in which an event can occur; otherwise errors will occur in working even the simplest problems.

In our example with the two dice, suppose we take as value for each pair, not the total number of dots appearing but simply the presence of a 2 or a 6 or the absence of both, so that value $(1,1)$ = absence; value $(1,2)$ = presence; etc. Then the population is the class of pairs

[absence, (1,1)]   [presence, (1,2)]   . . .   [presence, (1,6)]
[presence, (1,2)]   [presence, (2,2)]   . . .   [presence, (2,6)]
.   .   . . .   .
.   .   . . .   .
.   .   . . .   .
[presence, (6,1)]   [presence, (6,2)]   . . .   [presence, (6,6)]

The fr.f. is the class of pairs $(\frac{5}{9}, \text{presence})$, $(\frac{4}{9}, \text{absence})$.

Now suppose we paint three faces on the red die blue and three faces on the blue die red, and we take as the value of each pair simply the number of red faces turning up. Naming the six faces on each die by red_1, red_2, red_3, $blue_1$, $blue_2$, $blue_3$, the population becomes

$[2, (\text{red}_1, \text{red}_1)]$ $[2, (\text{red}_1, \text{red}_2)]$ . . . $[1, (\text{red}_1, \text{blue}_3)]$

$[2, (\text{red}_2, \text{red}_1)]$ $[2, (\text{red}_2, \text{red}_2)]$ . . . $[1, (\text{red}_2, \text{blue}_3)]$

.   .   . . .   .

.   .   . . .   .

.   .   . . .   .

$[1, (\text{blue}_3, \text{red}_1)]$ $[1, (\text{blue}_3, \text{red}_2)]$ . . . $[0, (\text{blue}_3, \text{blue}_3)]$

The fr.f. is therefore $(\frac{1}{4},0)$, $(\frac{1}{2},1)$, $(\frac{1}{4},2)$.

EXERCISES

1.7.1. We plan to toss a coin twice. What is the frequency function of the population of all possible results, taking as value the number of heads appearing?

1.7.2. We plan to toss a coin three times. What is the frequency function of the population of all possible results, taking as value the number of heads appearing? What is the cumulative distribution function?

1.7.3. What is the fr.f. of all possible pairs of letters from the word "simple," taking as value the number of s's?

1.7.4. What is the fr.f of all possible pairs of letters from the word "statistics," taking as value the number of s's? What is the c.d.f.?

1.7.5. What is the fr.f. of all possible pairs of letters from the word "Mississippi," taking as value the number of s's? What is the c.d.f.?

1.7.6. Illustrate the answers to Exercises 1.7.3 to 1.7.5 with five different graphic methods.

1.7.7. Find the fr.f. and the c.d.f. (if one exists) for each of the following populations:

a. (x_1,X_1), (x_1,X_2), (x_2,X_3), (x_1,X_4), (x_3,X_5)

b. $(1,X_1)$, $(1,X_2)$, $(-1,X_3)$, $(1,X_4)$, $(0,X_5)$, $(1,X_6)$

c. (absence, Y_1), (absence, Y_2), (presence, Y_3), (absence, Y_4)

d. (for, Jones), (against, Smith), (against, Doe), (for, Brown)

1.7.8. Find the fr.f. and the c.d.f. (if it exists) for each of the following populations:

a. All possible different outcomes (in terms of gene pairs) of a mating of a male with gene pair (a,b) with a female with gene pair (a,b), where each of the progeny gets one gene from each parent. (The gene pairs are not ordered.)

b. Same as *a*, except that parents have gene pairs (a,b) and (a,a).

c. All possible mutual communication channels that can be formed among four people, each channel connecting two or more people and having as value the number of people it connects together.

d. All possible communication networks that can be formed among four people, a network being defined as a particular arrangement of mutual communication channels and having as value the largest number of people mutually connected in that particular arrangement. In a given network there may be people not connected with anyone else, but every network must include at least one channel.

e. All possible routes of minimum length that a rat could take in finding its way from the starting point S to the goal G of the maze shown in the accom-

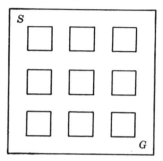

panying diagram, taking the number of right turns minus the number of left turns as the value of each route.

1.8. Some Combinatorial Considerations. The process of listing members of a finite population is usually rather tedious. Fortunately, the distribution of a finite population can often be determined by simple combinatorial considerations. Let us suppose that we have an urn which contains eight white and five black balls. What is the distribution of all possible pairs of balls, each pair having as value the number of white balls in the pair? There are three possible values, 0, 1, and 2. The proportion of pairs having a certain value is the number of pairs having that value divided by the number of pairs in all, that is,

$$f(0) = \frac{\text{number of ways of choosing 2 balls from 5 black balls}}{\text{number of ways of choosing 2 balls from 13 balls}}$$

$$f(1) = \frac{\text{number of ways of choosing 1 ball from 8 white and 1 ball from 5 black balls}}{\text{number of ways of choosing 2 balls from 13 balls}}$$

$$f(2) = \frac{\text{number of ways of choosing 2 balls from 8 white balls}}{\text{number of ways of choosing 2 balls from 13 balls}}$$

In order to prove a simple theorem giving the number of ways of choosing m objects from n objects, we need a more fundamental theorem, which we shall now prove.

Lemma.[1] If an event E_1 can occur in w_1 ways and a subsequent event can occur (after E_1 has occurred) in w_2 ways, then events E_1 and E_2 can occur in succession w_1w_2 ways.

Proof. For every one of the w_1 ways E_1 can occur there are w_2 ways E_2 can occur. These ways can be enumerated by the accompanying table; for example, the pair $(1, 2)$ means that the first way in which E_1 can occur can be paired with the second way in which E_2 can occur.

$$(1,1) \quad (1,2) \quad \ldots \quad (1,w_2)$$
$$(2,1) \quad (2,2) \quad \ldots \quad (2,w_2)$$
$$\cdot \qquad \cdot \qquad \cdots \qquad \cdot$$
$$\cdot \qquad \cdot \qquad \cdots \qquad \cdot$$
$$\cdot \qquad \cdot \qquad \cdots \qquad \cdot$$
$$(w_1,1) \quad (w_1,2) \quad \ldots \quad (w_1,w_2)$$

As the table has w_1 rows and w_2 columns, the total number of entries in the table is w_1w_2. Q.E.D.[2]

Our lemma can easily be generalized to any number of events. Consider, for example, three events, E_1, E_2, and E_3. Since the first two can occur in w_1w_2 ways and since the third can occur in w_3 ways for every one of the w_1w_2 ways in which the first two can occur, we can enumerate the ways in which the three events can occur by the accompanying table:

$$(1,1) \quad (1,2) \quad \ldots \quad (1,w_3)$$
$$(2,1) \quad (2,2) \quad \ldots \quad (2,w_3)$$
$$\cdot \qquad \cdot \qquad \cdots \qquad \cdot$$
$$\cdot \qquad \cdot \qquad \cdots \qquad \cdot$$
$$\cdot \qquad \cdot \qquad \cdots \qquad \cdot$$
$$(w_1w_2,1) \quad (w_1w_2,2) \quad \ldots \quad (w_1w_2,w_3)$$

Since there are w_1w_2 rows and w_3 columns, the total number of entries is $w_1w_2w_3$. Similarly, we could prove the proposition for 4, 5, 6, etc., events. In other words, if it is true for a certain

---

[1] A lemma is a proposition which is proved preliminary to a more important one.
[2] Q.E.D. is a commonly used abbreviation for "which was to be proved."

number of events then it is also true for that number of events plus one additional event.   We now state and prove our theorem rigorously.

Theorem 1.8.1.   If an event E_1 can occur in w_1 ways, and, after E_1 has occurred, a subsequent event E_2 can occur in w_2 ways, and, after E_1 and E_2 have occurred, a subsequent event E_3 can occur in w_3 ways, . . . , and, after E_1, E_2, . . . , E_{n-1} have occurred, a final event E_n can occur in w_n ways, then all n events can occur in a sequence in $w_1 w_2 \cdot \cdot \cdot w_n$ ways.

Proof.   By the lemma above, the theorem is true for $n = 2$. But if the theorem is true for any number of events n_1, it must also be true for $n_1 + 1$ events, because for every one of the $w_1 w_2 \cdot \cdot \cdot w_{n_1}$ ways that the first n_1 events can occur in a sequence there are w_{n_1+1} ways that event E_{n_1+1} can occur, as shown by the accompanying table:

(1,1)	(1,2)	. . .	$(1,w_{n_1+1})$
(2,1)	(2,2)	. . .	$(2,w_{n_1+1})$
.	.	. . .	.
.	.	. . .	.
.	.	. . .	.
$(w_1 w_2 \cdot \cdot \cdot w_{n_1},1)$	$(w_1 w_2 \cdot \cdot \cdot w_{n_1},2)$	. . .	$(w_1 w_2 \cdot \cdot \cdot w_{n_1},w_{n_1+1})$

The total number of entries in the table is $w_1 w_2 w_3 \cdot \cdot \cdot w_{n_1} w_{n_1+1}$ (rows $\times$ columns).   Therefore the theorem is true for $n = 2, 3, \ldots$.

As a matter of fact, we did not need our lemma at all; it is sufficient to point out that the theorem is true for $n = 1$ and to prove that if it is true for n_1 (that is, a particular value of n), it is true for $n_1 + 1$.   A proof of this kind is called *mathematical induction.*   Many theorems which are very difficult (in some cases, perhaps, impossible) to prove by other methods are easily proved by mathematical induction.

Theorem 1.8.2.   The number of permutations (arrangements) of n objects is $n(n - 1) \cdot \cdot \cdot (1)$ (read "n factorial" and abbreviated $n!$ or $\lfloor n$).

Proof.   We can fill the first position in n different ways; then, after filling the first position we can fill the second position in $n - 1$ different ways; . . . ; finally, we can fill the last position, after filling all the rest, in only 1 way. Thus, by Theorem 1.7.1, the number of permutations is n factorial ($n!$). Q.E.D.

We can now obtain a simple expression for the number of ways of choosing m from n objects.

Theorem 1.8.3. The number of ways of choosing m objects from n objects (abbreviated C_m^n) is equal to

$$\frac{n(n-1)\,\cdots\,(n-m+1)}{m!}$$

or, equivalently, $\dfrac{n!}{m!(n-m)!}$.

Proof. There are n ways of choosing the first object, $n-1$ ways of choosing the second object after choosing the first, $n-2$ ways of choosing the third object after choosing the first two, $\ldots$, $n-(m-1)=n-m+1$ ways of choosing the mth object after choosing the first $m-1$. Therefore, by Theorem 1.8.1, the number of ways of choosing a *sequence* of m objects is $n(n-1)\,\cdots\,(n-m+1)$. But this number of ways of choosing a sequence is equal to the number of ways (C_m^n) of choosing a combination of m objects times the number of ways of permuting m objects, which is $m!$; that is,

$$C_m^n m! = n(n-1)\,\cdots\,(n-m+1)$$

or
$$C_m^n = \frac{n(n-1)\,\cdots\,(n-m+1)}{m!}$$

Multiplying numerator and denominator by $(n-m)!$, we obtain

$$C_m^n = \frac{n!}{m!(n-m)!} \qquad \text{Q.E.D.}$$

We can now return to the problem at the beginning of this section: What is the distribution of all possible pairs of balls which can be drawn from an urn containing 8 white and 5 black balls, each pair having as value the number of white balls in the pair? The answer is

$$f(0) = \frac{C_2^5}{C_2^{13}}$$

$$f(1) = \frac{C_1^8 C_1^5}{C_2^{13}}$$

$$f(2) = \frac{C_2^8}{C_2^{13}}$$

That is, the fr.f. is the class of pairs $(C_2^5/C_2^{13}, 0)$ $(C_1^8 C_1^5/C_2^{13}, 1)$ $(C_2^8/C_2^{13}, 2)$.

Note that we can describe the fr.f. by the rule

$$f(x) = \frac{C_x^8 C_{2-x}^5}{C_2^{13}}$$

with the understanding that $0! = 1$ (hence $C_0^n = 1$). The rule $f(x) = \dfrac{C_x^8 C_{2-x}^5}{C_2^{13}}$ is merely a *rule* giving the frequency function, not the function itself, which is a class of ordered pairs.

EXERCISES

1.8.1. What is the fr.f. of all possible triples from a set of 7 men and 4 women, each triple having as value the number of sexes represented? What is the c.d.f.?

1.8.2. What is the fr.f. of all possible triples that can be chosen from a set of 7 men and 4 women, each triple having as value the number of women it contains? What is the c.d.f.?

1.8.3. What is the fr.f. of all quadruples that it is possible to choose from a set of 5 white, 4 black, and 3 red cards, each quadruple having as value the number of colors present? What is the c.d.f.?

1.8.4. There are three routes from A to B and seven routes from B to C. Of the seven routes from B to C, four have detours. What is the fr.f. of the population of all possible routes from A to C via B, taking as value the presence or absence of a detour?

1.8.5. There are 6 physicists and 4 biologists on a 10-man committee. What is the fr.f. of the population of all possible subcommittees of 2 members, each having as value the number of physicists it contains? What is the fr.f. if we take as value simply whether or not both members of the committee are in the same science?

1.8.6. How many different black and white patterns can be made with 4 black and 5 white cards, using all 9 cards each time in a row? (*Hint:* Find the number of ways each pattern can occur, that is, the number of permutations that look the same.)

1.8.7. Generalize your result in Exercise 1.8.6. to the number of discernibly different permutations of n objects of which n_1 look alike, n_2 look alike (though different from the first n_1), . . . , n_k look alike (though different from the first $k - 1$ groups), so that $n_1 + n_2 + \cdots + n_k = n$.

1.8.8. What is the fr.f. of all possible results of tossing three ordinary dice, taking as value the presence or absence of exactly two 6's?

1.8.9. What is the fr.f. of all possible results of tossing three ordinary dice, taking as value the sum of the numbers represented on the three faces?

1.8.10. What is the fr.f. of all possible results of tossing 4 dice, taking as value the number of 6's appearing?

1.8.11. What is the fr.f. of all possible triples of letters from the word "Mississippi," taking as value the number of s's?

1.8.12. What is the fr.f. of all possible quadruples of letters from the word "statistics," taking as value the number of s's?

1.8.13. What is the fr.f. of all possible ways in which a monkey can make a sequence of 30 choices in a learning experiment, at each choice being confronted with three alternatives, of which only one is correct (rewarded with food)? Take the number of correct choices as the value of each possible sequence.

Chapter 2

SAMPLING FROM A FINITE POPULATION

2.1. Expected Sampling Distributions. As we have stated before, a population is a class of ordered pairs, each member of a set being paired with its value. A *sample* is one or more of these ordered pairs, that is, a subclass of the population. A sample may vary in size from 1 to the size of the entire population.

Definition. A *sample* is a subclass of a population.

Example. A sample of size 1 from the population $(1,X_1)$, $(0,X_2)$, $(1,X_3)$, $(2,X_4)$, $(1,X_5)$, $(3,X_6)$ is the pair $(1,X_3)$. Another sample of size 1 is $(3,X_6)$. A sample of size 2 is $(0,X_2)$ and $(3,X_6)$. A sample of size 6 is the entire population.

Definition. A *statistic* is a characteristic of a sample.

Example. In sampling the above population, we might take as a statistic the arithmetic mean, that is, the sum of the values in the sample divided by the size of the sample. The mean of the sample $(1,X_3)$ is 1; the mean of the sample $(0,X_2)$ and $(3,X_6)$ is 1.5. The mean of the sample $(1,X_1)$, $(3,X_6)$, and $(1,X_3)$ is $\frac{5}{3}$.

Once we have decided upon a statistic, we can consider a population of all possible samples of a given size, each sample having as value the statistic. For example, the population of all possible samples of size 2 from the population $(1,X_1)$, $(4,X_2)$, $(0,X_3)$, and $(0,X_4)$, each sample having as value the arithmetic mean, is the class of pairs $[2.5, (X_1,X_2)]$, $[0.5, (X_1,X_3)]$, $[0.5, (X_1,X_4)]$, $[2, (X_2,X_3)]$, $[2, (X_2,X_4)]$, and $[0, (X_3,X_4)]$. The distribution (fr.f) of this latter population is $(\frac{1}{6},0)$, $(\frac{1}{3},0.5)$, $(\frac{1}{3},2)$, and $(\frac{1}{6},2.5)$ and is called the *expected sampling distribution of the arithmetic mean for random samples of size* 2 *from the population* $(1,X_1)$, $(4,X_2)$, $(0,X_3)$, *and* $(0,X_4)$.

Definition. The expected sampling distribution of a statistic z for random samples of size n from a finite population P is the distribution of the population of all possible samples of size n from the population P, each sample having as value the statistic z.

Example. Suppose there are 11 red and 6 blue marbles in a bowl. What is the sampling distribution of the number of red marbles in samples of size 4 drawn from this population? In this case the statistic is the number of red marbles in the sample of 4. There are C_4^{17} possible samples; of these, C_4^6 contain no red marbles, $C_1^{11}C_3^6$ contain 1 red marble, $C_2^{11}C_2^6$ contain 2 red marbles, $C_3^{11}C_1^6$ contain 3, and C_4^{11} contain 4. The expected sampling distribution is therefore $(C_4^6/C_4^{17}, 0)$, $(C_1^{11}C_3^6/C_4^{17}, 1)$, $(C_2^{11}C_2^6/C_4^{17}, 2)$, $(C_3^{11}C_1^6/C_4^{17}, 3)$, $(C_4^{11}/C_4^{17}, 4)$. This expected sampling distribution is conveniently given by the rule

$$f(z) = C_z^{11}C_{4-z}^6/C_4^{17}$$

2.2. Random Sampling. The term "random sample" is often used in books in statistics, and we shall use it also. Strictly speaking, however, a given sample can be no more random than any other sample; the term "random" refers to the method of drawing the sample rather than the sample itself. Usually two conditions are given as necessary and sufficient for random sampling:

1. Each member of the population is just as likely to be included in the sample as any other member.

2. The likelihood that any given member of the population will be included in the sample is not affected by the inclusion of any other particular member. In sampling a finite population this condition cannot literally be satisfied, that is, it must be modified slightly to read "is affected equally by" instead of "is not affected by."

It is possible to satisfy the first condition and not the second. For example, suppose that we have 4 chips in a bowl but that 2 of them are stuck together and the other 2 are also stuck together. We draw a sample of 2 members by drawing one of these pairs at random. Although each chip is equally likely to be included in the sample, the second condition is clearly not satisfied, as drawing any one chip ensures that we shall draw that chip which is attached to it.

It is also possible to satisfy the second condition and not the first. For example, suppose that one of the 4 chips (which are now separated) is stuck to the bottom of the bowl, and that this fact precludes our drawing it in the sample of 2. Then, provided we are as likely to draw any 2 of the remaining 3 as any other 2, we have satisfied the second condition but not the first.

Nearly all statistical inference assumes random sampling.[1] Unfortunately, however, the conditions for randomness often cannot be satisfied. For example, a psychologist may wish to draw a random sample of all human adults but may find that he has available only college sophomores taking elementary psychology at a certain college! In cases like this, the research worker usually tries to make some judgment about whether the bias introduced is at all relevant to the subject matter of his research, and if he is willing to assume, on the basis of this judgment, that his results will not be seriously biased, he goes ahead with the sample which he has. This procedure is often quite justifiable, as there are many problems in which one cannot see any reason for results' being biased by lack of randomness in sampling. However, even when the first condition must be violated, the research worker should, if at all possible, avoid the violation of the second condition. For example, suppose a psychologist is interested in a certain kind of phenomenon, which can be produced under experimental conditions. He makes three observations on each of 10 subjects. Can he say that he has a random sample of 30 observations? Obviously not, as including an observation on a given subject in the sample automatically implies an inclusion of two additional observations on the same subject. Treating a sample of n observations as though it were random when actually it is made up of k different sets of observations, each internally related, is an error which

[1] This is true even when the population is first divided into two or more parts ("stratified") and then sampled proportionately from each stratum, because in "stratified" or "representative" sampling it is usually assumed that within each stratum the members are drawn at random. It is possible to write down some sampling theory for biased sampling, but such theory is useful only if the amount of bias in sampling can be estimated, and this is ordinarily impossible.

accounts for a large proportion of invalid statistical inference, because, although it is obvious enough when simple statistics are used, it enters in a rather subtle manner when more complicated statistical manipulations are employed.

EXERCISES

2.2.1. Someone wishes to draw a random sample of 100 names from a book containing 20,000 short biographies in 2,150 pages. Which of the following procedures are random in the *strict* sense? If the procedure is not random, explain why.

a. Putting each name inside a capsule, mixing these capsules thoroughly, drawing a capsule randomly, drawing another capsule randomly, etc., until 100 capsules have been drawn.

b. Putting two names inside each capsule, mixing them thoroughly, drawing a capsule randomly, another capsule randomly, . . . , until 50 capsules have been drawn.

c. Putting each name inside a capsule, mixing them thoroughly, drawing handfuls of capsules randomly until 100 capsules have been drawn.

d. Putting each combination of 100 names inside a capsule, mixing them thoroughly, and drawing one capsule at random.

e. First choosing a page number by spinning a pointer (that can land on any numeral from 0 to 9) four times (letting 0372 give page 372, etc., and spinning the pointer again for any numeral that is "impossible"; for example, if the first spin yields 3, the pointer will be spun again until a 0, 1, or 2 is obtained), then spinning the pointer twice to obtain the particular name on the page. The procedure is repeated 99 times.

f. Following the same procedure as in *e*, except that the name so chosen and also the three following it (in the book) are taken, so that the procedure needs to be gone through only 25 times.

g. Taking the first name on every page whose number is divisible by 21, until 100 names are obtained.

h. Following the same procedure as in *g*, except choosing one of the first 9 pages as a starting page by spinning a pointer that can land on any numeral from 1 to 9.

2.2.2. For a straw poll, names were selected at random from telephone directories. If the population to be sampled is the population of voters, what condition does this method violate?

2.2.3. For a straw poll, a community is selected at random and then 50 people in the community are selected at random. Only registered voters are taken. Then another community is selected and an additional 50 voters are taken. This procedure is continued until a sample of 10,000 is obtained. Does this procedure violate one or both conditions of random sampling? Explain your answer.

2.2.4. Discuss each of the following sampling methods with respect to randomization:

a. In an agricultural survey, a field worker is assigned the job of sampling the weights of pigs of a certain age range and breed. He takes a sample of about 100 pigs by choosing at random 30 farmers in the area and then choosing at random several of each farmer's pigs meeting his specifications.

b. A physiologist obtains a sample of blood specimens at a university by getting a student to donate blood and then getting him to send other students to him. Each donor is in turn asked to send others; in this way 25 specimens are obtained.

c. On a large cattle ranch each animal has its own number. A sample of 30 is selected by writing down 30 numbers "at random" and then finding the corresponding animals.

d. In a study of working habits in a factory in which people work in pairs, a sample of 100 man-hours is obtained by studying for 1 hr each of 50 pairs of workers selected at random. The hour is selected at random from the working day for each pair.

e. A machine turns out a certain product at the rate of 100 units per hour and is operated for 8 hr per day. A sample of 48 units is taken each day by taking one at the beginning of each 10-min period during the day.

f. In the case of the machine mentioned in *e*, a sample of 50 is taken by taking 5 units at each of 10 randomly selected time intervals during the day.

2.2.5. Find the expected sampling distribution of the arithmetic mean of random samples of size 2 from each of the following populations:

a. $(0,X_1)$, $(0,X_2)$, $(0,X_3)$, $(0,X_4)$, $(0,X_5)$

b. $(-1,X_1)$, $(0,X_2)$, $(0,X_3)$, $(1,X_4)$

c. $(0,X_1)$, $(0,X_2)$, $(0,X_3)$, $(1,X_4)$, $(1,X_5)$

d. $(0,X_1)$, $(0,X_2)$, $(1,X_3)$, $(1,X_4)$, $(2,X_5)$

2.2.6. For each of the populations given in Exercise 2.2.5, find the expected sampling distribution of the arithmetic mean of random samples of size 3.

2.2.7. Do the same as in Exercise 2.2.5 for random samples of size 4.

2.2.8. Taking as a statistic the largest value in the sample (instead of the arithmetic mean), find the expected sampling distribution for random samples of size 2 from each of the populations given in Exercise 2.2.5.

2.2.9. Do the same as in Exercise 2.2.8 for random samples of size 3.

2.2.10. Do the same as in Exercise 2.2.8 for random samples of size 4.

2.2.11. Find the expected sampling distribution of the number of infected children in random samples of 5 from a population of 100 children of whom 70 are infected.

2.2.12. Find the expected sampling distribution of the number of newspaper readers in random samples of 10 from a population of 5,000 of whom 3,000 are newspaper readers.

2.3. Probability. Suppose that we draw a member at random from a finite population, that is, suppose we draw in such a manner that we are as likely to draw one member as another. We shall define[1] the *probability* that the member which we draw will have a certain value x as the proportion of the population having that value, that is, as $f(x)$.

Definition. The probability of obtaining, in a random draw from a finite population, a member having the value x is the proportion of the population having that value, that is, $f(x)$. The probability of obtaining a member having as value something not the value of any member is 0. Clearly $0 \leq \text{prob} \leq 1$.

Examples. 1. In a college with 2,400 undergraduates there are only 15 majoring in mathematics. If we plan to select an undergraduate at random, the probability that he will be a mathematics major is $15/2400 = 1/160 = .00625$. If there are no speech majors, the probability that he will be a speech major is 0. If all students are majoring in something the probability that he will be majoring in something is 1.

2. The probability of obtaining a 4 in a random toss of an ordinary six-sided die is $1/6$. (Here we are dealing with the population of six possible results.)

3. If we throw an ordinary six-sided die twice, the probability of obtaining a sum of 8 is $5/36$. (Here we are dealing with the population of 36 possible results; as we saw in Sec. 1.7, five of these results yield a sum of 8.)

Note that according to our definition the probability of drawing at random a sample of size n that will have a statistic (defined, of course, before drawing the sample) having the value z_1 is simply $f(z_1)$ in the expected sampling distribution of the statistic z for samples of size n. An expected sampling distribution can thus also be called a *probability distribution*.

EXERCISES

2.3.1. Five books, each by a different author, are arranged at random on a shelf. What is the probability that, reading from left to right, they will be in alphabetical order according to the author? (Each author has a different name.)

[1] This is not by any means the only way of defining "probability." There are difficulties with any definition that has been proposed; one difficulty with the definition given above lies in the vagueness of the expression "as likely to draw one member as another." For an interesting discussion of the diverse approaches to this controversial subject, see the monograph by Ernest Nagel, *Principles of the theory of probability* (International Encyclopedia of Unified Science, vol. 1, no. 6), Chicago: University of Chicago Press, 1939.

2.3.2. Ten people are paired at random in a tournament (making five pairs). What is the probability that Mr. Smith will be paired with Mr. Jones?

2.3.3. In a group of 90 people there are twice as many nonscientists as scientists. What is the probability that if a random sample of 7 is taken from this group it will contain

a. exactly 3 scientists?

b. at most 2 scientists?

c. at least 4 scientists?

d. no scientists?

2.3.4. If a monkey in a learning experiment chooses one of two objects (one containing food and the other not) at random on each of 10 trials, what is the probability that he will make exactly 8 correct choices (that is, choices of the object containing food)? Exactly 5 correct choices?

2.3.5. A sequence of two cards is to be drawn at random from an ordinary pack of 52 cards containing 13 spades, 13 hearts, 13 diamonds, and 13 clubs. Find the probability of drawing

a. first a spade and second a diamond

b. first either a spade or heart and second a diamond

c. first either a spade or a heart and second a heart

d. first a card which is not a heart and second a spade

2.3.6. Find the same probabilities as in Exercise 2.3.5 except under the condition that the first card is replaced before drawing the second.

2.3.7. A certain psychologist believes that if a subject is placed in a certain experimental situation a reaction of kind A is just as likely to occur as a reaction of kind B, and that if a sequence of reactions is obtained each reaction is independent of every other reaction. If this is true, what is the probability

a. that a subject will give exactly 4 reactions of kind A and 4 reactions of kind B in a sequence of 8 reactions?

b. that he will give exactly 7 reactions of kind A in a sequence of 8 reactions?

c. that he will give at most 7 reactions of kind A in a sequence of 8 reactions?

d. that he will give at least 2 reactions of kind A in a sequence of 6 reactions?

2.3.8. A bowl contains 4 orange chips, 3 black chips, and 2 white chips. If two chips are to be drawn at random, what is the probability

a. that neither is orange?

b. that one is orange and one is black?

c. that at least one is black?

d. that at most one is white?

2.3.9. If three chips are to be drawn at random from the bowl mentioned in Exercise 2.3.8, what is the probability

a. that one is orange, one is black, and one is white?

b. that one is orange and two are black?

c. that at least one is orange?

d. that at least one is orange and at least one is black?

e. that at most one is orange and at least one is black?

f. that at most one is orange and at most one is black?

2.3.10. If four chips are to be drawn from the bowl mentioned in Exercise 2.3.8, what is the probability

a. that 2 are orange and 1 is black and 1 is white?

b. that 2 are orange and 2 are white?

c. that at least 2 are orange and at most 1 is black?

d. that at least 1 is orange and at most 2 are black and at most 1 is white?

e. that at most 2 are orange and at most 2 are black and at least 1 is white?

2.3.11. A bowl contains 3 orange and 1 black chips. A second bowl contains 1 orange and 1 black chip. If a chip is to be drawn at random from the first bowl and placed into the second bowl and then a chip is to be drawn at random from the second bowl, what is the probability

a. that the chip drawn from the second bowl will be orange?

b. that the chip drawn from the second bowl will be black?

c. that the chip drawn from the second bowl will be of the same color as the chip drawn from the first bowl?

d. that the chip drawn from the second bowl will be of a different color from the chip drawn from the first bowl?

e. that the chip drawn from the first bowl will be orange and the chip drawn from the second bowl will be black?

f. that the chip drawn from the first bowl will be black and the chip drawn from the second bowl will be orange?

g. that both chips will be orange?

h. that both chips will be black?

i. that one of the chips will be orange and the other will be black?

j. that at least one of the chips drawn will be orange?

k. that at most one of the chips drawn will be black?

2.3.12. An urn contains 5 white and 2 black balls. A second urn contains 2 white and 1 black balls. It is decided that a ball will be drawn at random from the first urn and placed in the second urn; then a ball will be drawn at random from the second urn. What is the probability

a. that the ball drawn from the second urn will be white?

b. that the ball drawn from the second urn will be black?

c. that the ball drawn from the second urn will be the same color as the ball drawn from the first urn?

d. that the ball drawn from the second urn will be a different color from that of the ball from the first urn?

e. that both balls will be white?

f. that both balls will be black?

g. that at most one will be white?

h. that at least one will be white?

2.3.13. A bowl contains 9 orange and 16 black chips. A second bowl contains 4 orange and 9 black chips. Two chips are to be drawn at random from the first bowl and placed into the second and then a chip is to be drawn at random from the second bowl. What is the probability

a. that the chip drawn from the second bowl will be orange?

b. that the chip drawn from the second bowl will be black?

c. that the chip drawn from the second bowl will be of the same color as exactly one of those drawn from the first bowl?

d. that the chip drawn from the second bowl will be of a different color from both those drawn from the first bowl?

e. that all three chips will be orange?

f. that at least one chip will be orange?

g. that at least one chip will be orange and at least one chip will be black?

2.4. The Calculus of Probabilities. Consider two events such that the first event can be A or $\bar{A}$ (not A) and the second event B or $\bar{B}$. Now suppose there are n equally likely different ways in which these two events can occur, of which m_{11} are both A and B, m_{12} are A and $\bar{B}$, m_{21} are $\bar{A}$ and B, and m_{22} are $\bar{A}$ and $\bar{B}$. This situation can be represented by the accompanying table:

		Second event		Total
		B	$\bar{B}$	
First event	A	m_{11}	m_{12}	$m_{11} + m_{12}$
	$\bar{A}$	m_{21}	m_{22}	$m_{21} + m_{22}$
	Total	$m_{11} + m_{21}$	$m_{12} + m_{22}$	n

Now consider a population whose n members are pairs of events. Since each pair is equally likely, the probability that X will be a pair whose first member is A is

$$P(A) = \frac{m_{11} + m_{12}}{n}$$

Similarly,
$$P(\bar{A}) = \frac{m_{21} + m_{22}}{n}$$

$$P(A) + P(\bar{A}) = \frac{m_{11} + m_{12} + m_{21} + m_{22}}{n} = 1$$

or
$$P(\bar{A}) = 1 - P(A)$$

Similarly, $\quad P(A \text{ and } B) = \dfrac{m_{11}}{n}, P(A \text{ and } \bar{B}) = \dfrac{m_{12}}{n}$, etc.

Now suppose we raise the question, "What is the probability that the second event will be B if the first event is A?" This is the same as asking, "Of those pairs having A as the value of the first member, what proportion have B as the value of the second member?" The answer is clearly $m_{11}/(m_{11} + m_{12})$. We abbreviate "probability that the second event will be B if the first event is A" by $P(B|A)$ (read "probability that B, given A"). We have then

$$P(B|A) = \frac{m_{11}}{m_{11} + m_{12}}$$

But

$$P(A \text{ and } B) = \frac{m_{11}}{n}$$

and

$$P(A) = \frac{m_{11} + m_{12}}{n}$$

$$\therefore P(A \text{ and } B) = P(A)P(B|A)$$

or

$$P(B|A) = \frac{P(A \text{ and } B)}{P(A)}$$

$P(B|A)$ is also called the *conditional probability of B, given A*.

Examples. 1. There are 4 white and 3 black balls in an urn. What is the probability of drawing a white ball and then (without replacement) drawing a black ball? Let A denote drawing a white ball and B denote drawing a black ball. Then

$$P(A) = \tfrac{4}{7}$$
$$P(B/A) = \tfrac{3}{6} = \tfrac{1}{2}$$
$$P(A \text{ and } B) = (\tfrac{1}{2})(\tfrac{4}{7}) = \tfrac{2}{7}$$

We could have obtained this result directly by considering that there are $(4)(3) = 12$ ways of drawing a white and then a black ball and there are $(7)(6)$ ways of drawing 2 balls; thus

$$P(A \text{ and } B) = \frac{(4)(3)}{(7)(6)} = \frac{2}{7}$$

2. From an ordinary deck of 52 cards we draw a card and find that it is a heart. What is the probability that the next card drawn (without replacement of the first) will be a spade? Let A denote drawing a heart on the first draw and B denote drawing a spade on the second draw. Then

$$P(A \text{ and } B) = \frac{(13)(13)}{(52)(51)} = \frac{13}{204} \qquad P(A) = \frac{13}{52}$$
$$\therefore P(B|A) = \frac{(13)(13)/(52)(51)}{\tfrac{13}{52}} = \frac{13}{51}$$

This result could be obtained directly by considering that after the first draw there are 13 spades out of 51 cards left; thus

$$P(B|A) = {}^{13}\!/_{51}$$

3. What is the probability that if the first card drawn is not a heart the second card will be a spade? This is a more difficult problem than either of the above. Let A denote not getting a heart. Clearly $P(A) = \frac{3}{4}$. Let B denote getting a spade. To obtain $P(A$ and $B)$ consider that there are $(13)(12)$ ways of obtaining A and B with the first card a spade and $(26)(13)$ ways of obtaining A and B with the first card a club or a diamond. Thus there are $(13)(12) + (13)(26) = (13)(38)$ ways of obtaining A and B. Thus

$$P(A \text{ and } B) = \frac{(13)(38)}{(52)(51)} = \frac{19}{102}$$

$$\therefore P(B|A) = \frac{P(A \text{ and } B)}{P(A)} = \frac{{}^{19}\!/_{102}}{{}^{3}\!/_{4}} = \frac{38}{153}$$

Notice that without any restriction at all on the result of the first draw we would have $P(B) = \frac{1}{4} = {}^{38}\!/_{152}$.

Now let the first event be tossing a die and the second event be drawing a card. Let A denote obtaining a 5 and B denote drawing a king. What is $P(A$ and $B)$? In this case $P(B|A) = P(B)$, because the probability of drawing a king is unaffected by the fact that one has obtained a 5. Thus

$$P(A \text{ and } B) = P(B|A)P(A) = P(B)P(A) = (\tfrac{1}{6})(\tfrac{1}{13}) = \tfrac{1}{78}$$

Definition. A and B are *independent* events if and only if $P(B|A) = P(B)$.

It can be proved that if $P(B|A) = P(B)$, then $P(A|B) = P(A)$ as follows:

$$P(A|B) = \frac{P(A \text{ and } B)}{P(B)} = \frac{P(A \text{ and } B)}{P(B|A)} = P(A)$$

As an exercise the student should prove by mathematical induction that for a sequence of k events, A_1 or $\bar{A}_1$, A_2 or $\bar{A}_2$, $\ldots$, A_k or $\bar{A}_k$, respectively, $P(A_1$ and A_2 and $\cdots$ and $A_k) = P(A_1)P(A_2|A_1)P(A_3|A_1$ and $A_2) \cdots P(A_k|A_1$ and A_2 and $\cdots$ and $A_{k-1})$. When all events are independent this becomes simply

$$P(A_1 \text{ and } A_2 \text{ and } \cdots \text{ and } A_k) = P(A_1)P(A_2) \cdots P(A_k)$$

Suppose we consider our table again.   By "A or B" we mean either A occurs or B occurs or both occur.   Then

$$P(A \text{ or } B) = \frac{m_{11} + m_{12} + m_{21}}{n} = \frac{m_{11} + m_{12}}{n} + \frac{m_{21}}{n}$$

$$= \frac{m_{11} + m_{12}}{n} + \frac{m_{11} + m_{21}}{n} - \frac{m_{11}}{n}$$

$$= P(A) + P(B) - P(A \text{ and } B)$$

EXERCISES

2.4.1. There are twice as many men as women enrolled in course A.   There are equally many men and women enrolled in course B.   No person is enrolled in both courses.   One student is to be drawn at random from each course. Find the probability that

    a. both will be women.

    b. at least one will be a woman.

    c. exactly one will be a woman.

2.4.2. If E_1 (the first event) can be A or $\bar{A}$, E_2 can be B or $\bar{B}$, and E_3 can be C or $\bar{C}$, prove that if E_1, E_2, and E_3 are to occur,

$$P(A \text{ or } B \text{ or } C) = P(A) + P(B) + P(C) - P(A \text{ and } B) - P(A \text{ and } C)$$
$$- P(B \text{ and } C) + P(A \text{ and } B \text{ and } C)$$

2.4.3. Suppose that one-third of the members of a large community are laborers, and that three-fourths of these laborers want a change in city administration.   Suppose that of those who are not laborers, only one-eighth want a change.   Find the probability that

    a. a person picked at random from this community will be a laborer who does not want a change.

    b. a person picked at random will be either a laborer who does not want a change or a nonlaborer who does want a change.

    c. a person picked at random will not want a change.

    d. if two people are picked at random, one will be a laborer who does not want a change and the other will be a nonlaborer who does.

    e. if two people are picked at random one will be a laborer who wants a change and the other will be a nonlaborer who does not.

    f. if two people are picked at random, but in order, the *first* will be a laborer who wants a change and the *second* will be a nonlaborer who does not.

    g. if three people are picked at random, exactly one will be a nonlaborer and exactly two will want changes.

    h. a person picked at random either will be a laborer or will want a change.

2.4.4. A monkey is seated at a typewriter which contains only the 26 letters of the alphabet, striking keys at random.   Find the probability that in a given sequence of 10 letters *a.* the expression "monkeytype" will appear.

b. the word "monkey" will appear (all letters adjacent).

c. the letter *m* will appear at least once.

2.4.5. One-tenth of a large number of radio tubes are defective. What is the probability that if five tubes are randomly selected, none will be defective?

2.4.6. In a certain kind of vaccination, a vaccine to which 40 per cent of all people react is first given; if there is no reaction, a second vaccine is given to which 90 per cent of the remainder react. What is the probability that a person chosen at random will react only to the second vaccine?

2.4.7. In an oral examination a student is asked a question selected randomly from a large number. Only if he answers satisfactorily is he asked a second one, selected randomly from the remainder. If he actually can answer only 30 per cent of the questions, what is the probability that he will miss the second?

2.4.8. In an experiment on extrasensory perception five cards, each with a different symbol, are thoroughly shuffled and then placed in a pile. A subject, who knows the symbols, is to attempt to tell the order. Assuming that he has no ESP but guesses a sequence for the five symbols, what is the probability

a. that the subject will get the order entirely correct?

b. that he will get exactly three of the five correct?

2.4.9. In the same situation as the above, except that two red, two black, and two white cards are used, and assuming the subject has no ESP and guesses a possible sequence of six colors (two of each), what is the probability that

a. he will get the order entirely correct?

b. he will miss only two?

2.4.10. In an ESP experiment a coin was tossed five times. Each of 1,000 subjects (in a large auditorium but shielded so that no one could possibly receive any cues from any other subject or from the experimenter) wrote down a sequence. Exactly 173 subjects wrote down the correct sequence. The experimenter claimed that he had statistically significant results and that these results were evidence for ESP.

Write down the formula which the experimenter probably used (or approximated) in calculating his statistic. Why does this formula not apply? What would have to be done to make a valid statistical test?

Chapter 3

STATISTICAL INFERENCE

3.1. Expected Sampling Distributions Yielded by Different Hypotheses. Suppose that we have a bowl containing 8 chips, each being either orange or black. What is the expected sampling distribution of the number of orange chips in a sample for samples of size 4? Obviously we cannot answer this question, since we do not know how many of the 8 chips are orange; however, we can form hypotheses about the number of orange chips in the bowl and can find out what the expected sampling distribution *would be* on the basis of each hypothesis. If there are no orange chips in the bowl, the sampling distribution of the number of orange chips in a sample of size 4 is simply (1,0). If there is 1 orange chip in the bowl, the expected sampling distribution is $(C_0^1 C_4^7/C_4^8, 0)$, $(C_1^1 C_3^7/C_4^8, 1)$. If there are 2 orange chips in the bowl the sampling distribution is $(C_0^2 C_4^6/C_4^8, 0)$, $(C_1^2 C_3^6/C_4^8, 1)$, $(C_2^2 C_2^6/C_4^8, 2)$, etc. The expected sampling distribution corresponding to each hypothesis is shown in the appropriate row of Table 3.1.1, H_i indicating the hypothesis that there are i orange chips in the bowl.

EXERCISES

3.1.1. A sample of 2 is to be chosen at random from a dichotomous population containing 4 members (each either an A or a non-A). Make a table showing the expected sampling distribution of the number of A's in a sample on the basis of each possible hypothesis.

3.1.2. A sample of 3 is to be chosen at random from a population containing 24 members, each either an A or a B. Make a table showing the expected sampling distribution of the number of A's per sample for the hypothesis.

a. that the population contains 3 A's

b. that the population contains 12 A's

c. that the population contains 21 A's

TABLE 3.1.1. EXPECTED SAMPLING DISTRIBUTION OF NUMBER OF
ORANGE CHIPS IN SAMPLE OF FOUR DRAWN FROM BOWL
CONTAINING 8 CHIPS, FOR EACH POSSIBLE HYPOTHESIS
AS TO NUMBER OF ORANGE CHIPS IN BOWL

	Number of orange chips in sample				
	0	1	2	3	4
H_0	1	0	0	0	0
H_1	C_4^7/C_4^8 $= .5000$	$C_1^1 C_3^7/C_4^8$ $= .5000$	0	0	0
H_2	C_4^6/C_4^8 $= .2143$	$C_1^2 C_3^6/C_4^8$ $= .5714$	$C_2^2 C_2^6/C_4^8$ $= .2143$	0	0
H_3	C_4^5/C_4^8 $= .0714$	$C_1^3 C_3^5/C_4^8$ $= .4286$	$C_2^3 C_2^5/C_4^8$ $= .4286$	$C_3^3 C_1^5/C_4^8$ $= .0714$	0
H_4	C_4^4/C_4^8 $= .0143$	$C_1^4 C_3^4/C_4^8$ $= .2286$	$C_2^4 C_2^4/C_4^8$ $= .5143$	$C_3^4 C_1^4/C_4^8$ $= .2286$	C_4^4/C_4^8 $= .0143$
H_5	0	$C_1^5 C_3^3/C_4^8$ $= .0714$	$C_2^5 C_2^3/C_4^8$ $= .4286$	$C_3^5 C_1^3/C_4^8$ $= .4286$	C_4^5/C_4^8 $= .0714$
H_6	0	0	.2143	.5714	.2143
H_7	0	0	0	.5000	.5000
H_8	0	0	0	0	1

(left margin label: Hypothesis)

3.1.3. Four Ph.D. candidates are to be chosen at random from a group of 32
and given an extensive series of tests. Each tested candidate is given a final
rating as excellent, satisfactory, or unsatisfactory. Make a table showing the
expected sampling distribution of the number of excellent candidates per sample for the hypothesis
  a. that the population contains 4 excellent candidates
  b. that the population contains 16 excellent candidates
  c. that the population contains 24 excellent candidates
Why is it necessary that each tested candidate be rated independently of
the ratings of the others in order that this table have any validity?
3.1.4. A sample of blood specimens is to be chosen at random from a population of 21 and subjected to a thorough bioassay. On the basis of the
measurements, a complex ratio for each specimen is computed. Ratios of at

least ¾ are considered of significance. Make a table showing the expected sampling distribution of the number of ratios of at least ¾ for the hypothesis

   a. that the population contains 3 such ratios

   b. that the population contains 7 such ratios

   c. that the population contains 14 such ratios

3.1.5. An investor finds that nine stocks meet certain stringent requirements which should indicate an increase in value in the near future. He decides to choose three of these at random and invest in each of the three. Make a table showing the expected sampling distribution of the number of profitable stocks per sample for each of the theoretically possible hypotheses.

3.1.6. Fifty sites have been chosen as favorable for the drilling of oil wells. It is decided to drill wells on four of these, chosen at random. Find the expected sampling distribution of the number of strikes per sample on the hypothesis that 21 of the 50 sites actually contain oil.

3.1.7. Write a formula giving the expected sampling distribution under each of the following conditions:

   a. A sample of 8 drawn from 180 bombers on the hypothesis that 100 of the bombers fail to meet all specifications

   b. A sample of 15 drawn at random from 365 families on the hypothesis that 190 of the families have authoritarian structures

   c. A sample of 25 drawn at random from 2,000 school teachers on the hypothesis that one-half of the teachers are in favor of abolishing examinations

   d. A sample of size n drawn from a population containing N members on the hypothesis that N_1 members are A's

3.2. Testing Hypotheses about the Population.

Now suppose that, in complete ignorance about the actual contents of the bowl, we take a sample of 4 chips at random and observe that all 4 are orange. By referring to our table we see that if there were only 4 orange chips in the bowl (H_4) then the probability of drawing all 4 of them was only .0143, that is, out of all the $C_4^8 = 70$ different samples that we could have drawn, only one of them would have been 4 orange chips. Therefore, we would be rather suspicious of H_4. On the other hand, we would be less suspicious of H_5, since $f(4) = .0714$ on the basis of H_5. We would regard H_6, H_7, and H_8 each as quite tenable. One might be tempted to say that we should regard H_8 as the *most tenable* hypothesis, in view of the sample which we had drawn. If we should follow this procedure, however, we should have to say that H_0 is the most tenable hypothesis if our sample yields no orange chips, H_2 is the most tenable if our sample yields 1 orange chip, H_4 if 2, H_6 if 3, and H_8 if 4. Under no circumstances therefore would we be able to consider H_1, H_3, H_5, or H_7 the most tenable hypothesis, even though one of these were in fact the correct one! Before discussing this difficulty further let us consider a somewhat more interesting example.

Suppose that we know only that a bowl contains 4 chips, each either orange or nonorange. We plan to draw a chip at random, replace it, draw another, replace it, etc., drawing 10 times in all. What kind of inference can we make about the contents of the bowl? We can consider our 10 draws (in sequence) as a random sample of size 1 from the population consisting of all possible sequences of 10 draws, each sequence having as value the number of orange chips drawn. There are $4^{10} = 1,048,576$ sequences in the population (by Theorem 1.8.1). If there are no orange chips in the bowl, all these sequences have the value 0. If there is only one orange chip in the bowl (H_1), only $3^{10} = 59,049$ of these sequences have the value 0, because there are 3 ways of drawing the first nonorange chip, 3 ways of drawing the second, . . . , 3 ways of drawing the tenth. To see how many of the 1,048,576 sequences would have, on H_1, the value 1, consider that, if we draw the orange chip first, there are 3^9 ways of completing the sequence; in other words, there are $3^9 = 19,683$ sequences with an orange chip in the first place and nonorange chips in the other places. Similarly, there are 3^9 sequences with an orange chip in the second place, 3^9 sequences with an orange chip in the third place . . . , 3^9 squences with an orange chip in tenth place. Thus on H_1 there are $10\ (3^9) = 196,830$ sequences having the value 1. Similarly, on H_1 there are 3^8 sequences with orange chips in the first and second places, 3^8 sequences with orange chips in the first and third places, . . . , 3^8 sequences with orange chips in the ninth and tenth places. Since there are C_2^{10} pairs of places, there are $C_2^{10}(3^8) = 295,245$ sequences having the value 2. On H_1 there are $C_3^{10}(3^7) = 262,440$ sequences having the value 3, etc. In general, on the hypothesis H_i there are $C_x^{10}(i)^x(4 - i)^{10-x}$ sequences having the value x. The distribution (fr.f.) of the population of sequences on each hypothesis is given in Table 3.2.1.

Now suppose that we actually draw a sequence of 10 chips, replacing after each draw, and observe 4 orange chips. By

TABLE 3.2.1. DISTRIBUTION FOR EACH POSSIBLE HYPOTHESIS OF THE NUMBER OF ORANGE CHIPS IN ALL POSSIBLE SEQUENCES OF 10 CHIPS DRAWN FROM BOWL CONTAINING FOUR CHIPS, REPLACING AFTER EACH DRAW

Number of orange chips in a sequence of 10 choices

Hypothesis	0	1	2	3	4	5	6	7	8	9	10
H_0	1	0	0	0	0	0	0	0	0	0	0
H_1	$\frac{C_0^{10}(3^{10})}{4^{10}}$ $= .0563$	$\frac{C_1^{10}(3^9)}{4^{10}}$ $= .1877$	$\frac{C_2^{10}(3^8)}{4^{10}}$ $= .2816$	$\frac{C_3^{10}(3^7)}{4^{10}}$ $= .2503$	$\frac{C_4^{10}(3^6)}{4^{10}}$ $= .1460$	$\frac{C_5^{10}(3^5)}{4^{10}}$ $= .0584$	$\frac{C_6^{10}(3^4)}{4^{10}}$ $= .0162$	$\frac{C_7^{10}(3^3)}{4^{10}}$ $= .0031$	$\frac{C_8^{10}(3^2)}{4^{10}}$ $= .0004$	$\frac{C_9^{10}(3)}{4^{10}}$ $= .0000$	$\frac{C_{10}^{10}}{4^{10}}$ $= .0000$
H_2	$\frac{C_0^{10}(2^{10})}{4^{10}}$ $= .0010$	$\frac{C_1^{10}(2^9)(2^1)}{4^{10}}$ $= .0098$	$\frac{C_2^{10}(2^8)(2^2)}{4^{10}}$ $= .0439$	$\frac{C_3^{10}(2^7)(2^3)}{4^{10}}$ $= .1172$	$\frac{C_4^{10}(2^6)(2^4)}{4^{10}}$ $= .2051$	$\frac{C_5^{10}(2^5)(2^5)}{4^{10}}$ $= .2461$	$\frac{C_6^{10}(2^4)(2^6)}{4^{10}}$ $= .2051$	$\frac{C_7^{10}(2^3)(2^7)}{4^{10}}$ $= .1172$	$\frac{C_8^{10}(2^2)(2^8)}{4^{10}}$ $= .0439$	$\frac{C_9^{10}(2^1)(2^9)}{4^{10}}$ $= .0098$	$\frac{C_{10}^{10}(2^{10})}{4^{10}}$ $= .0010$
H_3	$\frac{C_0^{10}}{4^{10}}$ $= .0000$	$\frac{C_1^{10}(3^1)}{4^{10}}$ $= .0000$	$\frac{C_2^{10}(3^2)}{4^{10}}$ $= .0004$	etc. $.0031$	$.0162$	$.0584$	$.1460$	$.2503$	$.2816$	$.1877$	$.0563$
H_4	0	0	0	0	0	0	0	0	0	0	1

reference to our table we see that we can consider H_1 and H_2 each as quite tenable and that we can reject H_3 with considerable confidence (assuming that there is no other reason for considering H_3 as particularly reasonable). But just how confident should we be in rejecting H_3 in this particular case? Can we say that the number .0162 expresses the level of confidence with which we reject H_3? To answer this question, consider the following situation. Suppose we place 3 orange and 1 black chips in a bowl, that is, suppose we set up a situation in which H_3 is actually correct. Now suppose we were to draw a great many sequences, each time referring to our table and rejecting H_3 if the number of orange chips is 4, 3, 2, 1, or 0. Since H_3 is correct, each of our rejections will be a false assertion, and of our total number of assertions there will be approximately .0162 + .0031 + .0004 + .0000 + .0000 = .0197 false ones, if each possible sequence is drawn just as often as each other possible sequence. Therefore, since rejecting H_3 with the observation of 4 orange chips in the sample commits us to the rejection of H_3 with the observation of 3, 2, 1, or 0 orange chips, in rejecting H_3 with the observation of 4 orange chips we should consider ourselves as operating at the .0197 level of confidence rather than at the .0162 level. Similarly, if we plan to reject H_2 if there are 0, 1, 9, or 10 orange chips in the sequence, we must state, in rejecting H_2 with the observation of 1 orange chip in the sequence, that we reject H_2 at the

$$.0098 + .0098 + .0010 + .0010 = .0216$$

level of confidence, not the .0098 level.

The heavy black lines in the table include all those entries such that the hypothesis at the left is tenable if the sample value at the top is observed. The choice of which cells to include within the black lines is more or less arbitrary; however, it is conventional never to choose a confidence level which is greater than .05; in many cases .01 or even .001 is the level chosen.[1] In our table we can observe before drawing our sequence that if H_0 is correct we are in no danger at all of making a false assertion; if H_1 is

---

[1] The level of confidence chosen depends upon the purposes of the research worker. This question is discussed in Sec. 3.8.

correct then the probability that we are going to make a false assertion is .0197; if H_2 is correct, the probability is .0216; if H_3 is correct, the probability is .0197; if H_4 is correct, the probability is 0. Thus we can say before drawing our sample that *no matter which hypothesis is correct* the probability that we shall make a false assertion, that is, reject a hypothesis when it is the correct one, is some number not greater than .0216, the largest of the above probabilities. After drawing our sample, however, we should not speak of the *probability* that our assertion is false; we should say simply that we are rejecting a hypothesis at such and such a level of confidence.

EXERCISES

3.2.1. A bowl contains 100 chips. One chip is drawn at random; it is red. Test the hypothesis that
  a. the bowl contained only 1 red chip.
  b. the bowl contained only 2 red chips.
  c. the bowl contained only 20 red chips.
  d. the bowl contained all red chips.

3.2.2. A bowl contains 100 chips. Two chips are drawn at random. Both are black. Test the hypothesis that
  a. the bowl contained only 2 black chips.
  b. the bowl contained only 3 black chips.
  c. the bowl contained only 10 black chips.
  d. the bowl contained only 20 black chips.

3.2.3. A bowl contains 100 chips. One chip is drawn at random and replaced, then another chip is drawn. Both are black. Test the same hypotheses listed in Exercise 3.2.2.

3.2.4. A monkey makes 10 correct choices in a sequence of 12 choices. Test the hypothesis that the monkey is making choices at random. (Assume that in each trial there are exactly as many possible incorrect choices as correct.)

3.2.5. From a list of professors in a certain university we select a name at random, then we select another name at random (which may be the same as the first name), etc., selecting six names in all. We find that all six of these professors are from the East. Test the hypothesis that in the university there are as many non-Eastern professors as there are Eastern ones.

3.3. Confidence Intervals. The heavy black lines in the previous table indicate, for each value of the sample, which hypotheses are reasonable, using the .022 level of confidence. (See

Sec. 3.2 for the way in which the number .022 is obtained.) Thus, for an observed value of 0 we say, at the .022 level of confidence, that the number of orange chips in the bowl is either 0 or 1; for an observed value of 1 we say, at the .022 level of confidence that the number of orange chips in the bowl is 1; for an observed value of 2 we say, at the .022 level of confidence, that the number of orange chips in the bowl is 1 or 2; etc. The intervals 0–1 (inclusive), 1, 1–2, etc., are *confidence intervals*. We can say, before drawing our sequence of 10 chips, that the probability that we are going to make a false assertion about the limits within which the true number of orange chips lies is less than .022. Another way of stating this is as follows: Probability (our confidence interval will include the actual number of orange chips) > .978.

EXERCISES

3.3.1. From a bowl containing 3 chips, each either orange or black, we draw at random a sequence of 7 chips, of which 6 are orange. Find the .03 confidence interval for the number of orange chips in the bowl.

3.3.2. From a bowl containing 3 chips, each either orange or black, we draw at random a sequence of 20 chips, of which 18 are black. Find the .01 confidence interval for the number of orange chips in the bowl.

3.4. Power of a Test. In the case discussed in Sec. 3.3, suppose that the number of orange chips in the bowl is actually 0. In this case we are going to observe 0 as the value of our sequence; the .022 confidence interval for an observed value of 0 is the interval 0–1 inclusive. Thus there is *absolutely no chance of* rejecting H_1 if H_0 is correct. This situation is described by saying that the power of the test of H_1 is 0 if H_0 is correct.

Definition. The power of a test T of a hypothesis H is the probability of rejecting H, using T. The power of T is a function of which hypothesis is actually correct, as well as the level of confidence chosen; it is computed by summing probabilities of those observations which would entail the rejection of H.

Example. In the orange-chip problem, the power of our test of H_1 is 0 if H_0 is correct; the power of our test of H_1 is

$$.2051 + .1172 + .0439 + .0098 + .0010 = .3770$$

if H_2 is correct; the power of our test of H_1 is

$$.1460 + .2503 + .2816 + .1877 + .0563 = .9219$$

if H_3 is correct; the power of our test of H_1 is 1 if H_4 is correct. If H_1 is correct, the power of our test of H_0 is $1 - .0563 = .9437$; the power of our test of H_2 is

$$.0563 + .1877 + .0000 + .0000 = .2440$$

etc.

EXERCISES

3.4.1. Using the table in Sec. 3.2, make a table showing the power of our test of each hypothesis for each possible correct hypothesis.

3.4.2. Using the table in Sec. 3.1, make a table showing the power of a test (rejecting at the .03 level of confidence) of each hypothesis for each possible correct hypothesis.

3.5. Increasing the Power of a Test by Increasing the Number of Observations.

No matter which hypothesis is correct, that is, no matter what the true state of affairs, we can increase the power of our test of an incorrect hypothesis to as close to 1 as we wish by increasing the number of observations, that is, the size of the sequence which we draw from the bowl. The expected sampling distributions for a sequence of 100 chips drawn at random are shown by Table 3.5.1.

TABLE 3.5.1. EXPECTED SAMPLING DISTRIBUTIONS OF NUMBER OF ORANGE CHIPS IN SEQUENCE OF 100 CHIPS DRAWN RANDOMLY FROM BOWL CONTAINING FOUR CHIPS, REPLACING AFTER EACH DRAW

Number of orange chips in a sequence of 100 chips

	0–9	10–19	20–29	30–39	40–49	50–59	60–69	70–79	80–89	90–100
H_0	1	0	0	0	0	0	0	0	0	0
H_1	.000	.102	.749	.149	.000	.000	.000	.000	.000	.000
H_2	.000	.000	.000	.018	.443	.511	.028	.000	.000	.000
H_3	.000	.000	.000	.000	.000	.000	.149	.749	.102	.000
H_4	0	0	0	0	0	0	0	0	0	1

(Hypothesis)

In this table we have grouped the possible observed numbers of orange chips into intervals, but our heavy black lines indicate confidence intervals, as before, except that now we can say before drawing our sequence that the probability that we are going to make a false assertion (that is, reject a hypothesis when it is actually correct) is at most .018.   Whereas with a sequence of 10 the power of our test of H_1 if H_0 is correct is 0, with a sequence of 100 the power of our test of H_1 if H_0 is correct is 1.000.   Similarly, the power of our test of H_1, if H_2 is correct, has been increased from .3770 to .443 + .511 + .028 = .982. As an exercise the student should compute the increase of the power of our test of each hypothesis, given that each hypothesis in turn is the correct one.

To increase the power of our test still further we can take a sequence of 1,000.   The expected sampling distributions are shown by Table 3.5.2.

TABLE 3.5.2. EXPECTED SAMPLING DISTRIBUTION, FOR EACH POSSIBLE HYPOTHESIS, OF NUMBER OF ORANGE CHIPS IN SEQUENCE OF 1,000 RANDOM DRAWS, REPLACING AFTER EACH DRAW

Number of orange chips in a sequence of 1,000 draws

	0–99	100–199	200–299	300–399	400–499	500–599	600–699	700–799	800–899	900–1,000
H_0	1	0	0	0	0	0	0	0	0	0
H_1	.0000	.0001	.9998	.0001	.0000	.0000	.0000	.0000	.0000	.0000
H_2	.0000	.0000	.0000	.0000	.488	.512	.0000	.0000	.0000	.0000
H_3	.0000	.0000	.0000	.0000	.0000	.0000	.0001	.9998	.0001	.0000
H_4	0	0	0	0	0	0	0	0	0	1

Hypothesis

No matter which hypothesis is correct, the power of our test of any incorrect hypothesis is now approximately 1.   Another way of stating the law that the power can be increased to as close to 1 as desired is to say that the probability that the proportion of orange chips in the sequence will diverge more than a fixed amount from the proportion of orange chips in the bowl approaches 0 as a limit if we increase the size of the sequence. This is known as Bernoulli's theorem, which is usually stated in the following way: If the chance of an event occurring upon a single trial is p, and if a number of independent trials are made, the probability that the ratio of the number of successes to the number of trials differs from p by less than any preassigned quantity, however small, can be made as near certainty as may be desired by taking the number of trials sufficiently large.　As an exercise the student should satisfy himself that these statements are equivalent.

We summarize the effect of increasing the number of observations in Table 3.5.3.　This table shows the power of the test of each hypothesis, assuming the hypothesis at the left to be correct, for 10, 100, and 1,000 observations.

TABLE 3.5.3. POWER OF TEST OF EACH HYPOTHESIS IN CHIPS-IN-BOWL PROBLEM, FOR SEQUENCES OF 10, 100 (BOLDFACE), AND 1,000 (ITALICS), SHOWING HOW POWER INCREASES (IF HYPOTHESIS TESTED IS INCORRECT) AS NUMBER OF OBSERVATIONS INCREASES

| | | Hypothesis tested | | | | |
		H_0	H_1	H_2	H_3	H_4
	H_0	0 **0** *0*	0 **1** *1*	1 **1** *1*	1 **1** *1*	1 **1** *1*
	H_1	.944 **1.000** *1.000*	.020 **.000** *.000*	.244 **.999** *1.000*	.922 **1.000** *1.000*	1.000 **1.000** *1.000*
Correct hypothesis	H_2	.999 **1.000** *1.000*	.377 **.982** *1.000*	.021 **.018** *.000*	.377 **.972** *1.000*	.999 **1.000** *1.000*
	H_3	1.000 **1.000** *1.000*	.922 **1.000** *1.000*	.244 **.851** *1.000*	.020 **.000** *.000*	.944 **1.000** *1.000*
	H_4	1 **1** *1*	1 **1** *1*	1 **1** *1*	0 **1** *1*	0 **0** *0*

3.6. A Word of Caution. In Table 3.5.2 we see that the probability of obtaining between 300 and 399 orange chips in our sequence of 1,000 draws is very small no matter which hypothesis is correct. What then if we should actually draw a sequence containing, for example, 380 orange chips? At first it might appear that we should accept H_1 as the correct hypothesis, in view of the fact that .0001 is the largest probability in the column headed 300–399; however, since .0001 is itself such a small probability we should perhaps question our *method of drawing the chips;* it may be that our method contains some bias which would destroy the validity of the mathematical model which we have set up. In any practical situation the research worker should always be aware that unless he knows *some* hypothesis upon which the results which he obtained would be reasonably probable, he is perhaps using a mathematical model to which he has no scientific right. As a matter of fact, in the situation which we have been using as an example, it would be more prudent to construct Table 3.6.1.

With Table 3.6.1 before us, we can be confident (at the .05 level) that we are going to draw either 0, 224–276, 469–531, 724–776, or 1,000 orange chips. If we draw some other number of orange chips we may wish to reject (at the .05 level of confidence) our working assumption, namely, that our method of drawing is a random one. Furthermore, we can be confident at the .01 level that we are going to draw either 0, 216–284, 460–540, 716–784, or 1,000 orange chips; our failure to do so would make us even more suspicious of our method of drawing.

3.7. The Logic of Statistical Inference. The mathematical models which we have just been discussing are very special cases of statistical inference; in future chapters we shall take up models which can have a wider application. However, *the fundamental logic of the procedure will remain the same.* Always, in statistical inference, there are certain hypotheses about a population. If, on the basis of each hypothesis, the expected sampling distribution of a statistic can be determined, it is then possible to make some observations (that is, draw a sample) and then to reject certain hypotheses as untenable and to accept other hypotheses as tenable; in other words, to determine a set

TABLE 3.6.1. EXPECTED SAMPLING DISTRIBUTIONS, FOR ALL POSSIBLE HYPOTHESES, OF NUMBER OF ORANGE CHIPS IN SEQUENCE OF 1,000 RANDOM DRAWS FROM BOWL CONTAINING FOUR CHIPS*

Number of orange chips in 1,000 random draws

Hypothesis	0	1– 215	216– 223	224– 276	277– 284	285– 300	301– 425	426– 459	460– 468	469– 531	532– 540	541– 574	575– 699	700– 715	716– 723	724– 776	777– 784	785– 999	1,000
H_4	0	0	0	0	0	0	0	0	0	0	0	0	0	0	0	0	0	0	1
H_3	.000	.000	.000	.000	.000	.000	.000	.000	.000	.000	.000	.000	.000	.005	.020	.950	.020	.005	.000
H_2	.000	.000	.000	.000	.000	.000	.000	.005	.020	.950	.020	.005	.000	.000	.000	.000	.000	.000	.000
H_1	.000	.005	.020	.950	.020	.005	.000	.000	.000	.000	.000	.000	.000	.000	.000	.000	.000	.000	.000
H_0	1	0	0	0	0	0	0	0	0	0	0	0	0	0	0	0	0	0	0

* The values in this table were obtained by an approximation and some of the larger entries are significant to only two places.

42

of hypotheses (confidence interval) such that one is confident (at a certain level of confidence) that one of the hypotheses in the set is correct. The purpose of the foregoing discussion has been to give the student a firm grasp of this fundamental logic. He should now be able to handle problems like the following one. Upon a certain hypothesis H, the expected sampling distribution of a certain statistic z is given by the following table:

POSSIBLE VALUES OF THE STATISTIC z

z_1–z_4	z_5–z_7	z_8–z_{12}	z_{13}–z_{19}	z_{20}–z_{40}
.005	.020	.950	.020	.005

Suppose we draw a sample and obtain a value of z_{15} for our statistic. At what level of confidence can we reject H? If there are other hypotheses upon which the value of z_{15} is a reasonably probable one (that is, in relation to other possible values[1]), we can reject H at the .05 level of confidence.

EXERCISES

3.7.1. On the hypothesis H the expected sampling distribution of the statistic w is given by $f(w) = \dfrac{(5 - |w - 5|)^2}{85}$ when $w = 1, 2, \ldots, 9$. (The vertical lines mean the absolute value of whatever is between them. The absolute value of any number is positive, for example, $|3 - 7| = |-4| = 4$.) At what level of confidence can we reject H if the observed value of w turns out to be 9?

3.7.2. On the hypothesis H_1 the expected sampling distribution of the statistic y is given by $f(y) = \dfrac{(4 - |y - 4|)^3}{136}$ when $y = 1, 2, \ldots, 7$. The observed value of y is 6. Test H.

3.7.3. On the hypothesis H' (read "H prime") the expected sampling distribution of the statistic x is given by $f(x) = \dfrac{10 - x}{45}$ when $x = 1, 2, \ldots, 9$. The observed value of x is 9. Test H'.

3.7.4. On the hypothesis H the expected sampling distribution of z is given by $f(z) = \dfrac{(5 - |z - 4|)^3}{324}$ when $z = 1, 2, \ldots, 8$. The observed value of z is 8. Test H.

---

[1] In many situations the probability of any one specified value of a statistic is very small; what matters is the probability of that value in comparison with the probabilities of other specific values. If we flip a penny 1,000 times, the probability of obtaining 500 heads is small, yet larger than that of any other specified value.

3.7.5. On the hypothesis H_2 the expected sampling distribution of w is given by $f(w) = \dfrac{65 - w^2}{316}$ with $w = 1, 2, \ldots, 8$. The observed value is 7. Test H_2.

3.7.6. On the hypothesis H_N the expected sampling distribution of the statistic t is given (approximately) by the following table:

$(-7)-(-3.850)$	$(-3.850)-(-2.845)$	$(-2.845)-(-2.528)$
.0005	.0045	.005
$(-2.528)-(-2.086)$	$(-2.086)-(2.086)$	$(2.086)-(2.528)$
.015	.950	.015
$(2.528)-(2.845)$	$(2.845)-(3.850)$	$(3.850)-(7.000)$
.005	.0045	.0005

Test H_N for an observed value of $t = 2.7$.

3.7.7. On the hypothesis H_N the expected sampling distribution of the statistic CR is given (approximately) by the following table:

(-3.291) or lower	$(-3.291)-(-2.576)$	$(-2.576)-(-2.326)$
.0005	.0045	.005
$(-2.326)-(-1.960)$	$(-1.960)-(1.960)$	$(1.960)-(2.326)$
.015	.950	.015
$(2.326)-(2.576)$	$(2.576)-(3.291)$	(3.291) or higher
.005	.0045	.0005

The observed value is $CR = -2.0$. Test H_N.

3.7.8. On the hypothesis H the expected sampling distribution of the mean breaking strength in samples of 50 pieces of a certain kind of rope is given by the following table:

474 or lower	475–480	481–519	520–525	526 or higher
.005	.020	.950	.020	.005

A sample of 50 pieces of rope is drawn randomly and the mean breaking strength is found to be 479. Test H.

3.7.9. On the hypothesis H the expected sampling distribution of the mean intelligence-test score for 30 army officers drawn at random from a certain army base is given by the following table:

116 or lower	117–118	118–122	123–124	125 or higher
.01	.015	.950	.015	.01

A sample of 30 scores yields a mean of 116. Test H.

3.8. Two Types of Error. It is apparent from the previous discussion that either of two types of error can be made in drawing an inference about a population from a sample:

Type I Error. A hypothesis may be rejected when it is in fact correct. The level of confidence states the maximum probability of making a type I error.

Type II Error. A hypothesis may fail to be rejected when it is in fact incorrect. As the power of a test (P) states the probability that a hypothesis will be rejected, $1 - P$ is the probability of making a type II error, except when the hypothesis tested is correct, when the probability of making a type II error is, of course, zero.

TABLE 3.8.1. PROBABILITIES OF MAKING TYPE II ERROR WHEN USING
.0216 LEVEL OF CONFIDENCE (BOLDFACE TYPE) COMPARED WITH
THOSE WHEN USING .1344 LEVEL OF CONFIDENCE, IN
CHIP-IN-BOWL PROBLEM*

Hypothesis tested

		H_0	H_1	H_2	H_3	H_4
	H_0	**0** 0	**1** 0	**0** 0	**0** 0	**0** 0
	H_1	**.056** .056	**0** 0	**.756** .474	**.078** .020	**.000** .000
Correct hypothesis	H_2	**.001** .001	**.623** .376	**0** 0	**.623** .376	**.001** .001
	H_3	**.000** .000	**.078** .020	**.756** .474	**0** 0	**.056** .056
	H_4	**0** 0	**0** 0	**0** 0	**1** 0	**0** 0

* Data from Table 3.2.1.

We can decrease the probability of making a type I error by taking lower and lower levels of confidence. However, with the same number of observations, a lower level of confidence decreases the power of a test and thus increases the probability of a type II error. Consider, for example, Table 3.8.1, which

TABLE 3.8.2. PROBABILITIES OF MAKING TYPE II ERROR IN CHIP-IN-BOWL SITUATION FOR 10, 100 (BOLDFACE), AND 1,000 (ITALICS) OBSERVATIONS, WITH LEVEL OF CONFIDENCE = .0216 IN ALL CASES

		Hypothesis tested				
	H_0	H_1	H_2	H_3	H_4
H_0	0 **0** *0*	1 **0** *0*	0 **0** *0*	0 **0** *0*	0 **0** *0*
H_1	.056 **.000** *.000*	0 **0** *0*	.756 **.001** *.000*	.078 **.000** *.000*	.000 **.000** *.000*
H_2	.001 **.000** *.000*	.623 **.018** *.000*	0 **0** *0*	.623 **.028** *.000*	.001 **.000** *.000*
H_3	.000 **.000** *.000*	.078 **.000** *.000*	.756 **.149** *.000*	0 **0** *0*	.056 **.000** *.000*
H_4	0 **0** *0*	0 **0** *0*	0 **0** *0*	1 **0** *0*	0 **0** *0*

Correct hypothesis (row label for the entire set of rows)

shows the probability of a type II error for the .0216 level of confidence (boldface type) and also for the .1344 level of confidence for the situation illustrated in Table 3.2.1. Nevertheless, in testing any given hypothesis the probability of making a type II error can be made to approach zero by increasing the number of observations, keeping the level of confidence constant. Table 3.8.2 shows the probability of making a type II error with 10, 100 (boldface), and 1,000 (italics) observations, with level of confidence .0216 in all cases.

In many situations it is not feasible or perhaps even possible to increase the number of observations, and one must choose between taking a low level of confidence and thus increasing the probability of a type II error, or taking a higher level of confidence and thus increasing the probability of a type I error. Which course one follows depends upon the requirements of a particular situation. For example, if the rejection of a given hypothesis would imply that certain very costly changes should be made in a factory, school, or business, or in the case of scientific research that drastic changes must be made in a well-established theory, and if there are no other very compelling reasons to make these changes, then a very low level of confidence should probably be required, that is, the probability of making a type I error should be made very low. If, on the other hand, one must take some kind of action on the basis of the best possible evidence as to which hypotheses are most tenable, then a higher level of confidence should be taken with a resulting lower probability of a type II error.

3.9. Confidence Intervals with One Bound Only. In many cases we may be interested in ascertaining a confidence interval with lower bound only; that is, we may be interested in being able to say with a certain degree of confidence that the population characteristic (called a *parameter*) is at *least* as great as a certain value (lower bound). Conversely, we may wish to say that the parameter is at *most* as great as a certain value (upper bound). In either case we shall sum the cells in our table of expected sampling distributions in *one direction only*. Consider, for example, a population which has a parameter which must of necessity have one of the values a, b, c, d, e, or f, which are in ascending order. Let $z_1, z_2, \ldots, z_{11}$ be the possible values of a certain statistic, in ascending order. Let the expected sampling distributions of z be given by Table 3.9.1.[1]

The heavy black lines indicate the .05 confidence interval for the parameter for each observed value of the sample. For example, for an observed value of z_3 the .05 confidence interval is c–f inclusive, c being the lower bound. We are in this case not

---

[1] The question of whether we can think up an actual situation which fits this mathematical model is irrelevant to this discussion.

interested in the danger of including e and f in the interval, even though they seem rather unlikely; all we care about is that the parameter is at least c (at the .05 level of confidence). At first it may appear that we are merely giving up information contained in the sample, that we are gaining nothing by taking lower bound only. That this is not true can be seen by considering that with lower bound only we can say, with an observation of z_7, that the parameter is at least e (at the .05 level of confi-

TABLE 3.9.1. EXPECTED SAMPLING DISTRIBUTIONS OF z, ON EACH POSSIBLE HYPOTHESIS

Possible values of z in ascending order

		z_1	z_2	z_3	z_4	z_5	z_6	z_7	z_8	z_9	z_{10}	z_{11}
	H_f	.0000	.0000	.0000	.0000	.0000	.0000	.0203	.1010	.3152	.4779	.0856
	H_e	.0000	.0029	.0033	.0155	.0712	.1064	.3117	.2622	.1814	.0356	.0098
Hypothesis	H_d	.0176	.0202	.2163	.4403	.1985	.0571	.0215	.0154	.0097	.0025	.0008
	H_c	.2447	.4962	.1635	.0497	.0204	.0128	.0076	.0033	.0016	.0002	.0000
	H_b	.9215	.0371	.0196	.0102	.0058	.0034	.0015	.0008	.0001	.0000	.0000
	H_a	1	0	0	0	0	0	0	0	0	0	0

dence), whereas, if we had taken both upper and lower bounds we could say only that the parameter lies in the interval d–e inclusive. It may appear to the student that this juggling of confidence intervals is highly suspect, that statistics seems to be a highly arbitrary business. It is true that the method of selection of confidence intervals is to a certain extent arbitrary and depends upon the purposes of the investigator. However, the statistician can always justify his choice of a method of ascertaining a confidence interval (if that choice is made *before* a sample is drawn) by pointing out that before taking his sample the probability was p that he would make a false assertion about the limits within which the parameter lies.

A somewhat more convenient table in the foregoing type of problem is one which shows for each value z_i the probability of obtaining a value of z *at least as great* as z_i. Our table is transformed into Table 3.9.2.

TABLE 3.9.2. EXPECTED SAMPLING DISTRIBUTIONS OF z FOR EACH POSSIBLE HYPOTHESIS, SHOWING THE PROBABILITY OF OBTAINING A VALUE OF z AT LEAST AS GREAT AS z_i

Values of z, in ascending order

	z_1	z_2	z_3	z_4	z_5	z_6	z_7	z_8	z_9	z_{10}	z_{11}
H_f	1	1.0000	1.0000	1.0000	1.0000	1.0000	1.0000	.9797	.8787	.5635	.0856
H_e	1	1.0000	.9971	.9938	.9783	.9071	.8007	.4890	.2268	.0454	.0098
H_d	1	.9824	.9622	.7459	.3056	.1071	.0499	.0284	.0130	.0033	.0008
H_c	1	.7553	.2591	.0956	.0459	.0255	.0127	.0051	.0018	.0002	.0000
H_b	1	.0785	.0414	.0218	.0116	.0058	.0024	.0009	.0001	.0000	.0000
H_a	1	0	0	0	0	0	0	0	0	0	0

(Hypothesis)

With Table 3.9.2 the lower bound for the desired confidence interval can be seen at a glance. If we had desired an *upper bound* only, we would have summed in the opposite direction, that is, from left to right; our table would then show the c.d.f. on the basis of each hypothesis.

Chapter 4

PARAMETERS AND STATISTICS

4.1. Definitions

Definition. A *parameter* is a characteristic of a population or its distribution.

Examples. **1.** The proportion of the population of IQ's of California school children falling above 100.

2. The total range of values of the population of high jumps by athletes at the Olympic games in 1936.

3. The value occurring most frequently in the population of all possible ways in which two dice can land, each way having as value the sum of the numbers indicated by the two faces. (This value is, as we have seen, 7.)

We shall usually refer to parameters with Greek letters.

Definition. A *statistic* is any characteristic of a sample or its distribution.[1] *We shall refer to statistics with Latin letters.*

4.2. Measures of Central Tendency.

It is often useful to designate some value of a distribution which represents the *center* or *central tendency* in some sense. There are several kinds of center which we might choose; some of these are defined as follows.

Definition. The *mode* of a distribution is the value having the highest frequency, if there is such a value.

Examples. **1.** The parameter listed as Example 3 in Sec. 4.1.

2. The value schizophrenic in the distribution of patients in a certain hospital: ($\frac{2}{3}$, schizophrenic), ($\frac{7}{24}$, manic-depressive), ($\frac{1}{24}$, paranoiac).

3. The distribution ($\frac{1}{6}$, x_1), ($\frac{1}{3}$, x_2), ($\frac{1}{3}$, x_3), ($\frac{1}{6}$, x_4) has no mode.

[1] Later in our discussion the term "statistic" will also be used to include variables which are not determined by the sample alone but depend also upon some parameter; for example, if Y = sample mean − population mean, then Y is not a characteristic of either population or sample alone, but we choose to call Y a "statistic."

Definition. The *median* of a distribution is the value x such that $F(x) > .5$ and F(value just lower than x) $< .5$, if such a value exists. The median is therefore the middlemost value.

Examples. **1.** The value .3 in the c.d.f. (.1,0), (.2,.1), (.3,.2), (.6,.3), (1,.4). **2.** The fr.f. (.25,2), (.25,3), (.50,4) has no median.

Note that if a distribution is qualitative, that is, such that the values do not fall into a linear order, it does not have a median.

Definition. The *arithmetic mean* of a distribution is the sum of the products of the values and their corresponding proportions, that is, $x_1f(x_1) + x_2f(x_2) + \cdots + x_kf(x_k)$, assuming that the values are quantitative and do not indicate merely an order.

The arithmetic mean is, for finite populations, the same as the "average" used in school arithmetic. (As an exercise the student should prove this to himself.)

Examples. **1.** The arithmetic mean of the distribution ($\frac{1}{4}$,2), ($\frac{2}{4}$,3), ($\frac{4}{4}$,5) is $2(\frac{1}{4}) + 3(\frac{2}{4}) + 5(\frac{4}{4}) = 4$. **2.** The arithmetic mean of the distribution of all possible different results of tossing a die, taking the indicated number as value, is

$$1(\tfrac{1}{6}) + 2(\tfrac{1}{6}) + 3(\tfrac{1}{6}) + 4(\tfrac{1}{6}) + 5(\tfrac{1}{6}) + 6(\tfrac{1}{6}) = 3.5$$

Note that if the values are qualitative or ordinal (that is, such that they can be ordered but not such that we can assign distances between them) the arithmetic mean does not exist. For example, the population $(3,X_1)$, $(2,X_2)$, $(4,X_3)$, $(1,X_4)$, in which the values are *ranks*, does not have an arithmetic mean.

The arithmetic mean is also called the *expected value* of a member of the population (or sample) to be chosen at random, or the *mathematical expectation* of a member to be chosen at random. If we let X be an abbreviation for "a member of the set to be chosen at random" and E be an abbreviation for "expected value of" then $E(X)$ means the expected value of a member of the set to be chosen at random. We shall use $E(X)$ to refer indifferently to either the sample or the population mean; that is, a statement utilizing this symbol will hold for both population and sample. When speaking specifically of one or the other we shall use m for the sample mean and μ for the population mean.

The arithmetic mean is the *center of gravity* of a distribution in the sense that the sum of deviations from $E(X)$ is zero, the deviation of the member X_i being $x_i - E(X)$. (The student should prove this as an exercise.)

We can also define the expected value of any function of X as $E[g(X)] \equiv g(x_1)f(x_1) + g(x_2)f(x_2) + \cdots + g(x_k)f(x_k)$. For example, $E(X^2) = x_1^2 f(x_1) + x_2^2 f(x_2) + \cdots + x_k^2 f(x_k)$.

The reader should satisfy himself that, if g and h are any functions and c is a constant, then

$$E[cg(X) + h(X)] = cE[g(X)] + E[h(X)]$$

This important property of E is summed up by saying that E is a *linear operator*. Note also that $E(c) = c$. Remembering that any constant is a function of any variable, the student should note the special case $E[cg(X) + b] = cE[g(X)] + b$, where both b and c are constants.

Definition. The geometric mean of a distribution is the Nth root of the product of the values of all N members of the population (or sample), each value occurring in the product as many times as there are members in the set which have that value, that is, geometric mean $\equiv \sqrt[N]{w_1 w_2 \cdots w_N}$, in which w_i is the value of the ith member. Note that

$$w_1 w_2 \cdots w_N = (x_1)^{n_1}(x_2)^{n_2} \cdots (x_k)^{n_k}$$

in which x_i is a value different from every other value and n_i is the number of members of the set having that value. Thus

$$\text{Geometric mean} \equiv \sqrt[N]{w_1 w_2 \cdots w_N} = (w_1 w_2 \cdots w_N)^{1/N}$$
$$= x_1^{n_1/N} x_2^{n_2/N} \cdots x_k^{n_k/N} = x_1^{f(x_1)} x_2^{f(x_2)} \cdots x_k^{f(x_k)}$$

Example. The geometric mean of the distribution $(\frac{1}{4},1)$, $(\frac{1}{2},2)$, $(\frac{1}{8},3)$, $(\frac{1}{8},4)$ is $1^{\frac{1}{4}} 2^{\frac{1}{2}} 3^{\frac{1}{8}} 4^{\frac{1}{8}} = 1.924$.

Measures of central tendency other than those listed are rarely used.

4.3. Measures of Variability. It is useful to indicate the amount of variation in value among the members of a population or sample. The most obvious measure of variation is the range.

Definition. The *range* of a distribution is the difference between the highest and lowest values.

Example. In the distribution $(\frac{1}{8}, -4)$, $(\frac{1}{4}, 0)$, $(\frac{1}{2}, 1)$, $(\frac{1}{8}, 3)$ the range is $3 - (-4) = 3 + 4 = 7$.

By far the most frequently used measures of variability are the *variance*, and its square root, the *standard deviation*.

Definition. The *variance* of a distribution is the arithmetic mean of the squared deviations from the arithmetic mean; that is,

$$\text{Variance} \equiv [x_1 - E(X)]^2 f(x_1) + [x_2 - E(X)]^2 f(x_2)$$
$$+ \cdots + [x_k - E(X)]^2 f(x_k)$$

The *standard deviation* is the square root of the variance.

The variance of a population is denoted by σ^2, the variance of a sample by s^2. We shall use "Var" to denote either a population or sample variance. Note that $\text{Var} \equiv E\{[X - E(X)]^2\}$, that is, the variance of a distribution is the expected value of a squared deviation from the arithmetic mean.

Example. The distribution $(\frac{1}{6}, 1)$, $(\frac{1}{6}, 2)$, $(\frac{1}{6}, 3)$, $(\frac{1}{6}, 4)$, $(\frac{1}{6}, 5)$, $(\frac{1}{6}, 6)$ has the mean 3.5. (Unless otherwise indicated, "mean" in this text always refers to the arithmetic mean.) Therefore the variance is

$$(1 - 3.5)^2(\tfrac{1}{6}) + (2 - 3.5)^2(\tfrac{1}{6}) + (3 - 3.5)^2(\tfrac{1}{6}) + (4 - 3.5)^2(\tfrac{1}{6})$$
$$+ (5 - 3.5)^2(\tfrac{1}{6}) + (6 - 3.5)^2(\tfrac{1}{6}) = \tfrac{35}{12}$$

For computational purposes note that

$$E\{[X - E(X)]^2\} = E\{X^2 - 2XE(X) + [E(X)]^2\}$$
$$= E(X^2) - 2E(X)E(X) + [E(X)]^2 = E(X^2) - [E(X)]^2.$$

For example, we could have computed the variance $\frac{35}{12}$ by taking

$$E(X^2) = (1)(\tfrac{1}{6}) + (4)(\tfrac{1}{6}) + (9)(\tfrac{1}{6}) + (16)(\tfrac{1}{6})$$
$$+ (25)(\tfrac{1}{6}) + (36)(\tfrac{1}{6}) = \tfrac{91}{6}$$

Thus $\text{Var} = E(X^2) - [E(X)]^2 = \frac{91}{6} - \frac{49}{4} = \frac{35}{12}.$

EXERCISES

4.3.1. The following are sample data, each datum being the value of a member of the sample: 3, 2, 1, 1, 1, 3, 1, 4, 5, 1, 2, 4, 3, 2, 3, 5, 4, 2, 5, 1, 2.

Compute each of the following statistics, if it exists:

   a. The mode

   b. The median

   c. The arithmetic mean

   d. The variance (compute in two ways)

   e. The standard deviation

4.3.2. Compute the same statistics as in Exercise 4.3.1 for the following sample data: .00, .02, .00, .01, .03, .05, .00, .01, .03, .01, .05, .02, .01, .05, .04, .00, .01.

4.3.3. Compute the same statistics as in Exercise 4.3.1 for the following sample data: for, for, against, for, against, for, for, against, against, for, for, for, against, for, against, against, for.

4.3.4. Compute the same statistics as in Exercise 4.3.1 for the following sample data: 9, 8, 9, 9, 8, 7, 9, 6, 7, 7, 9, 8.

4.3.5. Find the arithmetic mean and the variance for each of the populations mentioned in the following exercises:

   a. Exercise 1.7.1

   b. Exercise 1.7.2

   c. Exercise 1.7.3

   d. Exercise 1.7.4

   e. Exercise 1.7.5

4.3.6. Find the arithmetic mean and the variance for each of the populations mentioned in the following exercises:

   a. Exercise 1.8.1

   b. Exercise 1.8.2

   c. Exercise 1.8.3

   d. Exercise 1.8.5

   e. Exercise 1.8.9

   f. Exercise 1.8.10

   g. Exercise 1.8.11

   h. Exercise 1.8.12

   i. Exercise 1.8.13

4.3.7. Find the arithmetic mean and the variance of the expected sampling distribution of the arithmetic mean of random samples of size 2 from each of the following populations:

   a. $(0,X_1)$, $(0,X_2)$, $(0,X_3)$, $(1,X_4)$, $(1,X_5)$

   b. $(0,X_1)$, $(0,X_2)$, $(1,X_3)$, $(1,X_4)$, $(2,X_5)$

Compare the arithmetic means which you have just computed with the arithmetic means of the two populations from which the samples are drawn.

4.3.8. Find the arithmetic mean and the variance of the expected sampling distribution of the arithmetic mean of random samples of size 3 from each of the following populations:

   a. $(0,X_1)$, $(0,X_2)$, $(1,X_3)$, $(1,X_4)$, $(1,X_5)$

   b. $(0,X_1)$, $(1,X_2)$, $(1,X_3)$, $(2,X_4)$, $(2,X_5)$

Compare the arithmetic means which you have computed with the arithmetic means of the two populations from which the samples are drawn.

4.3.9. Find the arithmetic mean and the variance of each row of Table 3.1.1. Compare the arithmetic mean in each case with the mean number of orange chips hypothesized, giving each orange chip in the bowl the value 1 and each black chip the value 0.

4.3.10. For the table which you constructed in Exercise 3.1.2, find the arithmetic mean and the variance for each of the three rows. Compare the arithmetic mean in each case with the arithmetic mean of the hypothesized population, giving each A the value 1 and each non-A the value 0.

4.3.11. Find the arithmetic mean and the variance for each row of Table 3.2.1. Compare the arithmetic mean in each case with that of the hypothesized population, giving each orange chip the value 1 and each black chip the value 0.

4.3.12. Prove that the arithmetic mean of the expected sampling distribution of arithmetic means for any size sample from a finite population is the arithmetic mean of the population, that is, that $E(m) = \mu$, where m is the sample mean and μ is the population mean.

4.4. Abbreviations. The student should by now desire an abbreviation for an expression like

$$x_1 f(x_1) + x_2 f(x_2) + \cdots + x_k f(x_k)$$

We shall abbreviate an expression of this kind by using the symbol Σ, called the *summation sign*. Using the summation sign, the above expression is abbreviated $\sum_{i=1}^{k} x_i f(x_i)$. The letter i in our abbreviation is called an *index*. Note that our index does not appear in the expression when it is fully written out; therefore, we could have used j or l or any other letter not appearing in the expression as the index. The expression $(3 - a)^c f(3) + (4 - a)^c f(4) + \cdots + (m - a)^c f(m)$ can be abbreviated $\sum_{x=3}^{m} (x - a)^c f(x)$. This latter expression is read "the summation of x minus a to the cth power times f of x with x running from 3 to m."

A product can be abbreviated in an exactly analogous way using the symbol Π. For example, the geometric mean is defined as $\prod_{i=1}^{k} x_i^{f(x_i)}$.

It is customary to drop the index and superscript when the context clearly indicates what should be summed or multiplied, and we shall follow this convention; for example, we shall write $\Sigma x f(x)$ for $\displaystyle\sum_{i=1}^{k} x_i f(x_i)$ when there is no danger of confusion.

EXERCISES

4.4.1. Abbreviate each of the following expressions:

a. $x_1^2 f(x_1) + x_2^2 f(x_2) + \cdots + x_k^2 f(x_k)$

b. $(x-1)^2 f(1) + (x-2)^2 f(2) + \cdots + (x-m)^2 f(m)$

c. $y_6 + y_7 + \cdots + y_i$

d. $(2-c)^2 + (3-c)^3 + \cdots + (b-c)^b$

e. $(1+a)^3 + (2+a)^4 + \cdots + (15+a)^{17}$

f. $(5)(6)(7) \cdots (40)$

4.4.2. Given that $\displaystyle\sum_{i=1}^{7} x_i^2 = 29$ and $\displaystyle\sum_{i=1}^{7} x_i = 15$, find, if possible,

a. $\displaystyle\sum_{i=1}^{7} (x_i - 2)^2$

b. $\displaystyle\sum_{j=1}^{7} (x_j + 3)^2$

c. $\displaystyle\sum_{j=1}^{7} (2x_j + 1)^2$

d. $\displaystyle\sum_{j=1}^{7} (x_j + j)^2$

e. $\displaystyle\sum_{i=1}^{7} i x_i$

4.4.3. Write an expression for the probability that a sample of 30 people chosen at random from a population of which 70 are above fifty and 30 are not above fifty will contain

a. from 15 to 25 people above fifty

b. at least 15 people above fifty

c. at most 20 people above fifty

4.4.4. Write an expression for the probability that a sample of n people chosen at random from a population of which N_1 are A's and N_2 are not A's will contain

a. from b to c A's (assuming $0 < b < c < n$)

b. at least $b + 4$ A's

c. at most $c - 2$ A's

4.4.5. Write an expression for the probability that a sequence of 30 choices (each choice having two alternatives, only one of which is correct) by a child in a problem which is too difficult for the child (so that the child chooses randomly) will contain

    a. at least 20 correct choices

    b. between 10 and 20 correct choices

    c. at most 25 correct choices

4.5. Moments. The mean and the variance of a distribution are merely special cases (though very important ones) of *moments* of that distribution.

Definition. The *k*th *moment about the point* *c* is the expected value of the *k*th power deviations from the point *c*; that is,

$$\mathrm{mom}_c^k \equiv E[(X - c)^k] = \sum_{\text{all } x} (x - c)^k f(x).$$

Examples. **1.** The arithmetic mean is the first moment about the origin, that is, $\mathrm{mom}_0^1 \equiv E(X) \equiv E[(X - 0)^1]$.

2. The variance is the second moment about the mean, that is, $\mathrm{mom}_{E(X)}^2$. The computational formula for the variance, derived in Sec. 4.3, is the second moment about the origin minus the square of the first moment about the origin; that is, $\mathrm{mom}_{E(X)}^2 = \mathrm{mom}_0^2 - (\mathrm{mom}_0^1)^2$ or $\mathrm{Var.} = E(X^2) - [E(X)]^2$.

The moments most frequently used are those about the origin ($c = 0$) and about the mean [$c = E(X)$]. The number k is called the *order* of the moment.

We can easily prove that the second moment about the point c is a minimum when $c = E(X)$, that is, the second moment about the mean is the smallest possible second moment. The proof is as follows:

$$
\begin{aligned}
E[(X - c)^2] - E\{[X - E(X)]^2\} &= E(X^2) - 2cE(X) + c^2 \\
-E(X^2) + [E(X)]^2 &= -2cE(X) + c^2 + [E(X)]^2 \\
&= [E(X) - c]^2
\end{aligned}
$$

which is positive unless $c = E(X)$.

4.6. Computation of Moments. It is more convenient to use frequencies than proportions in computing moments of samples (or finite populations). Suppose that we have the following sample data, each datum being the value of some member of the sample: 0, 5, 2, 1, 0, 0, 3, 2, 2, 1, 4, 5, 4, 3, 1, 1, 5, 0, 2, 3, 3, 4, 2, 3, 2.

We collect these values into a frequency table as follows:

x	frequency (x)
5	3
4	3
3	5
2	6
1	4
0	4

Instead of finding the proportion $f(x)$ for each value and then taking $m = \Sigma x_i f(x_i)$ we observe that

$$\sum x_i f(x_i) = \sum x_i \frac{\text{freq } (x_i)}{n} = \frac{\Sigma x[\text{freq } (x)]}{n}$$

The computation indicated by this formula can be conveniently performed in our table:

x	freq (x)	$x[\text{freq } (x)]$
5	3	15
4	3	12
3	5	15
2	6	12
1	4	4
0	4	0
	$\Sigma \text{freq } (x) = 25$	$\Sigma x[\text{freq } (x)] = 58$

Similarly, for the variance we observe that

$$\sum (x - m)^2 f(x) = \sum x^2 f(x) - \left[\sum x f(x)\right]^2 = \frac{\Sigma x^2[\text{freq } (x)]}{n}$$

$$- \left[\frac{\Sigma x[\text{freq } (x)]}{n}\right]^2 = \frac{n\Sigma x^2[\text{freq } (x)] - \{\Sigma x[\text{freq } (x)]\}^2}{n^2}$$

We compute both the mean and the variance in the following table:

x	x^2	freq (x)	$x[$freq $(x)]$	$x^2[$freq $(x)]$
5	25	3	15	75
4	16	3	12	48
3	9	5	15	45
2	4	6	12	24
1	1	4	4	4
0	0	4	0	0
Σ		25	58	196

$$m = {}^{58}\!/_{25} = 2.32$$

$$s^2 = \frac{25(196) - (58)^2}{(25)^2} = 2.4576$$

4.7. Transformations of Values for Computational Purposes.

Values are usually such that it is easier in computing the mean, variance, and other moments to transform the values, compute the desired moment, and then transform the computed moment into the value it would have had if the transformation had not been made. For example, suppose that we have the following sample data:

x	freq (x)
11,071	2
11,067	5
11,063	11
11,059	4
11,055	1

To simplify computation we subtract 11,063 from each value and divide the difference by 4; that is, we transform x into y so that $y = (x - 11,063)/4$. We then compute the mean and variance of Y as shown in the following table:

x	y	y^2	freq (y)	$y[$freq $(y)]$	$y^2[$freq $(y)]$
11,071	2	4	2	4	8
11,067	1	1	5	5	5
11,063	0	0	11	0	0
11,059	-1	1	4	-4	4
11,055	-2	4	1	-2	4
		Σ	23	3	21

$$m_y = {}^{3}\!/_{23} = 0.1304$$

$$s_y^2 = \frac{(23)(21) - 9}{(23)^2} = 0.89603$$

To obtain m_x and s_x^2 we observe that, since $x = 4y + 11{,}063$ [we can obtain this either directly from the table or by solving the equation $y = (x - 11{,}063)/4$ for x],

$$m_x = \frac{\Sigma x[\text{freq }(x)]}{n} = \frac{\Sigma(4y + 11{,}063)\text{freq }(y)}{n} = \frac{4\Sigma y[\text{freq }(y)]}{n}$$

$$+ \; 11{,}063 \, \frac{\Sigma \text{freq }(y)}{n} = 4m_y + 11{,}063$$

Therefore,

$$m_x = 4(0.1304) + 11{,}063 = 11{,}063.522$$

Similarly,

$$s_x^2 = \frac{\Sigma(x - m_x)^2 \text{freq }(x)}{n}$$

$$= \frac{\Sigma[4y + 11{,}063 - (4m_y + 11{,}063)]^2 \text{freq }(y)}{n}$$

$$= \frac{\Sigma(4y - 4m_y)^2 \text{freq }(y)}{n} = \frac{16\Sigma(y - m_y)^2 \text{freq }(y)}{n} = 16s_y^2$$

Therefore

$$s_x^2 = 16(0.89603) = 14.336$$

Instead of 11,063 we could have chosen any other value to transform into 0, and we could have chosen any interval for steps between y's. The student should be able to prove as an exercise that if $x = ay + b$, in which a and b are any constants, then $m_x = am_y + b$ and $s_x^2 = a^2 s_y^2$ and, further, that $\text{mom}_{E(X)}^3 = a^3\text{mom}_{E(Y)}^3$ and $\text{mom}_{E(X)}^4 = a^4\text{mom}_{E(Y)}^4$ and, more generally, $\text{mom}_{E(X)}^k = a^k\text{mom}_{E(Y)}^k$.

The number which is transformed into 0 is usually called an *arbitrary origin*.

EXERCISES

4.7.1. Each of the following data is the length of time (in seconds) that it took a subject in a psychological experiment to respond to the turning on of a light by pressing a key:

.15	.11	.14	.23	.20	.11	.14	.25
.10	.15	.17	.16	.11	.13	.16	.15
.21	.14	.22	.15	.15	.21	.12	.13
.17	.20	.18	.12	.16	.19	.19	.18

Find each of the following statistics, if it exists:

a. The mode

b. The median

c. The arithmetic mean

d. The variance

e. The standard deviation

4.7.2. Each of the following data is the intensity of a visual stimulus, measured in millilamberts, which had to be reached before a subject could recognize a word when it was exposed for .10 sec:

```
2.2   2.4   2.4   2.9   2.8   2.5   2.4
2.3   2.1   2.2   2.7   2.6   2.5   2.3
2.5   2.7   2.6   2.5   2.5   2.7   2.6
2.8   2.3   2.5   2.4   2.2   2.5   2.4
2.6   2.6   2.5   2.5   2.3   2.6   2.5
```

Find the statistics as in Exercise 4.7.1, a to e.

4.7.3. Find a convenient computational formula for $\text{mom}_{E(X)}^3$.

4.8. Grouping of Data into Class Intervals.

In most practical applications of statistics the data are spread out over a great many different values, so that computation becomes very laborious, even using the method given in Sec. 4.7. By grouping the data into *class intervals* and considering each datum as falling at the mid-point of its class interval, computation can be made much easier. For most data it has been found suitable to use between 10 and 20 classes. With fewer than 10 classes the calculation is usually not sufficiently accurate (obviously grouping throws away information); with more than 20 classes calculation is tedious. For example, suppose we have as data the number of cars passing over a certain bridge on each of 60 days selected at random from a large class of ordinary business days, and these numbers of cars range from 3,684 to 4,071, a range of 387. Following convention we therefore use some number between 20 and 39 as our class interval. If we use 25 as class interval it is convenient to take as mid-points 3,675, 3,700, 3,725, . . . , 4,075. The intervals are therefore 3,663–3,687, 3,688–3,712, . . . , 4,063–4,087. Any number falling between 3,663 and 3,687 (inclusive) is tabulated as 3,675, etc. We then proceed as in Sec. 4.7.

Example. The following are IQ scores of 200 children.

122	110	99	112	118
88	96	103	105	98
97	101	114	108	92
115	134	107	98	103
98	115	97	129	107
102	90	105	104	131
106	112	92	91	96
94	100	105	111	100
83	127	98	92	99
111	111	115	116	124
97	98	126	156	101
129	106	120	103	118
91	102	113	100	85
113	97	104	94	102
111	101	145	108	100
95	107	119	109	97
126	94	99	95	104
99	110	103	101	99
112	113	100	117	100
104	122	111	102	111
117	109	107	100	112
100	98	96	109	108
93	105	100	97	100
109	123	110	100	92
106	108	99	107	101
101	157	94	88	110
97	103	148	114	107
102	142	100	101	119
126	109	114	96	103
161	118	107	104	92
115	124	96	111	136
94	107	116	92	102
101	95	105	103	98
108	105	113	117	113
116	116	129	104	95
97	139	110	120	105
100	99	92	95	100
107	102	121	119	128
119	112	106	100	111
99	117	108	104	117

The highest IQ is 161, the lowest 83, giving a range of 78. By taking an interval of length 5, we obtain about 16 intervals. It is convenient to take multiples of 5 as mid-points. Our grouped distribution together with a transformation and calculation of moments is shown in the following table:

IQ (mid-point)	y	y^2	freq (y)	y freq (y)	y^2 freq (y)
160	11	121	1	11	121
155	10	100	2	20	200
150	9	81	1	9	81
145	8	64	1	8	64
140	7	49	2	14	98
135	6	36	2	12	72
130	5	25	5	25	125
125	4	16	7	28	114
120	3	9	13	39	117
115	2	4	27	54	108
110	1	1	21	21	21
105	0	0	34	0	0
100	-1	1	45	-45	45
95	-2	4	25	-50	100
90	-3	9	12	-36	108
85	-4	16	2	-8	32
			200	102	1,406

$$m_y = {}^{102}\!/_{200} = 0.51$$

$$s_y^2 = \frac{200(1,406) - (102)^2}{(200)^2} = 6.7699$$

From the table we see that $x = 5y + 105$. Thus,

$$m_x = 5m_y + 105 = 107.55$$

and $s_x^2 = 25s_y^2 = 169.2475$.

Chapter 5

HYPERGEOMETRIC AND BINOMIAL
DISTRIBUTIONS

5.1. Hypergeometric Distributions. We have already considered cases in which we draw a random sample of n from a population having N members, of which N_1 are of one kind and $N - N_1$ are of another kind, for example, drawing a random sample of 4 chips from a bowl containing 6 orange chips and 2 black chips. We saw that the expected sampling distribution (probability distribution) in any such case is given by $f(x) = C_x^{N_1} C_{n-x}^{N-N_1} / C_n^N$ in which x is the number of members in the sample which are of the first kind. Any distribution given by a rule of this form is a *hypergeometric distribution.*

Definition.[1]   A hypergeometric distribution is any distribution given by a rule of the form $f(x) = C_x^{N_1} C_{n-x}^{N-N_1} / C_n^N$. The expected sampling distribution of the number of A's in a sample of size n from a population of size N such that N_1 are A's and the rest are non-A's is a hypergeometric distribution.

Example.   The expected sampling distribution of the number of orange chips in a sample of 4 chips from a bowl containing 6 orange and 2 nonorange chips is given by $f(x) = C_x^6 C_{4-x}^2 / C_4^8$.

5.2. Moments of a Hypergeometric Distribution. It can be shown that the first moment about the origin, that is, the arithmetic mean, is nN_1/N, as follows.

First we note that, because of the way in which the hyper-

---

[1] This is the special case of one variable; our definition can easily be generalized to any number of variables.

geometric expression was derived,

$$\sum_{x=0}^{n} \frac{C_x^{N_1} C_{n-x}^{N-N_1}}{C_n^N} = 1$$

Thus

$$\sum_{x=0}^{n} C_x^{N_1} C_{n-x}^{N-N_1} = C_n^N = C_{x+n-x}^{N_1+N-N_1}$$

Let us write this result

$$\sum_{y=0}^{m} C_y^b C_{m-y}^k = C_m^{b+k}$$

in which m, b, and k are positive integers. Then

$$E(X) = \sum_{x=0}^{n} \frac{x C_x^{N_1} C_{n-x}^{N-N_1}}{C_n^N} = 0 + \frac{1}{C_n^N} \sum_{x=1}^{n} x \frac{N_1!}{x!(N_1 - x)!} C_{n-x}^{N-N_1}$$

$$= \frac{N_1}{C_n^N} \sum_{x=1}^{n} \frac{(N_1 - 1)!}{(x - 1)!(N_1 - x)!} C_{n-x}^{N-N_1} = \frac{N_1}{C_n^N} \sum_{x-1=0}^{n-1} C_{x-1}^{N_1-1} C_{n-x}^{N-N_1}$$

Note that if we let $y = x - 1$, $m = n - 1$, $b = N_1 - 1$, and $k = N - N_1$ the summation is in the form $\sum_{y=0}^{m} C_y^b C_{m-y}^k$. Thus we have

$$\frac{N_1}{C_n^N} C_{n-1}^{N-1} = \frac{N_1 n!(N - n)!}{N!} \frac{(N - 1)!}{(n - 1)!(N - n)!} = \frac{n N_1}{N}$$

In a similar but slightly more complicated way it can be shown that the second moment about the mean, that is, the variance, is

$$\frac{n N_1 (N - N_1)(N - n)}{N^2 (N - 1)}.$$

5.3. Binomial Distributions. In addition to the case in which we draw a random sample from a finite population, we have also in Chap. 3 considered the case in which we draw a sample of 1, replace it, draw another sample of 1, replace it, etc., drawing as many times as we wish. We considered our final sequence of n draws as a random sample of size 1 from the population of all possible sequences of n draws. In the population containing

N_1 A's and $N_2(= N - N_1)$ non-A's, the number of ways of drawing x A's and then $n - x$ non-A's (replacing after each draw) is $(N_1)^x(N - N_1)^{n-x}$; similarly, the number of ways of drawing $x - 1$ A's and then a non-A and then another A and then $n - x - 1$ non A's is also $(N_1)^x(N - N_1)^{n-x}$; there are as many such kinds of sequences as there are ways of choosing x positions out of n positions, that is, C_x^n; therefore, the number of ways of drawing x A's and $n - x$ non-A's in a sequence of n draws is $C_x^n(N_1)^x(N - N_1)^{n-x}$. As there are N^n possible sequences in all, the probability of drawing x A's in a sequence of n draws is $\dfrac{C_x^n(N_1)^x(N - N_1)^{n-x}}{N^n}$. We summarize this result in the following theorem.

Theorem 5.3. Consider the population consisting of all possible sequences of n random draws (with replacement after each draw) from a set in which N_1 are A's and $N - N_1$ are non-A's, each sequence having as value the number of A's drawn. The distribution of the population of sequences is given by

$$f(x) = \frac{C_x^n(N_1)^x(N - N_1)^{n-x}}{N^n}.$$

It is convenient to rewrite this formula as follows:

$$f(x) = C_x^n p^x q^{n-x}$$

in which p and $q(= 1 - p)$ are the proportions of A's and non-A's.

Examples 1. Suppose we plan to flip a penny 10 times. What is the probability of obtaining 6 heads? In this case $N = 2$; $N_1 = 1$; $n = 10$; $x = 6$. Thus $f(6) = C_6^{10}(\frac{1}{2})^{10}$.

2. One-third of an unknown number of chips in a bowl are white. What is the probability that 15 chips out of 35 drawn at random (replacing after each draw) will be white?   Ans. $C_{15}^{35}(\frac{1}{3})^{15}(\frac{2}{3})^{20}$.

Another way of obtaining the term $C_x^n p^x q^{n-x}$ is by reasoning as follows. The probability of obtaining an A on each draw is p, and that of obtaining a non-A is q. Therefore, in accordance with the multiplication of probabilities of independent events, the probability of drawing a particular sequence containing x A's and $n - x$ non-A's is $p^x q^{n-x}$. This is the probability for only one sequence; there are C_x^n such sequences; therefore, in accordance with the addition of probabilities of independent events, the probability of obtaining any sequence containing x A's is $C_x^n p^x q^{n-x}$.

By the same line of reasoning we can easily show that $C_x^n p^x q^{n-x}$ is the general term in the expansion of $(p + q)^n$, which is the *binomial* expansion.   Consider

$$(p + q)^n = (p + q)_1 (p + q)_2 \cdots (p + q)_n$$

If we multiply these n factors together, we will obtain $pp \cdots p$ $+ pp \cdots pq + pp \cdots pqp + \cdots + qq \cdots qp + qq$ $\cdots q$, such that *each term is obtained by choosing either p or q from each of the n factors.*   [For example,

$$(p + q)^3 = ppp + ppq + pqp + qpp + pqq + qpq$$
$$+ qqp + qqq]$$

We now ask, how many of these terms contain p as a factor x times and q as a factor $n - x$ times?   As we have one term for each sequence of n choices, obviously there are as many terms containing p as a factor x times as there are ways of choosing p x times, that is, of choosing x of the n factors enclosed in parentheses, that is, C_x^n.   Therefore the coefficient of $p^x q^{n-x}$ is

C_x^n and we obtain $(p + q)^n = \sum\limits_{x=0}^{n} C_x^n p^x q^{n-x}$.   If the reader is disturbed by the fact that this series writes the expansion backward,

he can instead write $(p + q)^n = \sum\limits_{x=0}^{n} C_{n-x}^n p^{n-x} q^x$.

Definition.   A binomial distribution is any distribution given by a rule of the form $f(x) = C_x^n p^x q^{n-x}$.

The reader should not rely on this abstract definition of a binomial distribution; instead he should keep firmly in mind the type of situation in which binomial distributions arise, the type described in Theorem 5.3.   This type of situation arises frequently in many fields of research.

5.4. Moments of a Binomial Distribution.   In the type of situation referred to in Theorem 5.3, what is $E(X)$?   Intuitively we feel that a sequence of n random draws should "on the average" contain the same proportion of A's as there are in the set, that is, $N_1/N(= p)$. Thus the mean number of A's in a sequence of n draws should be np. We can obtain the result $E(X) = np$ for all binomial distributions in a rigorous manner as follows:

$$E(X) = \sum_{x=0}^{n} xC_x^n p^x q^{n-x} = 0 + \sum_{x=1}^{n} x \frac{n!}{x!(n-x)!} p^x q^{n-x}$$

$$= \sum_{x=1}^{n} \frac{n!}{(x-1)!(n-x)!} p^x q^{n-x}$$

$$= np \sum_{x-1=0}^{n-1} \frac{(n-1)!}{(x-1)!(n-x)!} p^{x-1} q^{n-x}$$

$$= np \sum_{x-1=0}^{n-1} \frac{(n-1)!}{(x-1)![(n-1)-(x-1)]!} p^{x-1} q^{n-1-(x-1)}$$

$$= np(p+q)^{n-1}$$

$$= np(1)^{n-1} = np \qquad \text{Q.E.D.}$$

If the student does not see that

$$\sum_{x-1=0}^{n-1} \frac{(n-1)!}{(x-1)![(n-1)-(x-1)]!} p^{x-1} q^{n-1-(x-1)} = (p+q)^{n-1}$$

it will help him to rewrite the expression letting $y = x - 1$ and $m = n - 1$.

Similarly we can prove that the variance is npq. This proof involves a few algebraic tricks like the above, but followed step by step, it is actually very simple. One trick which may be new to the student is writing $x^2 - x + x$ for x^2. In higher mathematics such apparently useless expansions are often found extremely helpful. First we obtain $E(X^2)$ and then we use the formula. $\text{Var} = E(X^2) - [E(X)]^2$.

$$E(X^2) = \sum_{x=0}^{n} x^2 C_x^n p^x q^{n-x} = \sum_{x=0}^{n} (x^2 - x + x) C_x^n p^x q^{n-x}$$

$$= \sum_{x=0}^{n} x(x-1) \frac{n!}{x!(n-x)!} p^x q^{n-x} + \sum_{x=0}^{n} xC_x^n p^x q^{n-x}$$

$$= 0 + 0 + \sum_{x=2}^{n} x(x-1) \frac{n!}{x!(n-x)!} p^x q^{n-x} + np$$

$$= n(n-1)p^2 \sum_{x=2}^{n} \frac{(n-2)!}{(x-2)!(n-x)!} p^{x-2} q^{n-x} + np$$

$$= n(n-1)p^2 \sum_{x-2=0}^{n-2} \frac{(n-2)!}{(x-2)![(n-2)-(x-2)]!}$$

$$p^{x-2} q^{(n-2)-(x-2)} + np$$

$$= n(n-1)p^2(p+q)^{n-2} + np = n(n-1)p^2(1) + np$$

$$= n^2 p^2 - np^2 + np = n^2 p^2 + np - np^2 = n^2 p^2$$

$$+ np(1-p) = n^2 p^2 + npq$$

$$\therefore \text{Var} = n^2 p^2 + npq - (np)^2 = npq \qquad \text{Q.E.D.}$$

EXERCISES

5.4.1. For each of the following statistics, indicate whether its expected sampling distribution is a hypergeometric distribution, a binomial distribution, or neither. Write a rule for the distribution if it is hypergeometric or binomial. Write an expression for the mean and variance of each expected sampling distribution, if it is hypergeometric or binomial.

a. The number of high-anxiety-level students in a sample of 20 drawn at random from a population of 600 students.

b. The number of 6's in 50 throws of an ordinary die.

c. The number of 6's and 5's in 50 throws of an ordinary die.

d. The number of 8's in 50 throws of two ordinary dice.

e. The number of correct answers on a true-false test of 100 items, for a student who does not understand any of the questions.

f. The number of hearts drawn in 10 draws (without replacement) from an ordinary pack of 52 cards.

g. The number of heads-tails-heads-tails-heads sequences in 50 sequences of 5 flips each of an ordinary coin.

h. The number of black chips drawn on the third draw in the following situation. There are 3 black and 4 white chips in urn *A* and 5 black and 7 white chips in urn *B*. A chip is drawn at random from *A* and placed into *B*. A chip is then drawn at random from *B* and placed into *A*. A chip is then drawn at random from *A*.

i. The number of black chips drawn on the second draw in the situation described in *h*.

j. The mean (arithmetic) diameter of oranges in a sample of 20 taken at random from an orchard of 100,000 oranges.

5.4.2. Follow instructions as in Exercise 5.4.1.

a. The number of names of distinguished scientists in a sample of 20 different names taken at random from a biographical dictionary which contains the names of 20,000 scientists, of whom 500 are distinguished.

b. The number of married students in a sample of 50 from a college containing both married and unmarried students.

c. The number of *a*'s typed by a monkey hitting a typewriter keyboard 30 times at random, there being 40 keys on the keyboard.

d. The number of correct answers to a multiple-choice question (with 4 answers) in a sample of 25 papers if the students were answering at random.

e. The number of defective tubes in a random sample of 100, if the factory output is .5 per cent defective.

f. The number of draws until an ace is drawn from a pack of 52 cards of which 4 are aces, without replacing after each draw.

g. The number of draws until an ace is drawn, replacing after each draw.

h. The proportion of positive reactions to a vaccine given to n army recruits.

5.4.3. Find the mean and variance of a dichotomous population of which p members have the value 1 and $q(= 1 - p)$ members have the value 0.

5.4.4. Prove that the variance of the expected sampling distribution of the mean of a sample drawn at random from the dichotomous population described in Exercise 5.4.3 is pq/n, in which n is the size of the sample and the population is so large that we can neglect the fact of depletion.

5.4.5. Prove that the variance of the expected sampling distribution of the proportion of A's drawn from a dichotomous population (neglecting depletion) is pq/n by making use of the theorem mentioned in Sec. 4.7.

5.4.6. A radioactive substance emits electrons independently of one another, that is, whether an electron has or has not been emitted in the recent past has no influence on emissions in the present. Suppose that a careful record has been made of the times of electron emission for a given piece of radioactive material, and that during a given time interval L exactly N electrons have been emitted. Suppose we plan to sample the records by choosing at random a subinterval l of L. What is the probability that we shall find that 10 electrons have been emitted during l?

5.5. Binomial as Limit of Hypergeometric.

Suppose that we draw a random sample of size n from a dichotomous population of size N such that N is *very large* in comparison with n. In this case it does not matter appreciably whether we draw a sample of size n or whether we draw a sequence of size n, replacing after each draw, because the depletion of the population by a few members does not appreciably affect what happens on the next draw. If, for example, $N = 800,000$ and $n = 30$, then no matter what the value of p (the proportion of A's in the population), the sampling distribution of X (the number of A's in a sample) for samples of size n is approximately the same as the distribution of all possible sequences of n draws from a population in which the proportion of A's is p, replacing after each draw. This means that, with a fixed sample of size n and with a fixed proportion p, as the population size N gets larger and larger the hypergeometric distribution approaches closer and closer to the binomial distribution with the same n and p. We can prove this in a rigorous manner as follows.

Given a dichotomous population of size N and with a proportion p of A's, the sampling distribution of X, the number of A's, for samples of size n is given by

$$f(x) = \frac{C_x^{pN} C_{n-x}^{N-pN}}{C_n^N} = \frac{\dfrac{(pN)!}{x!(pN-x)!} \dfrac{(N-pN)!}{(n-x)!(N-pN-n+x)!}}{\dfrac{N!}{n!(N-n)!}}$$

$$= \frac{(pN)!}{x!(pN-x)!} \frac{(N-pN)!}{(n-x)!(N-pN-n+x)!} \frac{n!(N-n)!}{N!}$$

$$= \frac{n!}{x!(n-x)!} \frac{(pN)!}{(pN-x)!} \frac{(N-pN)!}{(N-pN-n+x)!} \frac{(N-n)!}{N!}$$

$$= C_x^n pN(pN-1) \cdots$$
$$(pN-x+1)(N-pN)(N-pN-1) \cdots$$
$$(N-pN-n+x+1) \frac{1}{N(N-1) \cdots (N-n+1)}$$

$$= C_x^n \frac{pN(pN-1) \cdots (pN-x+1)}{N(N-1) \cdots (N-x+1)}$$
$$\frac{(N-pN)(N-pN-1) \cdots (N-pN-n+x+1)}{(N-x)(N-x-1) \cdots (N-n+1)}$$

Noting that $N - n + 1 = N - x - n + x + 1$, we can write the above expression as

$$C_x^n \frac{pN}{N} \frac{pN-1}{N-1} \cdots \frac{pN-x+1}{N-x+1} \frac{N-pN}{N-x} \frac{N-pN-1}{N-x-1}$$
$$\cdots \frac{N-pN-n+x+1}{N-x-n+x+1}$$

Dividing the numerator and denominator of each term by N, we obtain

$$C_x^n \frac{p}{1} \frac{p - 1/N}{1 - 1/N} \cdots \frac{p - \dfrac{x-1}{N}}{1 - \dfrac{x-1}{N}} \frac{1 - p}{1 - \dfrac{x}{N}} \frac{1 - p - \dfrac{1}{N}}{1 - \dfrac{x+1}{N}} \cdots$$

$$\frac{1 - p - \dfrac{n - x - 1}{N}}{N - \dfrac{x + n - x - 1}{N}}$$

All we have done so far is to rewrite the hypergeometric expression; now observe that as $N \to \infty$ (approaches infinity) each of the terms $\dfrac{1}{N}, \dfrac{2}{N}, \cdots \dfrac{x-1}{N}, \dfrac{x}{N}, \dfrac{x+1}{N}, \ldots, \dfrac{n-x-1}{N} \to 0$.

Therefore each of the terms $\dfrac{p - \dfrac{1}{N}}{1 - \dfrac{1}{N}}, \cdots, \dfrac{p - \dfrac{x-1}{N}}{1 - \dfrac{x-1}{N}} \to p$ and

each of the terms

$$\frac{1 - p}{1 - \dfrac{x}{N}}, \frac{1 - p - \dfrac{1}{N}}{1 - \dfrac{x+1}{N}}, \cdots, \frac{1 - p - \dfrac{n - x - 1}{N}}{1 - \dfrac{x + n - x - 1}{N}} \to 1 - p = q$$

Therefore, the entire expression approaches $C_x^n p^x q^{n-x}$.   Q.E.D.

This example should give the student some idea of what the mathematical statistician means when he says that one distribution approaches another as a limiting form or that in the limit the distribution of a certain random variable is a certain distribution. Unfortunately most of such proofs are far beyond the scope of this text; the above is one of the most elementary examples possible.

EXERCISES

5.5.1. Find the binomial approximation for each of the following hypergeometric distributions:

a. $f(x) = \dfrac{C_x^{100} C_{50-x}^{200}}{C_{50}^{300}}$

b. $f(x) = \dfrac{C_x^{N_1} C_{n-x}^{N-N_1}}{C_n^N}$

5.5.2. Find a hypergeometric distribution for which each of the following binomial distributions could be approximations:

a. $f(x) = C_x^{100}(.3)^x(.7)^{100-x}$

b. $f(x) = C_x^n p^x q^{n-x}$

5.5.3. If the proportion of Bostonians in favor of a certain bill is p, what is the probability that fewer than 10 in a random sample of 25 will favor the bill?

5.5.4. It is known that one-fifth of the students in a large university are members of ZXZXZ. A student committee is to be selected at random. How large a committee must be selected to make the probability of having fewer than two members of ZXZXZ on the committee less than .01?

5.6. Fitting a Binomial to Sample Data. We may have theoretical or empirical reasons for believing (or doubting) that a certain population has a binomial distribution. If a random sample from the population is available, we can examine the sample distribution to see how similar it is to a binomial. For this purpose we construct a binomial distribution which is like our sample distribution in some respects, and then we compare the two distributions, observed and constructed. Let the sample distribution be $[f(0),0]$, $[f(1),1]$, . . . , $[f(n),n]$, with mean m. Since in a binomial distribution $E(X) = np$, we set $m = np$, solve for p, and use n and p to construct a binomial distribution to compare with the sample. The constructed binomial distribution will thus have the same mean as our sample, but if the distribution sampled is not a binomial, the constructed binomial distribution may differ greatly from the sample distribution in other respects.

Examples. 1. A large random sample has the distribution $(.01,0)$, $(.09,1)$, $(.39,2)$, $(.51,3)$. Then $m = 0(.01) + 1(.09) + 2(.39) + 3(.51) = 2.40$; therefore $p = m/n = 2.40/3 = .80$. Using $p = .80$, $n = 3$ we obtain the binomial distribution $(.008,0)$, $(.096,1)$, $(.384,2)$, $(.512,3)$, which agrees very closely with our sample distribution.

2. A large random sample has the distribution $(.071,0)$, $(.232,1)$, $(.605,2)$, $(.092,3)$. Then $m = 1.718$; $p = .573$. Using these two values we obtain the binomial distribution $(.078,0)$, $(.314,1)$, $(.420,2)$, $(.187,3)$, which departs considerably from our sample distribution.

In some cases we may hypothesize, for theoretical reasons, a value of p for the population, in which case we use the hypothesized value instead of that obtained from the sample mean in fitting a binomial to the sample. For example, if we toss a coin "at random" for 100 sequences of 4 tosses each, we would use $n = 4$, $p = \frac{1}{2}$ in comparing our 100 observations with those theoretically expected.

In Chap. 10 we shall discuss a method for determining whether the departure of our sample distribution from that theoretically expected can reasonably be attributed to random sampling.

EXERCISES

5.6.1. Fit a binomial to the following sample data (each datum being the value of an observation):

```
2 1 1 0 0 1 3 1 0 1
1 0 2 1 1 0 0 1 1 1
1 2 0 0 1 0 1 0 0 1
1 1 2 1 1 1 1 0 1 0
3 1 0 2 2 0 1 2 0 0
5 0 1 1 0 1 1 1 0 1
3 1 2 1 0 0 2 0 1 1
3 4 0 1 3 1 0 0 1 0
0 1 1 1 1 2 2 0 1 1
1 0 0 0 0 1 2 1 1 1
0 2 1 1 2 1 0 0 1 0
3 2 1 0 1 0 2 0 1 2
2 2 1 0 0 0 1 0 2 1
0 1 2 1 1 1 1 1 0 0
0 1 0 0 2 0 2 1 2 1
1 2 1 1 0 1 2 1 0 1
2 0 0 1 0 0 0 1 0 0
2 0 1 1 0 0 0 1 0 0
0 1 0 0 1 0 0 0 1 0
0 0 2 6 0 2 4 0 3 2
```

5.6.2. Fit a binomial to the following sample data:

Value	Frequency	Value	Frequency
5	1	2	98
4	13	1	100
3	47	0	41

Chapter 6

POISSON DISTRIBUTIONS

6.1. A Poisson as an Approximation to a Binomial. In many problems which can be solved by the binomial formula the computations become tedious; for example, computing $C_8^{75}(\frac{1}{9})^8(\frac{8}{9})^{67}$ is quite a task. Fortunately there are ways of approximating probabilities for a binomial distribution which involve very little computation; one of these can be used when n *is large and p is small;* that is, the larger the size of n and the smaller the size of p, the better the approximation. We shall now derive this approximation by starting with the general term in the binomial expansion and letting $n \to \infty$ and $p \to 0$ in such a way that their product np remains constant.

$$C_x^n p^x q^{n-x} = \frac{n!}{x!(n-x)!}\, p^x q^{n-x}$$

$$= \frac{n(n-1)\,\cdots\,(n-x+1)}{x!}\, p^x q^{n-x}$$

Let $\alpha \equiv np$; then, replacing p by α/n we obtain

$$\frac{n(n-1)\,\cdots\,(n-x+1)}{x!}\left(\frac{\alpha}{n}\right)^x\left(1-\frac{\alpha}{n}\right)^{n-x} = \frac{n}{n}\frac{(n-1)}{n}$$

$$\cdots\,\frac{(n-x+1)}{n}\frac{\alpha^x}{x!}\left(1-\frac{\alpha}{n}\right)^n\left(1-\frac{\alpha}{n}\right)^{-x}$$

With x and α fixed, as n approaches infinity each of the terms $\dfrac{(n-1)}{n},\ \dfrac{(n-2)}{n},\ \ldots,\ \dfrac{(n-x+1)}{n}$ has 1 as its limit; thus their product has 1 as its limit. We state without proof that the term $(1-\alpha/n)^n$ has $e^{-\alpha}$ as a limit.[1] The term $(1-\alpha/n)^{-x}$ has

[1] The numerical value of e is approximately 2.718. It is the natural logarithmic base.

1 as a limit, as the term within parentheses has 1 as a limit and the exponent is fixed. Therefore, the limit of the total expression is $\alpha^x e^{-\alpha}/x!$.

The reason that the approximation is better the larger the size of n and the smaller the size of p can be seen from the derivation. We let $n \to \infty$ as α (that is, np) remained fixed; therefore, as $n \to \infty$, p must approach 0. The reader may be surprised, however, to find that the approximation is as good as it is with relatively small sizes of n and relatively large values of p.

Examples. 1. Consider the binomial distribution corresponding to $(\frac{1}{3} + \frac{2}{3})^3$. Since $\alpha \equiv np = 1$, the approximating Poisson distribution is given by $f(x) = 1^x e^{-1}/x!$. Part of each distribution is given in Table 6.1.1. This approximation is not very good because n is not large nor is p small.

TABLE 6.1.1. POISSON APPROXIMATION TO BINOMIAL FOR
$p = \frac{1}{3}, n = 3$

x	$f(x)$ (binomial)	$f(x)$ (Poisson approximation)
0	.296	$e^{-1} = .368$
1	.444	$e^{-1} = .368$
2	.222	$\dfrac{e^{-1}}{2} = .189$
3	.037	$\dfrac{e^{-1}}{6} = .061$

2. The binomial distribution corresponding to $(.1 + .9)^3$ is approximated by $f(x) = .3^x e^{-.3}/x!$, as shown in Table 6.1.2. This approximation is much

TABLE 6.1.2. POISSON APPROXIMATION TO BINOMIAL FOR
$p = \frac{1}{10}, n = 3$

x	$f(x)$ (binomial)	$f(x)$ (Poisson approximation)
0	.729	.741
1	.243	.222
2	.027	.033
3	.001	.003

better because p is considerably smaller than in Example 1.

3. The binomial distribution corresponding to $(\frac{1}{3} + \frac{2}{3})^{10}$ is approximated by $f(x) = \dfrac{(1\frac{2}{3})^x e^{-1\frac{2}{3}}}{x!}$, as shown in Table 6.1.3. This approximation is somewhat better than that in Example 1 because n is larger.

TABLE 6.1.3. POISSON APPROXIMATION TO BINOMIAL FOR
$$p = \tfrac{1}{3},\ n = 10$$

x	$f(x)$ (binomial)	$f(x)$ (Poisson approximation)
0	.017	.036
1	.086	.119
2	.195	.198
3	.260	.220
4	.226	.183
5	.137	.122
6	.057	.070
7	.016	.032
8	.003	.013
9	.000	.004
10	.000	.001

4. The binomial distribution corresponding to $(.1 + .9)^{10}$ can be approximated by a Poisson distribution more closely than any of the distributions mentioned in the three examples above.

It should be obvious to the student that by "good approximation" we mean that the differences between proportions are small fractions of 1. For example, in Example 3 the largest difference is .043 [for $f(4)$]; the difference may be, however, and usually is in the case of extreme values, a very large proportion of $f(x)$. For example, $f(10)$ in Example 3 is .00002, whereas the approximation is .00124, a very large error relative to $f(10)$.

EXERCISES

6.1.1. Write the expression for the Poisson approximations to the following binomial distributions:

a. $f(x) = C_x^{20}(\frac{1}{20})^x(1\frac{9}{20})^{20-x}$

b. $f(x) = C_x^n p^x q^{n-x}$

6.1.2. Write the expressions for the binomial approximations and then the Poisson approximations to the following hypergeometric distributions:

a. $f(x) = \dfrac{C_x^{5,000} C_{100-x}^{1,000,000}}{C_{100}^{1,005,000}}$

b. $f(x) = \dfrac{C_x^{N_1} C_{n-x}^{N-N_1}}{C_n^N}$

6.2. Computation of a Poisson. The computation of a Poisson distribution is greatly simplified by observing that

$$f(x+1) = \frac{\alpha^{x+1} e^{-\alpha}}{(x+1)!} = \frac{\alpha^x e^{-\alpha}}{x!} \frac{\alpha}{x+1} = f(x) \frac{\alpha}{x+1}$$

In other words, we can calculate $f(0)$, then $f(1) = f(0) \frac{\alpha}{1}$; $f(2) = f(1) \frac{\alpha}{2}$; $f(3) = f(2) \frac{\alpha}{3}$; etc. This kind of method, which is often used in mathematics, is called an *iterative* or *recursive* method.

6.3. Definition. So far we have considered $\alpha^x e^{-\alpha}/x!$ merely as a way of approximating $C_x^n p^x q^{n-x}$. We can, however, consider $\alpha^x e^{-\alpha}/x!$ as giving the distribution of a purely mathematical or conceptual population of infinitely many members.

Definition. A Poisson distribution is a distribution given by a rule of the form $f(x) = \alpha^x e^{-\alpha}/x!$, in which the values are 0 and all positive integers.

Example. The rule $f(x) = 2^x e^{-2}/x!$ gives the Poisson distribution $(e^{-2}, 0)$, $(2e^{-2}, 1)$, $(2e^{-2}, 2)$, $(4e^{-2}/3, 3)$, ...

Our definition assumes, of course, that $\displaystyle\sum_{x=0}^{\infty} \frac{\alpha^x e^{-\alpha}}{x!} = 1$. This is a necessary consequence of the way in which we derived the Poisson; further, it follows immediately from the relation $e^c = \displaystyle\sum_{x=0}^{\infty} \frac{c^x}{x!}$, in which c is any positive number:

$$\sum_{x=0}^{\infty} \frac{\alpha^x e^{-\alpha}}{x!} = e^{-\alpha} \sum_{x=0}^{\infty} \frac{\alpha^x}{x!} = e^{-\alpha} e^{\alpha} = \frac{e^{\alpha}}{e^{\alpha}} = 1$$

6.4. Moments of a Poisson Distribution. It is a necessary consequence of the way in which we derived the Poisson that the mean is α and the variance is also α (because as $n \to \infty$ np

remains fixed; thus $p \to 0$ and $q \to 1$; thus $npq \to np = \alpha$). However, we can easily give an independent derivation. First we extend the definition of the arithmetic mean $E(X)$ and the variance $E\{[X - E(X)]^2\}$ to distributions having infinitely many values by defining $E(X)$ as $\sum_{\text{all } x} x f(x)$ and $E\{[X - E(X)]^2\}$

as $\sum_{\text{all } x} [X - E(X)]^2 f(x)$. Remembering that $e^\alpha = \sum_{x=0}^{\infty} \frac{\alpha^x}{x!}$, we have

$$E(X) = \sum_{x=0}^{\infty} x \frac{\alpha^x e^{-\alpha}}{x!} = 0 + \sum_{x=1}^{\infty} x \frac{\alpha^x e^{-\alpha}}{x!} = e^{-\alpha} \sum_{x=1}^{\infty} \frac{\alpha^x}{(x-1)!}$$

$$= \alpha e^{-\alpha} \sum_{x=1}^{\infty} \frac{\alpha^{x-1}}{(x-1)!} = \alpha e^{-\alpha} \sum_{x=0}^{\infty} \frac{\alpha^x}{x!} = \alpha e^{-\alpha}(e^\alpha) = \alpha$$

$$E(X^2) = \sum_{x=0}^{\infty} x^2 \frac{\alpha^x e^{-\alpha}}{x!} = \sum_{x=0}^{\infty} (x^2 - x + x) \frac{\alpha^x e^{-\alpha}}{x!}$$

$$= \sum_{x=0}^{\infty} x(x-1) \frac{\alpha^x e^{-\alpha}}{x!} + \sum_{x=0}^{\infty} x \frac{\alpha^x e^{-\alpha}}{x!} = 0 + 0$$

$$+ \sum_{x=2}^{\infty} x(x-1) \frac{\alpha^x e^{-\alpha}}{x!} + \alpha = \alpha^2 \sum_{x=2}^{\infty} \frac{\alpha^{x-2} e^{-\alpha}}{(x-2)!} + \alpha$$

$$= \alpha^2 e^{-\alpha} \sum_{x=0}^{\infty} \frac{\alpha^x}{x!} + \alpha = \alpha^2 e^{-\alpha}(e^\alpha) + \alpha = \alpha^2 + \alpha$$

$$\therefore \text{Var} = E(X^2) - [E(X)]^2 = \alpha^2 + \alpha - \alpha^2 = \alpha \qquad \text{Q.E.D.}[1]$$

Thus both the mean and variance of a Poisson distribution are equal to α.

We can fit a Poisson to sample data in a way similar to that in which we fit a binomial, that is, by computing $E(X)$ for the sample and then setting $\alpha = E(X)$. Alternately, we could compute the variance of the sample and set $\alpha = \text{Var}$; we state without proof that it is best in fitting a Poisson to use $E(X)$ as an estimate of α rather than Var or any combination of $E(X)$ and Var.

[1] Actually in this last step we are making use of a theorem which we have proved only for the finite case, but which also holds for all cases.

6.5. Poisson Distributions as Exact. Thus far we have discussed Poisson distributions only as approximations to binomial distributions. There are numerous situations, however, in which Poisson distributions are theoretically exact. These situations are those in which events are distributed in time (or space) in such a way that not only will information about the position of one event not help to predict the position of any other specific event, but even information about how many events occur in one interval of time (or region of space) does not help to predict how many events occur in any other interval. These two conditions are stated briefly by saying that the events are distributed *individually and collectively at random.*

In Exercise 5.4.6 we mentioned the emission of electrons by a radioactive substance as being such that whether an electron has been emitted in the recent past has nothing to do with whether one will be emitted in the present. In that exercise we brought this situation within the scope of a binomial by providing the information that N electrons had been emitted during a certain interval and then asking what we should expect if we examine part of the records. This maneuver was highly artificial, however. If we are interested in predicting not what we shall find in the records but what the substance will itself do in a specified interval, obviously we cannot know N, that is, the total number of electrons emitted during the interval L from which our specified interval l is drawn. If, however, we know, from previous observations (or from theoretical considerations), the mean value of N, we can find the probability that x electrons will be emitted during the interval l, and this probability is given exactly not by the binomial but by the Poisson. As the expectation for the number emitted during L is N, the expectation for the number emitted during l is lN/L. The probability that x electrons will be emitted is given by

$$f(x) = \frac{(lN/L)^x}{x!} \, e^{-(lN/L)}$$

Unlike the case in which the Poisson is used as an approximation, no restrictions need be placed on the relative sizes of l, L, or N. Furthermore, the Poisson rule applies to the total interval (that is, $l = L$) as well as to any subinterval; that is, the probability that x electrons will be emitted during L is given by

$$f(x) = \frac{N^x e^{-N}}{x!}$$

The proof that the Poisson rule is exact for the type of situation just described is beyond the scope of this text.[1]

EXERCISES

6.5.1. The mean number of cars passing over a toll bridge during the time interval 3 to 4 P.M. is 600. The cars pass individually and collectively at random. Write an expression for the probability that not more than 2 cars will pass during the one-minute interval 3:39 to 3:40.

6.5.2. During the time interval 4:45 to 5 P.M., telephone calls in a certain exchange are placed individually and collectively at random, the average being 1,000. Write an expression for the probability that fewer than 1,500 calls will be placed during this interval.

6.5.3. Approximate, by means of a Poisson, the probability that a random sample of 60 bearings will contain 4 or fewer defectives, if the proportion of defective bearings being turned out is $\frac{1}{20}$.

6.5.4. Records were kept at each of 500 observation stations of the number of flying saucers spotted during the year. Fit a Poisson to the following data which were obtained:

Saucers	Frequency
0	75
1	152
2	147
3	98
4	41
5	16
6	5

[1] A proof and further discussion of the Poisson is given by Fry (7).

Chapter 7

DISCRETE DISTRIBUTIONS

7.1. Definition. Up to this point we have discussed only populations having as values either qualitative categories or numbers which are "spread out" along the number axis in the sense that no value is a point about which infinitely many values cluster (we shall define this kind of spreading out precisely); furthermore, a nonzero proportion of the population falls at each value. It may seem to the student that these conditions should hold for almost all distributions. It turns out, however, that there is another very important class of distributions, which we shall discuss in the following chapters. The distributions which we have already discussed form a special class known as *discrete distributions*.

Definition. A *discrete population* is a population such that a nonzero proportion of the population falls at each value and each finite interval of the number axis contains at most a finite number of values.

Definition. A *discrete distribution* is the distribution of a discrete population, i.e. the class of all ordered pairs such that the second member of each pair is a value and the first member of each pair is the (nonzero) proportion of the population having the second member as value.[1]

Examples. **1.** All distributions of finite populations. Obviously any finite population satisfies the conditions necessary and sufficient for a discrete population. (Note that there is nothing in the definition requiring the values to be numbers; it merely excludes the case, to be discussed later, in which a finite interval of the number axis contains infinitely many values.)

---

[1] This is the fr.f. We could have defined "distribution" in terms of the c.d.f.; however, the c.d.f. does not always exist.

2. Any Poisson distribution, for example, the distribution given by

$$f(x) = \frac{e^{-3}3^x}{x!}$$

in which $x = 0, 1, 2, \ldots$.

7.2. The Logic of Statistical Inference for Discrete Distributions.

In Sec. 3.7 a short statement was made about the logic of statistical inference; we shall now give a somewhat more sophisticated statement. We start with a population Ω with a discrete distribution and consider drawing a sample O_n at random. If we define a statistic z, then z will have a sampling distribution, depending upon n and the distribution of Ω. If we make hypotheses about the distribution of Ω, we can derive hypothetical sampling distributions of z, one for each hypothesis. In each hypothetical sampling distribution we can mark out a region of values ω such that probability $z\epsilon\omega$ (the probability that z will have a value in ω) is low, if the hypothetical sampling distribution is in fact the sampling distribution. We then draw a sample O_n, calculate z, and reject all hypotheses for which the value of z we obtained is in the region ω. In most of the cases of statistical inference which we have discussed, we have known the functional form of the population (for example, that it is dichotomous), and we have needed to hypothesize only values of one or more parameters. In such cases rejection of a hypothesis about the distribution of Ω amounts to a rejection of a hypothesis about the value of one or more of its parameters.

Chapter 8

CONTINUOUS DISTRIBUTIONS

8.1. Continuous Populations. Suppose for the moment that we could construct a pointer that could land with equal likelihood on any point between 0 and 1. Suppose further that we plan to spin this pointer a large number of times. What is the expected proportion of spins that will result in the pointer's landing at exactly $\frac{1}{3}$? Upon reflection, we see that the only answer that we can give is zero. For suppose that we should choose some very small proportion, say .0000001, as our answer; clearly we would, to be consistent, have to give this same answer for any other point. It can easily be shown that, if we should do this, the sum of all the expected proportions would be greater than 1 (in fact, would be infinite), thus demonstrating that our choice must have been incorrect. To prove that no matter how small a proportion ϵ is chosen for each point we will obtain a sum greater than 1, we need merely consider the sequence of points 1, $\frac{1}{2}$, $\frac{1}{3}$, $\frac{1}{4}$, $\frac{1}{5}$, . . . (which of course does not by any means exhaust all the points on the interval 0–1). Take any integer N greater than $1/\epsilon$ and then take the first N members of the above sequence; their expected proportions will have a sum greater than 1, showing that we must take 0 as the expected proportion.

Although we cannot construct a pointer[1] that can land on any point between 0 and 1, this imaginary case provides a way of thinking about conceptual or mathematical entities called *continuous populations* and *continuous distributions*.

8.2. Proportion Density. Let us compare our imaginary pointer that can land anywhere between 0 and 1 with a pointer

---

[1] Even the best of pointers can of course be read only to a limited precision, that is, there is a finite number of *discriminably different* points on the dial.

that can land anywhere between 0 and 2. Although in both cases the expected proportion at each value is zero, for a large number of spins the results are clustered more thickly or *densely* in the case of the 0–1 pointer, so that for a region of a given size, for example, the region between ¼ and ½, a greater proportion of the spins will be expected to lie in that region in the case of the 0–1 pointer than in the case of the 0–2 pointer. It is this notion of *proportion density* or *probability density* that we shall use in defining *continuous distribution* so that we can distinguish one continuous distribution from another.

Before we can define *proportion density* we must define *cumulative distribution function* (c.d.f.) for a continuous population.

Definition. The *cumulative distribution* function (c.d.f.) of a continuous population is the class of all pairs such that the second member of each pair is a value and the first member is the proportion of the population having values less than or equal to that value. This definition is identical with that for a c.d.f. of a discrete population given in Chap. 3, although in the continuous case we can leave out the words "or equal to" because a zero proportion lies at each value. Note that in each case F (lowest value) $= 0$ and F (highest value) $= 1$. Further, if $x_1 < x_2$, then $F(x_1) \leq F(x_2)$. No function which fails to satisfy these conditions can be a c.d.f.

Now let us see what the expected c.d.f. is for a large number of random spins of a pointer which can land on any point between 0 and 1. In order to do this we must introduce another definition.

Definition. If a certain kind of event can occur at any point of a region of size L, and if each point is judged as likely to be the locus of the event as any other point, then in the occurrence of a large number of events of this kind, the expected proportion which will occur in a subregion of size K is K/L.

According to our definition, the expected proportion of spins resulting in the 0–1 pointer's landing between 0 and any point x is simply $x/1 = x$. In other words, the expected $F(x) = x$ when $0 \leq x \leq 1$. Similarly, the expected F for spins of the pointer which can land anywhere between 0 and 2 is given by $F(x) = x/2$ when $0 \leq x \leq 2$.

We can also imagine a pointer ranging between 0 and 1 with variable friction so that the expected c.d.f. is given by $F(x) = x^2$ when $0 \leq x \leq 1$.

We might even consider such c.d.f.'s as those given by

$$F(x) = \frac{x^2 + x}{2} \qquad \text{when } 0 \leq x \leq 1$$

$$F(x) = \frac{x^3 + 2x^2 + 5x}{8} \qquad \text{when } 0 \leq x \leq 1$$

$$F(x) = xe^{x-1} \qquad \text{when } 0 \leq x \leq 1$$

$$F(x) = \frac{x \log (x + 1)}{\log 2} \qquad \text{when } 0 \leq x \leq 1$$

Now we are in a position to build up the concept of *proportion density*. In the first place, the c.d.f. (F) increases as we increase x, and the proportion density at a point x_1 is merely the *rate of increase of F* at that point x_1. To see exactly what is meant by *rate of increase*, consider taking a very small region of length Δx extending from x_1 to $x_1 + \Delta x$. Call the proportion of the population falling in this region $\Delta F(x)$. The ratio $\Delta F(x)/\Delta x$ represents a kind of average proportion density in this region, and the *limit*[1] of $\Delta F(x)/\Delta x$ as $\Delta x \to 0$ is the proportion density at the point x_1.

Definition. The proportion density at a point x_1 is the rate of increase of $F(x)$ with respect to x at the point x_1, that is, it is the limit of $\Delta F(x)/\Delta x$ as $\Delta x \to 0$.

The limit of $\Delta F(x)/\Delta x$ as $\Delta x \to 0$ is also called the *derivative of the c.d.f. with respect to x* and is written $dF(x)/dx$, the symbol d being used to indicate the approach to 0.

It is very easy to find $dF(x)/dx$ when F is given by any rule of the form

$$F(x) = \frac{a_n x^n + a_{n-1} x^{n-1} + \cdots + a_1 x + a_0}{b_m x^m + b_{m-1} x^{m-1} + \cdots + b_1 x + b_0}$$

in which the a's and b's are constants and at least one b is not zero. (A function given by a rule of this form is called an

---

[1] It is assumed that the student has an intuitive concept of limit; for a precise definition, see Appendix B.

"algebraic function.") One effective process is the four-step rule, as follows:

First Step. In $F(x)$ replace x by $x + \Delta x$ and calculate the value of $F(x) + \Delta F(x)$.

Second Step. Subtract $F(x)$ from $F(x) + \Delta F(x)$ to obtain $\Delta F(x)$.

Third Step. Divide $\Delta F(x)$ by Δx to obtain $\Delta F(x)/\Delta x$.

Fourth Step. Find the limit of $\Delta F(x)/\Delta x$ by setting $\Delta x = 0$.

Examples. 1. $F(x) = \dfrac{x^2 + x}{2}$ when $0 \leq x \leq 1$. This is in the form described above with $a_2 = 1$, $a_1 = 1$, $b_0 = 2$, and all the other a's and b's $= 0$.

First step:

$$F(x) + \Delta F(x) = \frac{(x + \Delta x)^2 + (x + \Delta x)}{2} = \frac{x^2 + 2x\,\Delta x + (\Delta x)^2 + x + \Delta x}{2}$$

$$= \frac{x^2 + x}{2} + \frac{2x\,\Delta x + \Delta x + (\Delta x)^2}{2}$$

Second step:

$$F(x) + \Delta F(x) - F(x) = \Delta F(x) = \frac{2x\,\Delta x + \Delta x + (\Delta x)^2}{2}$$

Third step:

$$\frac{\Delta F(x)}{\Delta x} = \frac{2x + 1 + \Delta x}{2}$$

Fourth step:

$$\lim_{\Delta x \to 0} \frac{\Delta F(x)}{\Delta x} = \frac{2x + 1}{2} = x + \frac{1}{2}$$

$$\text{when } 0 \leq x \leq 1$$

or

$$\frac{dF(x)}{dx} = x + \frac{1}{2}$$

2. $F(x) = \dfrac{x^3 + 2x^2 + 5x}{8}$ when $0 \leq x \leq 1$.

$$F(x) + \Delta F(x) = \frac{(x + \Delta x)^3 + 2(x + \Delta x)^2 + 5(x + \Delta x)}{8}$$

$$\Delta F(x) = \frac{3x^2\,\Delta x + 3x(\Delta x)^2 + (\Delta x)^3 + 4x\,\Delta x + 2(\Delta x)^2 + 5\,\Delta x}{8}$$

$$\frac{\Delta F(x)}{\Delta x} = \frac{3x^2 + 3x\,\Delta x + (\Delta x)^2 + 4x + 2\,\Delta x + 5}{8}$$

$$\lim_{\Delta x \to 0} \frac{\Delta F(x)}{\Delta x} = \frac{3x^2 + 4x + 5}{8} \quad \text{or} \quad \frac{dF(x)}{dx} = \frac{3x^2 + 4x + 5}{8} \quad \text{when } 0 \leq x \leq 1$$

Transcendental functions, that is, functions which cannot be given by a rule of the form described, such as those given by

$$F(x) = xe^{x-1} \text{ when } 0 \leq x \leq 1, \quad F(x) = \frac{\log (x + 1)}{\log 2} \text{ when } 0 \leq$$

$x \leq 1$, $F(x) = \sin x$ when $0 \leq x \leq 90°$, require more subtle procedures; fortunately, however, differentiation has been reduced to simple rules which can be found in any calculus textbook;[1] for example, if $F(x) = cx^k$, in which c and k are constants, then $dF(x)/dx = kcx^{k-1}$. Further, if $F(x) = G(x) + H(x)$, in which G and H are functions, then $dF(x)/dx = dG(x)/dx + dH(x)/dx$. Using these two rules jointly, we can immediately obtain the answers for the examples just given; the details are left to the student.

We shall denote proportion density not only by $dF(x)/dx$ but also by $f(x)$, that is, $f(x) \equiv dF(x)/dx$. Whereas in the discrete case $f(x)$ means the proportion having the value x, in the continuous case it means the proportion (or probability) density.

8.3. Continuous Distributions. We can now define "continuous distribution" in the following way.

Definition. A continuous distribution is the distribution of a continuous population, that is, the class of pairs such that the second member of each pair is a value, and the first member of the pair is the proportion density (probability density) for that value; in other words, the class of all pairs of the form $[f(x), x]$.* In the continuous case we can never actually list the class of pairs; we must rely upon a rule.

Now suppose that we are given the frequency function f and asked to find the cumulative distribution function F. Obviously, since $f(x) = dF(x)/dx$, then F is simply a function such that $dF(x)/dx = f(x)$ and also such that F (highest value) $= 1$. To find F, therefore, we "guess" and then check our answer by differentiating; or, even better, we look in a table showing, for a given function, another function of which the first is the derivative. Such a function is called a "primitive function" of the first. F is therefore a primitive function of f.

Examples. **1.** If f is given by $f(x) = 1$ when $0 \leq x \leq 1$, what is F? We see from our table of primitive functions in Appendix C that a function of x whose derivative is a constant a is ax plus a constant c. We have therefore

---

[1] Many of these "rules" are given in Appendix C; they are actually theorems, which can be derived from the definition of the derivative.

* This definition is in terms of the frequency function. We could have used the c.d.f., as in the continuous case the c.d.f. always exists.

$F(x) = x + c$ when $0 \leq x \leq 1$. Also, since f is a probability density function, $F(1) = 1$. Thus $F(1) = 1 + c = 1$. Therefore $c = 0$. The answer is $F(x) = x$ when $0 \leq x \leq 1$.

2. If f is given by $f(x) = \dfrac{6x^2 + 5}{62}$ when $1 \leq x \leq 3$, what is F? From our table we see that if $f(x) = a_n x^n + a_{n-1}x^{n-1} + \cdots + a_1 x + a_0$, then

$$F(x) = \frac{a_n x^{n+1}}{n+1} + \frac{a_{n-1}x^n}{n} + \cdots + a_0 x + c$$

In this case we have $n = 2$, $a_2 = \frac{6}{62}$, $a_1 = 0$, $a_0 = \frac{5}{62}$. Therefore

$$F(x) = \frac{2x^3 + 5x}{62} + c$$

Also, since f is a probability density function, $F(3) = 1$. Therefore, $c = \frac{7}{62}$. [Since F (lowest value) must be equal to 0, it would have been easier in this case to set $F(1) = 0$ and solve for c. Regardless of which is used, a check should always be made to see whether F for each extreme value has the proper value, either 0 or 1. If such is not the case, then either we have made an error in finding F or the f with which we started was not in fact a probability density function.]

EXERCISES

8.3.1. We plan to spin a pointer that can land on any point between .01700 . . . and .82500 . . . , all points being equally likely. Find the probability that the point will land
  a. between .020 and .025 inclusive
  b. between .020 and .025, excluding the end points
  c. on the point .750
  d. on the interval .030–.035 or the interval .150–.165
  e. on a point greater than .750
  f. on a point not greater than .750

8.3.2. Suppose we put variable friction on a pointer so that $F(x) = 4x^2$ when $0 \leq x \leq .5$. Find
  a. the probability density at the point .250
  b. the probability that the pointer will land between .30 and .45
  c. the probability that the pointer will land on a point not less than .40

8.3.3. Suppose we put variable friction on a pointer running from 0 to 2 so that the probability density at a given point is directly proportional to the distance of that point from 2. Find
  a. an expression giving the probability density
  b. the probability density at the point 1
  c. an expression giving the c.d.f.
  d. the probability that the pointer will land between 1 and 1.5
  e. the probability that the pointer will land on a point at least as great as .7

8.3.4. Suppose we put variable friction on a pointer running from 0 to 3 so that the probability density at a given point is directly proportional to the distance of that point from 0.   Find

  a. an expression giving the probability density
  b. the probability density at the point 2
  c. an expression giving the c.d.f.
  d. the probability that the pointer will land between 1.5 and 2.0

8.3.5. Suppose the probability density is given by $f(x) = ax^2 - \frac{1}{6}$ when $1 \leq x \leq 2$.   Find

  a. $f(x)$ (that is, find the value of a)
  b. $F(x)$
  c. the probability between 1.5 and 2.0

8.3.6. Suppose the probability density is given by $f(x) = x - \frac{1}{2}$ when $a \leq x \leq 2$.   Find

  a. $F(x)$
  b. the value of a

8.3.7. Suppose the c.d.f. is given by $F(x) = \log x$ when $1 \leq x \leq e$.   Find

  a. $f(x)$
  b. the probability between 1.5 and 2.0

8.3.8. Suppose $F(x) = e^x - 1$ when $0 \leq x \leq \log 2$.   Find

  a. $f(x)$
  b. the probability between .3 and .5

8.3.9. Suppose the probability density is given by $f(x) = ax^2 + x$ when $1 \leq x \leq 2$.   Find

  a. $f(x)$
  b. $F(x)$

8.4. Definite Integrals. Let us consider another way in which we can obtain F from f.   Suppose that we know f and we wish to find the proportion of the population falling between two definite limits, a and b (with a less than b), that is, we wish to find $F(b) - F(a)$.   We can proceed as follows.

Divide the interval a to b into n equal subintervals, each of length $(b - a)/n$, which we shall call Δx.   Within each subinterval, choose any value of $f(x)$ as the estimated average proportion density for that interval; call this estimate $f(x_i)$.   Then for each subinterval i the approximate proportion (or probability) falling within i is the estimated average proportion density times the length of the interval, that is, $f(x_i)\,\Delta x$.   For the entire interval, therefore, the approximate proportion is $\sum_{i=1}^{n} f(x_i)\,\Delta x$.   The approximation will tend to become better and better as n gets larger and larger, and, as a matter of fact, the approximation will approach the correct value $F(b) - F(a)$ as n approaches infinity, that is, $\lim\limits_{n\to\infty} \sum\limits_{i=1}^{n} f(x_i)\,\Delta x = F(b) - F(a)$.

Our approximation process can be illustrated by plotting $f(x)$ as the ordinate versus x as the abscissa. The estimated probability $f(x_i)\,\Delta x$ is the rectangle of height $f(x_i)$ and length Δx. As $\Delta x \to 0$, the "corners" which extend beyond the curve $y = f(x)$ become smaller and smaller; as a matter of fact,

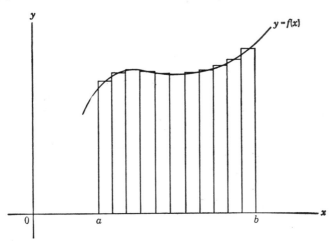

FIG. 8.4.1. The approximation $\Sigma f(x_i)\,\Delta x$ to the amount of probability between a and b.

$\lim\limits_{\Delta x\to 0} \Sigma f(x_i)\,\Delta x$ can be used as a *definition* of the area under the curve $y = f(x)$.

We abbreviate the expression "$\lim\limits_{n\to\infty} \sum\limits_{i=1}^{n} f(x_i)\,\Delta x$ taken over the interval a to b" by $\int_a^b f(x)\,dx$, the sign $\int$ indicating that we are taking the limit of a sum (it comes from an old form of the letter S) and dx indicating the fact that as $n \to \infty$, $\Delta x \to 0$.

$\int_a^b f(x)\,dx$ is called the *definite integral of f of x* between the limits a and b. The sign $\int$ is called the *integral sign*.

In summary we state that *the definite integral of a probability density function between the limits a and b gives the amount of* *probability between those limits.* It is the area under the curve given by the density function.

If we take for a the lowest value in the distribution (or the lower limit of the values) we have

$$\int_a^b f(x)\ dx = F(b) - F(a) = F(b) - 0 = F(b)$$

If the values extend to $-\infty$, as in the case of a type of distribution we shall describe in the next chapter,[1] then we take the limit of $\int_a^b f(x)\ dx$ as $a \to -\infty$. We abbreviate " $\lim\limits_{a \to -\infty} \int_a^b f(x)\ dx$" by $\int_{-\infty}^b f(x)\ dx$. Therefore, for a distribution whose values extend to $-\infty$ we have $\int_{-\infty}^b f(x)\ dx = F(b)$. If the values extend also to ∞, we can take the limit of $\int_{-\infty}^b f(x)\ dx$ as $b \to \infty$, calling this limit $\int_{-\infty}^\infty f(x)\ dx$. This limit is of course always 1 for any probability density function f.

As we saw before, $\lim \Sigma f(x_i)\ \Delta x = F(b) - F(a)$, or

$$\int_a^b f(x)\ dx = F(b) - F(a)$$

This statement says that the definite integral of f of x is the difference between two definite values of the primitive function $F(x)$.

For any integrable functions g and h and any constant c,

$$\int_R [cg(x) + h(x)]\ dx = c \int_R g(x)\ dx + \int_R h(x)\ dx$$

in which R indicates that we are integrating over some range. This important property is summed up in the statement that the integral is a *linear operator*.

8.5. Indefinite Integrals. Suppose that we replace the constant b with the variable x in the definite integral $\int_a^b f(x)\ dx$. We then have $\int_a^x f(x)\ dx = F(x) - F(a)$. As $-F(a)$ is a constant, which will be different for each different choice of a, we can write $\int_a^x f(x)\ dx = F(x) + c$, or more briefly $\int f(x)\ dx = F(x) + c$. This is called the *indefinite integral of f of x.* If we differentiate

---

[1] Mathematicians usually extend the range of values in any distribution to include the entire number axis by setting $f(x) = 0$ for all numbers outside what is called in this text the range of values; we follow this convention in the Appendix.

the indefinite integral we obtain the probability density function, that is, $\dfrac{d[F(x) + c]}{dx} = \dfrac{dF(x)}{dx} = f(x)$. Therefore *the indefinite integral is a primitive function.*[1]

Unfortunately, integration cannot be reduced to rules as thoroughly as differentiation, and in courses in the calculus considerable time is spent in learning techniques of integration. However, many indefinite (as well as some definite) integrals are given in tables in calculus texts. This text contains a few of these in Appendix C.

Examples. 1. Given $f(x) = 4x^3/15$ when $1 \leq x \leq 2$, what is F? We find in tables of indefinite integrals that $\displaystyle\int ax^n \, dx = \dfrac{ax^{n+1}}{n+1} + c$. Therefore

$$F(x) = \int \frac{4x^3}{15} \, dx = \frac{x^4}{15} + c$$

But since f is a probability density function, it must be the case that $F(2) = 1$; therefore $F(2) = 1 + \frac{16}{15} + c$ and $c = -\frac{1}{15}$. Therefore

$$F(x) = \frac{x^4}{15} - \frac{1}{15}$$

2. Given $f(x) = \dfrac{1}{(x - 4) \log 3}$ when $5 \leq x \leq 7$, what is F? From tables,

$$\int \frac{a}{x + b} \, dx = a \log (x + b) + c. \quad \text{Note that } a = 1/\log 3, \, b = -4.$$

$$\therefore \int \frac{1}{(x - 4) \log 3} \, dx = \frac{1}{\log 3} \log (x - 4) + c = F(x)$$

But $F(7) = 1$.

$$\therefore \frac{1}{\log 3} \log (7 - 4) + c = 1 \qquad \frac{\log 3}{\log 3} + c = 1 \qquad c = 0$$

$$\therefore F(x) = \frac{\log (x - 4)}{\log 3}$$

EXERCISES

8.5.1. Let a distribution be given by $F(x) = e^{2x} - b$ when $\dfrac{\log 2}{2} \leq x \leq \dfrac{\log 3}{2}$.
Find
a. b
b. the probability in the interval .5–.6

[1] This is the fundamental theorem of the calculus. We have not proved this theorem, although we hope that our discussion has made it seem plausible. A proof is given in the Appendix, Sec. B.8.

8.5.2. Let a distribution be given by $f(x) = cx - 1$ when $1 \leq x \leq (1 + \sqrt{5})/2$. Find

a. c

b. $F(x)$

c. the probability in the interval 1–1.1

8.5.3. Let a distribution be given by $f(x) = 2/x$ when $a \leq x \leq e^2$. Find

a. $F(x)$

b. a.

c. the probability in the interval $e^{1.75}$–$e^{1.90}$

8.5.4. Suppose we have a pointer that can land between $0°$ and $90°$ and with variable friction so that $f(x) = b \cos x$. Find

a. $F(x)$

b. the probability that the pointer will land between $45°$ and $75°$

8.5.5. Which of the following rules *cannot* give distributions for the interval $1 \leq x \leq 2$?

a. $f(x) = x^2 + 2x - 4$

b. $f(x) = ax^2 + 2x - 4$

c. $F(x) = x$

d. $F(x) = cx$

e. $F(x) = x^2 - 3$

f. $F(x) = ax^2 - 3$

g. $f(x) = \log x$

h. $f(x) = a \log x$

i. $f(x) = \log x + c$

j. $F(x) = x^3 - 2x^2 - 1$

k. $F(x) = x^3 - cx - 1$

8.6. A Physical Model for Distributions.

It is often useful to conceptualize a distribution in the following way. Suppose we take a unit mass of soft clay and spread it on the values so that in case the distribution is discrete each value has that proportion of the unit mass which is paired with it in the distribution (fr.f.), and in case the distribution is continuous each value has the corresponding density. In other words, in the discrete case we would place a certain amount of clay (probability) at each value; in the continuous case we would spread out the clay so that although at a given point there is no clay (which is perfectly reasonable since a point has zero volume) yet the *density* of clay at that point is the proportion or probability density paired with it in the distribution.

8.7. Moments of Continuous Distributions.

The *expected value* or *expectation* of a member drawn at random from a continuous population is defined as $E(X) \equiv \int_R x f(x)\, dx$, in which R is the total range of values for which $f(x)$ is defined. This expected value is also called the *arithmetic mean* (see Sec. 4.2).

Examples. 1. If $f(x) = x$ when $0 \leq x \leq \sqrt{2}$, then

$$E(X) = \int_0^{\sqrt{2}} x^2\, dx = \frac{(\sqrt{2})^3}{3}$$

2. If $f(x) = 1/x$ when $1 \leq x \leq e$, then $E(X) = \int_1^e dx = e - 1$.

We also define the expected value of a function g as

$$E[g(X)] \equiv \int_R g(x) f(x)\, dx$$

Note that if c is a constant and g and h are two functions of X, then it follows from the linear nature of the integral that $E[cg(X) + h(X)] = cE[g(x)] + E[h(X)]$. Thus E is a *linear operator*. Note also that $E(c) = c$. It was stated earlier that E has these properties in the finite case, and we state without proof that it has these properties in the discrete case in general, as well as in the continuous case.

Definition. The kth moment about the point c is the expected value of the kth power deviation from the point c, that is,

$$\text{mom}_c^k \equiv E(X - c)^k \equiv \int_R (x - c)^k f(x)\, dx$$

Examples. 1. If $k = 1$, $c = 0$, we have the arithmetic mean.
2. If $k = 2$, $c = E(X)$, we have the variance.

EXERCISES

8.7.1. Find the mathematical expectation and variance of X for each of the distributions given in Exercises 8.3.1 to 8.3.9.

8.7.2. Find the mathematical expectation and variance of X for each of the distributions given in Exercises 8.5.2 to 8.5.4.

8.7.3. If $f(x) = ce^x$ when $-\infty < x \leq 0$, find
a. the mean of X
b. the variance of X

8.7.4. If $F(x) = c \cos x$ when $90° \leq x \leq 180°$, find
a. mom_0^1
b. $\text{mom}_{E(X)}^2$

Chapter 9

NORMAL DISTRIBUTIONS

9.1. A Normal Distribution as an Approximation to a Binomial Distribution. In Sec. 5.3 we discussed binomial distributions and the kind of situation in which a binomial distribution arises. A binomial distribution was defined as one given by $f(x) = C_x^n p^x q^{n-x}$, in which n is an integer, p lies between zero and one, $q = 1 - p$, and x takes only the values $0, 1, \ldots, n$. We now state without proof the following theorem.

Theorem 9.1. An approximation to $C_x^n p^x q^{n-x}$ is

$$\frac{1}{\sqrt{2\pi}\ \sqrt{npq}}\ e^{-(\frac{1}{2}npq)(x-np)^2}$$

or, more precisely,

$$\lim_{n \to \infty} C_x^n p^x q^{n-x} = \frac{1}{\sqrt{2\pi}\ \sqrt{npq}}\ e^{-(\frac{1}{2}npq)(x-np)^2}$$

if, as $n \to \infty$, $\dfrac{(x - np)^3}{n^2} \to 0$.

Unfortunately the proof of this theorem is beyond the scope of this book.[1] The reader should be aware of the following points, however:

1. The approximation is better the larger the size of n, as illustrated in Table 9.1.1 for the case $p = \frac{1}{2}$, $x = np$.

2. The approximation is better the closer to $\frac{1}{2}$ the value of p, as illustrated in Table 9.1.2 for the case $n = 100$ and $x = np$.

3. The approximation is better in terms of per cent error the smaller the absolute size of $x - np$, with fixed n and p; in other words, the closer x is to the mean, the better the approximation, as illustrated in Table 9.1.3 for the case $n = 100$, $p = \frac{1}{2}$.

[1] A proof is given by Feller (4).

TABLE 9.1.1. NORMAL APPROXIMATION TO BINOMIAL FOR $p = \frac{1}{2}$, $x = np$

	$C_x^n p^x q^{n-x}$	Approximation	Difference	Per cent error
$n = 10$ $x = 5$	.2461	.2523	.0062	2.50
$n = 100$ $x = 50$	.0796	.0798	.0002	0.25
$n = 1,000$ $x = 500$	.0252	.0252	.0000	0.00

TABLE 9.1.2. NORMAL APPROXIMATION TO BINOMIAL FOR $n = 100$, $x = np$

	$C_x^n p^x q^{n-x}$	Approximation	Difference	Per cent error
$p = \frac{1}{10}$ $x = 10$	.1318	.1330	.0012	0.91
$p = \frac{1}{4}$ $x = 25$	.0918	.0921	.0003	0.33
$p = \frac{1}{2}$ $x = 50$	.0796	.0798	.0002	0.25

TABLE 9.1.3. NORMAL APPROXIMATION TO BINOMIAL FOR $n = 100$, $p = \frac{1}{2}$

$x - np$	$C_x^n p^x q^{n-x}$	Approximation	Difference	Per cent error
4	.000023	.000026	.000003	13.04
2	.01084	.01080	.00004	0.37
0	.0796	.0798	.0002	0.25

In the discussion above, $\dfrac{1}{\sqrt{2\pi}\,\sqrt{npq}}\,e^{-(\frac{1}{2}npq)(x-np)^2}$ has been considered a *probability*, defined only for $x = 0, 1, \ldots, n$. We can, however, consider this quantity a *probability density*, defined for all values of x from $-\infty$ to $+\infty$. Considered in this way, the approximation for $C_x^n p^x q^{n-x}$ becomes

$$\int_{x-.5}^{x+.5} \frac{1}{\sqrt{2\pi}\,\sqrt{npq}}\,e^{-(\frac{1}{2}npq)(y-np)^2}\,dy$$

that is, the area under the curve between $x - .5$ and $x + .5$. There is a great advantage in doing this (in addition to an increase in accuracy); for example, suppose that we wish to approximate $\displaystyle\sum_{x=10}^{20} C_x^n p^x q^{n-x}$. We need merely take

$$\int_{9.5}^{20.5} \frac{1}{\sqrt{2\pi}\,\sqrt{npq}}\,e^{-(\frac{1}{2}npq)(x-np)^2}\,dx$$

as our approximation. As a matter of fact, we do not even have to perform this integration but instead can use tables, as will be demonstrated in Sec. 9.4.

When $\dfrac{1}{\sqrt{2\pi}\,\sqrt{npq}}\,e^{-(\frac{1}{2}npq)(x-np)^2}$ is considered a probability density, we have a *normal* distribution, a definition of which follows in the next section.

9.2. Definition of Normal Distributions

Definition. A normal distribution is any continuous distribution given by $f(x) = (1/\sqrt{2\pi}\,k)e^{-(\frac{1}{2}k^2)(x-c)^2}$ in which c and k are constants and x ranges over all numbers.

We already know, by the definition of "distribution," that for a function f to be a distribution it must be the case that $\int_R f(x)\,dx = 1$, in which R indicates that we are integrating over the range for which the probability density is defined. It must also be the case that $f(x)$ is nonnegative for all values of x in R. Since $e^{-(\frac{1}{2}k^2)(x-c)^2}$ is positive for any values of c and k, our total expression will be positive if k is positive. Furthermore, we state without proof[1] that for any value of c and any positive

---

[1] A proof is given in the Appendix, Sec. B.21.

value of k,

$$\int_{-\infty}^{\infty} \frac{1}{\sqrt{2\pi}\,k}\, e^{-(\frac{1}{2}k^2)\,(x-c)^2}\, dx = 1$$

Therefore, a rule of this form will *always* give a distribution, provided only that k is positive.

Examples. **1.** Since $\sqrt{npq}$ and np are constants (for any given binomial distribution), we see, by setting $k^2 = npq$ and $c = np$, that

$$f(x) = \frac{1}{\sqrt{2\pi}\,\sqrt{npq}}\, e^{-(\frac{1}{2}npq)(x-np)^2}$$

gives a normal distribution, as stated in the last paragraph of Sec. 9.1.

2. With $k = 1$ and $c = 0$ we obtain the special case $f(x) = (1/\sqrt{2\pi})\, e^{-(x^2/2)}$. This special case is so important that it is sometimes referred to as *the* normal distribution (see Sec. 9.4).

Note that $(x - c)^2 = [-(x - c)]^2$; for example, if x is 5 units above c, so that $x - c = 5$, we obtain the same value for $f(x)$ that we obtain if x is 5 units below c, so that $x - c = -5$. This means that $f(x)$ is *symmetrical* about c.

Furthermore, it is easy to prove that $f(x)$ has its maximum value at c as follows:

$$e^{-(\frac{1}{2}k^2)\,(x-c)^2} = \frac{1}{e^{(\frac{1}{2}k^2)(x-c)^2}}$$

which is less than 1 unless $x = c$, because e to any positive power is greater than 1.

Further, if $x = c$, then $e^{-(\frac{1}{2}k^2)\,(x-c)^2} = e^0 = 1$. Therefore,

$$\frac{1}{\sqrt{2\pi}\,k}\, e^0 > \frac{1}{\sqrt{2\pi}\,k}\, e^{-(\frac{1}{2}k^2)\,(x-c)^2} \qquad \text{when } x \neq c$$

The foregoing discussion implies that when plotted a normal distribution will slope symmetrically away from its mode.

EXERCISES

9.2.1. Which of the following rules can give normal distributions? For each one which can, find c and k.

a. $f(x) = e^{-x^2}$

b. $f(x) = \dfrac{1}{\sqrt{2}}\, e^{-(\pi/2)\,x^2}$

    c. $f(x) = 3e^{-9\pi(x-3)^2}$
    d. $f(x) = 3e^{-9\pi(x+3)^2}$
    e. $f(x) = be^{-x^2}$
    f. $f(x) = e^{-bx^2+6bx-9b}$

9.2.2. Which of the following rules can give normal distributions? For each such rule, find the values of *c* and *k*.

    a. $f(x) = be^{-2x^2}$
    b. $f(x) = be^{-x^2-2x-1}$
    c. $f(x) = \pi e^{-dx^2}$
    d. $f(x) = b\pi e^{-x^2}$

9.2.3. Write an approximation for the probability that of 147 chips drawn at random from a bowl containing 5 black chips and 2 white chips, replacing after each draw, between 80 and 120 inclusive will be black.

9.2.4. Write an approximation for the probability that of 100 chips drawn at random from a bowl containing a very large number of chips, of which $\frac{1}{4}$ are white, between 20 and 30 inclusive will be white.

9.2.5. Write an approximation to the probability that not more than 150 clocks in a shipment of 1,000 will be defective, if the factory is shipping out 10 per cent defectives on the average.

9.2.6. Write an approximation to the probability that more than 80 per cent of a sample of 200 randomly selected students will be from urban areas, if the percentage of urban students in the entire population is 75 per cent.

9.3. Moments of Normal Distributions. The definition of the arithmetic mean (the first moment about zero) of a continuous distribution was $E(X) \equiv \int_R xf(x)\, dx$. In the case of a normal distribution we have therefore

$$E(X) \equiv \int_{-\infty}^{\infty} x\, \frac{1}{\sqrt{2\pi}\, k}\, e^{-(\frac{1}{2}k^2)(x-c)^2}\, dx$$

We state without proof[1] that

$$\int_{-\infty}^{\infty} x\, \frac{1}{\sqrt{2\pi}\, k}\, e^{-(\frac{1}{2}k^2)(x-c)^2}\, dx = c$$

Therefore the constant *c* is the arithmetic mean $E(X)$. Actually, this follows from the fact demonstrated in Sec. 9.2 that a normal distribution is symmetrical about *c*, because the center of any symmetrical distribution is the arithmetic mean.[2]

---

[1] A proof is given in the Appendix, Sec. B.21.
[2] Unless the mean does not exist at all. See Sec. 11.1 for an example.

We state also without proof[1] that

$$E[(X - c)^2] \equiv \int_{-\infty}^{\infty} (x - c)^2 \, \frac{1}{\sqrt{2\pi} \, k} \, e^{-(\frac{1}{2}k^2)(x-c)^2} \, dx = k^2$$

Therefore the constant k^2 is the variance and k is the standard deviation.

Because of these results, the equation for a normal distribution is usually written $(1/\sqrt{2\pi} \, \sigma)e^{-(\frac{1}{2}\sigma^2)(x-\mu)^2}$ using the conventional symbols μ and σ for the mean and standard deviation respectively.

We shall abbreviate the expression $(1/\sqrt{2\pi} \, \sigma)e^{-(\frac{1}{2}\sigma^2)(x-\mu)^2}$ by simply $\phi(\mu,\sigma^2)$. To say, for example, that X is distributed according to $\phi(5,49)$ means that $f(x) = (1/\sqrt{2\pi} \, 7)e^{-(\frac{1}{98})(x-5)^2}$.

We shall also use the abbreviation $N(\mu,\sigma^2)$ for the longer expression "a normal distribution with mean μ and variance σ^2," or, depending upon the context, "a normal population with mean μ and variance σ^2."

It should be obvious from the equation for a normal distribution that a normal distribution is *completely specified* if we know its mean and variance. In other words, there cannot be two normal distributions which have the same mean and variance and yet which differ in some other parameter.

We state without proof[1] that *in any normal distribution the amount of probability between the mean μ and a point b standard deviations from μ depends only upon b, not upon the size of μ or σ.* This is stated formally as follows:

$$\int_{\mu_1}^{\mu_1+b\sigma_1} \phi(\mu_1,\sigma_1^2) \, dx = \int_{\mu_2}^{\mu_2+b\sigma_2} \phi(\mu_2,\sigma_2^2) \, dx$$

for any values of μ_1, μ_2, σ_1, σ_2, and b. It so happens that $\int_{\mu}^{\mu+b\sigma} \phi(\mu,\sigma^2) \, dx = .3413$ for $b = 1$, $.4772$ for $b = 2$, and $.4987$ for $b = 3$. These probabilities are indicated in Fig. 9.3.1.

The probability density (height of the curve) varies, of course, with different values of σ, even when b is the same. This is the

[1] A proof is given in the Appendix, Sec. B.21.

reason that we cannot put a numerical scale on the ordinate in Fig. 9.3.1.

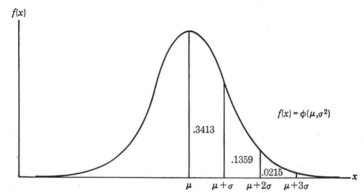

FIG. 9.3.1. A normal distribution with mean μ and standard deviation σ.

9.4. The Special Case c $(=\mu)$ $= 0$ and $k(=\sigma) = 1$. In Sec. 4.7 the student was asked to prove that if a variate X is transformed by a linear transformation into a variate Y, that is, if $y_i = ax_i + b$, in which a and b are constants, then $m_y = am_x + b$ and $s_y^2 = a^2 s_x^2$, in which m means the arithmetic mean and s means the standard deviation.

This result, which can also be obtained for continuous distributions (the student should prove this as an exercise), implies that we can take a normally distributed variate X and by a suitable transformation obtain a new variate Y such that the mean of Y is 0 and the variance is 1. To find values of a and b which accomplish this, simply set $a\mu_x + b = 0$ and $a^2\sigma_x^2 = 1$. Then $a^2 = 1/\sigma_x^2$ or $a = 1/\sigma_x$ (taking positive root only) and $b = -a\mu_x = -\mu_x/\sigma_x$.

We state without proof[1] that a linear transformation leaves the functional *form* of a normal distribution unchanged; therefore, that Y will also be normally distributed.

In summary we state the following theorem.

Theorem 9.4. If X is distributed according to $\phi(\mu_x, \sigma_x^2)$ and

$$y_i = \frac{1}{\sigma_x} x_i - \frac{\mu_x}{\sigma_x} = \frac{x_i - \mu_x}{\sigma_x}$$

then Y is distributed according to $\phi(0,1)$.

[1] A proof is given in the Appendix, Sec. B. 21.

Because of the great usefulness of normal distributions (see Sec. 9.5 below) and because any normally distributed variate can be so easily transformed into a variate having the distribution $N(0,1)$, extensive tables showing $N(0,1)$ can be found in most books on statistics. In this book tables can be found in Appendix D.

The relation of $N(0,1)$ to any other normal distribution can be understood by examining the equation whereby we transformed x_i into y_i, that is, $y_i = (x_i - \mu_x)/\sigma_x$. The numerator is the distance between the value x_i and the mean μ_x. When we divide this distance by the standard deviation σ_x, we obtain the *number of standard deviations a given value is from the mean of the distribution*. (This statement holds regardless of whether X is normally distributed or not.) Theorem 9.4 therefore implies that the probability that a normal variate X will take a value which is b standard deviations or more from the mean is simply $\int_b^\infty \phi(0,1)\,dx$, which is given in the tables. The probability that X will have a value b standard deviations or more in the negative direction is $\int_{-\infty}^{-b} \phi(0,1)\,dx$. Similarly, the probability that x will lie *within* b standard deviations of the mean is $\int_{-b}^{b} \phi(0,1)\,dx$. More generally, the probability that x will lie between b standard deviations and d standard deviations from the mean, where $b < d$, is $\int_b^d \phi(0,1)\,dx$.

We now see how we can use tables to approximate any desired portion of a binomial distribution, as stated in Sec. 9.1. Suppose, for example, that $n = 100$ and $p = \frac{1}{3}$ and we wish to approximate $\sum_{x=25}^{40} C_x^{100}(\frac{1}{3})^x(\frac{2}{3})^{100-x}$. Since $np = 33\frac{1}{3}$ and $\sqrt{npq} = 10\frac{2}{3}$, we find the number of σ's that 24.5 is from the mean by taking

$$\frac{24\frac{1}{2} - 33\frac{1}{3}}{10\frac{2}{3}} = \frac{-5\frac{5}{6}}{20\frac{6}{6}} = -2.65$$

Similarly 40.5 is 2.15 σ's from the mean. Therefore our approximation is $\int_{-2.65}^{2.15} \phi(0,1)\, dx$, which by our tables we find to be

.9802. More generally, to approximate $\sum_{x=a}^{b} C_x^n p^x q^{n-x}$ we take

$\int_{\frac{a-.5-np}{\sqrt{npq}}}^{\frac{b+.5-np}{\sqrt{npq}}} \phi(0,1)\, dx$, which we find from the tables.

$\phi(0,1)$ and $\phi(0,100)$ are illustrated in Fig, 9.4.1.

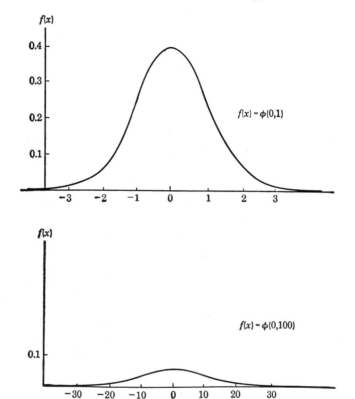

FIG. 9.4.1. Normal distributions with 0 mean and variances of 1 and 100 respectively.

EXERCISES

9.4.1. Find μ and σ for each of the following distributions:

a. $f(x) = 3e^{-9\pi x^2}$

b. $f(x) = \dfrac{1}{2\sqrt{\pi}}\, e^{-\frac{x^2}{4} - \frac{x}{2} - \frac{1}{4}}$

9.4.2. Find μ and σ for each of the following distributions:

a. $f(x) = \dfrac{1}{\pi} e^{-\frac{1}{\pi}x^2}$

b. $f(x) = \dfrac{2}{\sqrt{\pi}} e^{-\frac{x^2}{8} + \frac{3x}{4} - \frac{9}{8}}$

9.4.3. Find the probability between -1 and 2 for each of the distributions in Exercise 9.4.1.

9.4.4. Find the probability between 1 and 3 for each of the distributions in Exercise 9.4.2.

9.4.5. For the distribution $N(2,9)$, find the proportion

a. between 3 and 4

b. less than 3

9.4.6. If scores on an aptitude test have approximately the distribution $N(100,100)$, find the proportion of scores

a. between 115 and 130

b. greater than 70

9.4.7. Evaluate the approximation obtained in Exercise 9.2.3.

9.4.8. Evaluate the approximation obtained in Exercise 9.2.4.

9.4.9. Find the probability that a randomly selected member of a normally distributed population will lie within 2 standard deviations of the mean.

9.4.10. Find the probability whose approximation was asked for in Exercise 9.2.5.

9.5. Tests of Hypotheses and Confidence Intervals.

Suppose we know X to be distributed normally and we know the variance σ^2 but not the mean μ. We hypothesize a value μ_H. How can we test our hypothesis by drawing a member of the population at random? The student should, on the basis of our discussion of tests of hypotheses in Chap. 3, be able to answer this question for himself, but we shall describe the procedure.

According to our hypothesis, .95 of the population lie within 1.96 σ's (whose value we know) of μ_H, .96 of the population lie within 2.06 σ's of μ_H, etc. [We obtain these values from our tables of $N(0,1)$.] Therefore, we draw a member of the population at random. If this member lies too far from μ_H, then we reject our hypothesis at the appropriate confidence level. In other words, we compute $(x - \mu_H)/\sigma$ (the number of σ's that x lies from μ_H), which, if our hypothesis were correct, would have the distribution $N(0,1)$. If our result departs too far from expectation, then we reject our hypothesis at the appropriate confidence level.

Example. We know that a certain population has the distribution $N(\mu,25)$. We wish to test the hypothesis that $\mu = 100$. We draw a member of the population at random and observe its value to be 115. We compute

$$\frac{x - \mu_H}{5} = \frac{115 - 100}{5} = 3.00$$

Thus, referring to our tables of $N(0,1)$, we reject our hypothesis at the .003 level of confidence.

Suppose we wish to test the hypothesis that μ has the value μ_H *or greater.* In this case, we decide before drawing our sample that we shall make our test in *one direction only.* In other words, we are so confident that x is going to have a value smaller than μ_H that we give up the possibility of making a test in case x turns out to be greater than μ_H. From tables of $N(0,1)$ we see that if μ has the value μ_H then the probability that $(x - \mu_H)/\sigma$ will have a value less than -1.65 is .05, less than -1.75 is .04, etc. If our result departs too far from expectation, we can reject our hypothesis at the indicated level of confidence.

Example. We know that X is distributed according to $N(\mu,100)$. We wish to test the hypothesis that μ is at least 80 (80 or greater). We draw a member at random and find its value to be 62. We compute

$$\frac{62 - 80}{10} = -1.80$$

Referring to our table, we see that we can reject our hypothesis at the .04 level of confidence. If we had obtained a value of 98, however, we could not have rejected the hypothesis that $\mu = 80$. (Why not?)

The reader may feel that drawing a sample of size 1 is not going to give us a very powerful test of our hypothesis. He is quite right. By taking larger samples we can increase the power of our test tremendously.

We now state without proof[1] the following theorem.

Theorem 9.5.1. Let X_1 be distributed according to $\phi(\mu_1,\sigma_1^2)$, X_2 be distributed according to $\phi(\mu_2,\sigma_2^2)$, . . . , X_n be distributed according to $\phi(\mu_n,\sigma_n^2)$. Then if all the X's are chosen independently, the sum $\sum_{i=1}^{n} X_i$ is distributed according to

[1] A proof is given in the Appendix, Sec. B.21.

$\phi(\mu,\sigma^2)$, where $\mu = \sum\limits_{i=1}^{n} \mu_i$ and $\sigma^2 = \sum\limits_{i=1}^{n} \sigma_i^2$. (The sum of n mutually independent normally distributed variates is normally distributed with a mean equal to the sum of the means and a variance equal to the sum of the variances.)

Corollary. Consider a random sample of size n from a population having the distribution $N(\mu,\sigma^2)$. Then $\sum\limits_{i=1}^{n} X_i$ has the distribution $N(n\mu,n\sigma^2)$.

Remembering that m (the sample mean) $= \dfrac{\sum\limits_{i=1}^{n} x_i}{n}$ and using the relation stated at the beginning of Sec. 9.4, we have

$$\mu_m = \frac{\mu_\Sigma}{n} = \frac{n\mu}{n} = \mu \qquad \text{and} \qquad \sigma_m^2 = \frac{\sigma_\Sigma^2}{n^2} = \frac{n\sigma^2}{n^2} = \frac{\sigma^2}{n}$$

In summary we state the following theorem.

Theorem 9.5.2. Consider a random sample of size n drawn from a population having the distribution $N(\mu,\sigma^2)$. Then the mean of the sample m will have the distribution $N(\mu, \sigma^2/n)$.

Corollary. $\dfrac{m - \mu}{\sigma/\sqrt{n}}$ will have the distribution $N(0,1)$.

Thus we see that by taking a sample of size n we multiply our ratio $(m - \mu_H)/\sigma$ by $\sqrt{n}$, thus greatly increasing the power of our test.

Example. We know that a certain population is distributed according to $N(\mu,36)$. We wish to test the hypothesis that $\mu = 20$. We draw a sample of 9 and find that $m = 23.6$. We compute

$$\frac{m - \mu_H}{\sigma/\sqrt{n}} = \frac{23.6 - 20}{6/3} = 1.80$$

Therefore we cannot reject our hypothesis.

Using the same kind of reasoning as above we can easily obtain a confidence interval for μ, if we know σ^2.

First we consider a sample of size 1. We know that

$$f(x) = \phi(\mu,\sigma^2)$$

This means that prob $(a < x < c) = \int_a^c \phi(\mu,\sigma^2) \, dx$, in which a and c are any two constants. Let us choose a and c so that they are b standard deviations from μ, that is, let $a = \mu - b\sigma$ and $c = \mu + b\sigma$. We then have

$$\text{prob} (\mu - b\sigma < x < \mu + b\sigma) = \int_{\mu-b\sigma}^{\mu+b\sigma} \phi(\mu,\sigma^2) \, dx$$

But prob $(\mu - b\sigma < x < \mu + b\sigma)$ is just the probability that x will lie within b standard deviations of μ. Now obviously if x lies within b σ's of μ, then μ lies within b σ's of x and vice versa. That is, if $\mu - b\sigma < x < \mu + b\sigma$ then $x - b\sigma < \mu < x + b\sigma$ and vice versa.[1] Therefore

$$\text{prob} (x - b\sigma < \mu < x + b\sigma) = \text{prob} (\mu - b\sigma < x < \mu + b\sigma)$$
$$= \int_{\mu-b\sigma}^{\mu+b\sigma} \phi(\mu,\sigma^2) \, dx$$

which, by our discussion in Sec. 9.4, is simply $\int_{-b}^{b} \phi(0,1) \, dx$. In summary we state the following theorem.

Theorem 9.5.3. Consider a random variate X from $N(\mu,\sigma^2)$. Then prob $(x \pm b\sigma$ includes $\mu) = \int_{-b}^{b} \phi(0,1) \, dx$.

We can therefore find the p confidence interval by finding from our tables of $N(0,1)$ the value of b for which

$$\int_{-b}^{b} \phi(0,1) \, dx = 1 - p$$

Example. We know that a certain population is distributed according to $\phi(\mu,25)$. We wish to find the .01 confidence interval for μ. We draw a member of the population at random and find its value to be 75. Referring to tables of $N(0,1)$ we see that our confidence interval is

$$75 \pm 2.58 \ (5) = 75 \pm 12.90$$

If we had decided beforehand that our interval would have a lower bound only, we should have found our interval to be $75 - 2.33 \ (5)$ to ∞.

Similarly, using Theorem 9.5.2, that $f(m) = \phi(\mu, \sigma^2/n)$, we can prove that prob $\left(m \pm b \dfrac{\sigma}{\sqrt{n}} \text{ includes } \mu\right) = \int_{-b}^{b} \phi(0,1) \, dx$.

---

[1] The equivalence can be proved formally by adding $-\mu - x$ to each term of the first inequality (adding equals to unequals leaves them unequal) and then multiplying through by -1 (which changes the direction of the inequality signs). The same procedure changes the second into the first.

Example. We know a certain population to be distributed according to $\phi(\mu,81)$. We wish to find the .05 confidence interval. Drawing a sample of 4, we find m to be 50. Our confidence interval is $50 \pm 1.96(\%) = 50 \pm 8.82$.

Remember that we can speak of the *probability* that $m \pm b \dfrac{\sigma}{\sqrt{n}}$ includes μ only *before* we draw our sample. Afterward we are more or less *confident* that it includes μ.

EXERCISES

9.5.1. If X is distributed according to $\phi(5,4)$, what is the probability that a member of the population chosen at random will have a value

    a. in the interval 4–6?

    b. in the interval 3–6?

    c. greater than 6?

9.5.2. If X is distributed according to $\phi(1,9)$, what is the probability that a sample of 9 will have a mean

    a. in the interval 0–2?

    b. in the interval (-1)–2?

    c. less than 3?

9.5.3. Suppose X is normally distributed with known variance of 225. Find the value a sample of 1 would have to have in order to reject (at the .05 level of confidence) the hypothesis

    a. that the mean is 30

    b. that the mean is at least 30

    c. that the mean is less than 100

9.5.4. If X is distributed according to $\phi(\mu,25)$, show how, with a sample of 1, you can obtain a .05 confidence interval for μ.

9.5.5. If $f(x) = \phi(\mu_x,4)$ and $f(y) = \phi(\mu_y,9)$, what is $f(x + y)$? (Assume X and Y are chosen independently.)

9.5.6. Show how, with a sample of 5 drawn from $N(\mu,4)$, you can test the hypothesis that

    a. $\mu = 0$

    b. $\mu \leq 1$

9.5.7. The following is a sample of 4 drawn from $N(\mu,16)$: $(2.5,X_1)$, $(3,X_2)$, $(2,X_3)$, $(2.5,X_4)$. Find the .01 confidence interval for μ based on this sample.

9.5.8. The mean of a sample of 9 drawn from $N(\mu,100)$ is 38. Find the .02 confidence interval for μ with

    a. both upper and lower bound

    b. lower bound only

    c. upper bound only

9.5.9. In Exercise 9.5.3, find the power of the test of each hypothesis if μ is actually

a. 50
b. 10
c. 110

9.5.10. In Exercise 9.5.6, find the power of the test of each hypothesis (requiring the .01 level for rejection) if μ is actually

a. 2
b. 3

9.5.11. The weight of a certain canned product is distributed approximately normally with a variance of 25 oz. Find the size sample necessary to estimate, at the .01 level of confidence, the mean weight within 1 oz.

9.6. The Central-limit Theorem. We now come to one of the most remarkable and useful theorems in the field of statistics, which we state without proof.[1]

Central-limit Theorem. Consider any population, discrete or continuous, with finite mean μ and finite variance σ^2. The sampling distribution of m, the mean of a random sample of size n, will approach $N(\mu, \sigma^2/n)$ as n approaches infinity; more precisely,

$$\lim_{n \to \infty} \text{prob}\ (a \leq m \leq b) = \int_a^b \phi(\mu, \sigma^2/n)\ dx$$

in which a and b are any constants.

Corollary.

$$\lim_{n \to \infty} \text{prob}\left(a \leq \frac{m - \mu}{\sigma/\sqrt{n}} \leq b\right) = \int_a^b \phi(0,1)\ dx$$

This theorem implies, among other things, that we can make up a hypothesis about the size of μ, draw a sample, and, provided that n is large, test our hypothesis by using the tables for $N(0,1)$. To make this test we simply compute the mean of the sample m and the variance s^2; then, using s^2 as our estimate[2] of

---

[1] Proofs are given by Cramer (3), Wilks (12), Hoel (8), and Mood (9).

[2] It should seem reasonable to the student to use s^2 as an estimate of σ^2. This estimate is justified by the fact that, for any $\epsilon > 0$, $\lim_{n \to \infty} \text{prob}\ (|s^2 - \sigma^2| > \epsilon) = 0$. An estimate having this property is called *consistent*. Although consistent, s^2 is *biased* in that its mean value for any n is not σ^2 but $\sigma^2(n - 1)/n$ (a proof is given in the Appendix, Sec. B.20). An unbiased estimate of σ^2 is $s^2n/(n - 1)$, which is also consistent, and for this reason the sample variance is sometimes *defined* as $\dfrac{\Sigma(x - m)^2}{n - 1}$ $[=s^2n/(n - 1)]$. For large n the factor $n/(n - 1)$ is negligible.

σ^2, compute $\dfrac{m - \mu_H}{s/\sqrt{n}}$, in which μ_H is the hypothesized value of μ.

If our hypothesis is correct, that is, if $\mu_H = \mu$, then $\dfrac{m - \mu_H}{s/\sqrt{n}}$ will have the approximate distribution $N(0,1)$. If our actual result departs too far from expectation, then we reject our hypothesis at the indicated confidence level. The reader may raise the objection that our estimate of the population variance may be incorrect. This is true. However, we used a good estimate, and there is no reason for believing the variance estimate to be seriously wrong; therefore, the best working hypothesis is that our hypothesis about the population mean is incorrect. Furthermore, with large samples s^2 nearly always has a very small percentage error.

Examples. **1.** We wish to test the hypothesis that the mean of a population is 5. We draw a sample of size 100 and find that the mean of our sample m is 20 and the population variance estimate $\hat{\sigma}^2(= s^2)$ is 2,500. We then compute

$$y = \frac{m - \mu_H}{\hat{\sigma}/\sqrt{n}} = \frac{20 - 5}{\sqrt{2,500/100}} = \frac{15}{\sqrt{25}} = 3$$

If our hypothesis were correct, we see by our table of $N(0,1)$ that the probability of obtaining a value of 3 or greater would have been less than .0014. Similarly, the probability of obtaining a value of -3 or smaller would have been less than .0014. Therefore, the probability of obtaining this great a deviation from our expected value, 0, would have been less than .003. Therefore, we reject our hypothesis at the .003 level of confidence. Further, we can assert at the .003 level of confidence that the population mean is *greater* than 5, because a hypothesized mean less than 5 would have given us an even greater deviation and enabled us to reject that hypothesis at an even lower level of confidence.

2. We wish to test the hypothesis that the mean of a population is 100 *or less*. We draw a sample of 100 and find that m is 117 and $\hat{\sigma}^2$ is 10,000. Then

$$y = \frac{m - \mu_H}{\hat{\sigma}/\sqrt{n}} = \frac{117 - 100}{100/\sqrt{100}} = 1.7$$

We are justified in rejecting our hypothesis at the .05 level of confidence, because before drawing our sample we assumed that our sample mean would be greater than 100; in other words, we decided to make our test *in a certain direction only*. If m had turned out to be 83, we could not reject the hypothesis that $\mu = 100$ at the .05 level of confidence, because doing so would imply that, before drawing our sample, the probability of rejecting our hypothesis at the .05 level of confidence would have actually been .10, if μ were actually 100. Our previous decision to make our test in one direction only, however, made the probability of rejecting our hypothesis at the .05 level of confidence only .05 (if the mean μ were 100), as it should be. If m had turned out to be much smaller than 100, say 70, we might be very suspicious of the hypothesis that $\mu = 100$, but the proper level of confidence at which to reject this hypothesis would require considerable thought.

It should be kept in mind that in computing $\dfrac{m - \mu_H}{\hat{\sigma}/\sqrt{n}}$ we are finding the approximate number of standard deviations our sample mean departs from the population mean in the *expected sampling distribution of the mean*, because μ_H is the hypothetical mean of the expected sampling distribution of the mean and $\hat{\sigma}/\sqrt{n}$ is our estimate of the standard deviation of the sampling distribution of the mean. If this is not perfectly clear to the student he should reread the discussion of the relation between $N(\mu,\sigma^2)$ and $N(0,1)$ given in Sec. 9.4.

The statistic $\dfrac{m - \mu_H}{\hat{\sigma}/\sqrt{n}}$ is called the "critical ratio."

Definition. The standard error of the mean σ_m is the standard deviation of the sampling distribution of the mean.

In sampling *any* population, $\sigma_m = \sigma/\sqrt{n}$; therefore, the critical ratio may be written $\dfrac{m - \mu_H}{\hat{\sigma}_m}$.

How large must n be for $\int_a^b \phi(0,1)\, dx$ to be a close enough approximation to prob $\left(a \leq \dfrac{m - \mu}{\sigma/\sqrt{n}} \leq b \right)$ and for s^2 to be a close enough approximation to σ^2 to justify the use of the critical ratio in testing hypotheses and finding confidence intervals? There is no general answer to this question, for the closeness of approximation depends not only upon n but also upon the distribution of the population sampled. A dichotomous population is the one *least* favorable to the generation of a normal sampling distribution, and if neither proportion is less than .20, a quite reasonable approximation is obtained with a sample of about 30. If one of the proportions is about .10, n should be about 100 for a reasonable fit. For a population whose distribution is roughly bell-shaped, a sample of less than 15 can give a close approximation. Obviously any general statement about the size of n has to be vague; many research workers adopt 30 as a kind of rule-of-thumb definition of "large." For many, perhaps most, nondichotomous populations encountered in practice, 30 is ample for a good approximation.

The central-limit theorem is of considerably greater generality than the student will probably recognize at first. For example, it enables one to test hypotheses about *proportions*. Consider a dichotomous population with two *qualitative* values instead of quantitative ones. Call the values A and B, and call the proportion of A's in the population p. If we transform the qualitative values A and B into the quantities 1 and 0 respectively, then the mean μ of the transformed population is simply p. Furthermore, the mean m of a sample with transformed values is simply p', the proportion of A's in the sample. According to the central-limit theorem, $\lim \text{prob} (a < p' < b) = \int_a^b \phi(p, \sigma^2/n)\, dx$. For the transformed dichotomous population with mean p, the variance is

$$E[(X - \mu)^2] = p(1 - p)^2 + (1 - p)(0 - p)^2 = p(1 - p)$$

Note that $q = 1 - p$ is the proportion of B's. Therefore the variance can be written pq. The central-limit theorem becomes

$$\lim_{n \to \infty} \text{prob} (a < p' < b) = \int_a^b \phi(p, pq/n)\, dx$$
$$\therefore \lim_{n \to \infty} \text{prob} [a < (p' - p)/\sqrt{pq/n} < b] = \int_a^b \phi(0,1)\, dx$$

The testing of a hypothesis about the mean of the transformed population is thus a test of a hypothesis about the proportion of A's! Note that in this test we do not need to estimate σ^2 from the sample; our hypothesis about p provides us with our estimate of σ^2.

9.7. Confidence Interval for a Mean of a Nonnormal Population. On the basis of the central-limit theorem we can easily derive a theorem which enables us, with a large sample, to obtain a confidence interval for the mean of any population whatsoever (as long as it has finite mean and finite variance) with very little computation.

The central-limit theorem states

$$\lim_{n \to \infty} \text{prob} \left(a < \frac{m - \mu}{\sigma/\sqrt{n}} < c \right) = \int_a^c \phi(0,1) \, dx$$

Reasoning in exactly the same way that we did in Sec. 9.5, we obtain

$$\lim_{n \to \infty} \text{prob} \left(m \pm b \frac{\sigma}{\sqrt{n}} \text{ includes } \mu \right) = \int_{-b}^b \phi(0,1) \, dx$$

Example. We wish to find the .01 confidence interval for the mean of a population with a completely unknown distribution (except that we know that it has finite mean and finite variance). We draw a large sample, say $n = 100$, and compute the sample mean and the estimate of the population variance s^2. We find that $m = 60$ and $s^2 = 81$. We then compute $m \pm b(s/\sqrt{n})$, which in this case is 60 ± 2.58 ($9/10$).

An important special case is that of finding a confidence interval for the proportion of members having a specified value in a dichotomous population. As in Sec. 9.6, we transform the specified value into 1 and the other values into 0. The proportion p having the specified value is then the mean of the transformed population. As before we have

$$\lim_{n \to \infty} \text{prob} \left(a < \frac{p' - p}{\sqrt{pq/n}} < c \right) = \int_a^c \phi(0,1) \, dx$$

in which p' is the proportion for a sample of size n. Then

$$\lim_{n \to \infty} \text{prob} \left(p' \pm b \sqrt{pq/n} \text{ includes } p \right) = \int_{-b}^b \phi(0,1) \, dx$$

To find the confidence limits for p we take

$$p' + b \sqrt{\frac{pq}{n}} = p$$

$$p' - b \sqrt{\frac{pq}{n}} = p$$

and solve for the values of p. Note that these two equations become

$$p' - p = -b \sqrt{\frac{pq}{n}}$$

$$p' - p = b \sqrt{\frac{pq}{n}}$$

Squaring, we obtain

$$(p')^2 - 2pp' + p^2 = \frac{b^2 pq}{n} = \frac{b^2 p(1-p)}{n} = \frac{b^2 p}{n} - \frac{b^2 p^2}{n}$$

$$\left(\frac{b^2}{n} + 1\right) p^2 - \left(\frac{b^2}{n} + 2p'\right) p + (p')^2 = 0$$

The solution to a quadratic equation $ax^2 + bx + c = 0$ is $x = \dfrac{-b \pm \sqrt{b^2 - 4ac}}{2a}$, thus

$$p = \frac{(b^2/n) + 2p' \pm \sqrt{(b^4/n^2) + (4b^2 p'/n) + 4(p')^2 - 4b^2(p')^2/n - 4(p')^2}}{(2b^2/n) + 2}$$

which simplifies to

$$\frac{(2np') + b^2 \pm b \sqrt{b^2 + 4np' - 4n(p')^2}}{2b^2 + 2n}$$

EXERCISES

9.7.1. A sample of 49 from a population with unknown distribution has a mean of 50 and a variance of 9.
   a. Test the hypothesis that $\mu = 52$.
   b. Find the .05 confidence interval for μ.

9.7.2. In an experiment on reaction time, 81 subjects gave a mean reaction time of 354 msec, with a variance of 400 msec. Find the .05 confidence interval for μ for the population from which these 81 reaction times can be considered a random sample.

9.7.3. In Exercise 9.7.2, what would be the difficulty with this procedure if all 81 reaction times had come from the same subject?

9.7.4. Nine hundred IQ scores are pulled at random from files containing the scores of 1,000,000 school children. The sample mean and variance are 101 and 9 respectively.

a. Test the hypothesis that $\mu \leq 100$.

b. Find a .01 confidence interval for μ with lower bound only.

9.7.5. Eighteen patients are selected at random from a large hospital. Each one is tested on two tests which are supposed to measure neurotic tendencies. The 36 scores have a mean of 105 and a variance of 25. The investigator wanted to test the hypothesis that the mean score in the hospital is 100. He took the critical ratio $\dfrac{105 - 100}{\frac{5}{6}} = 6$, and rejected the hypothesis at the .001 level of confidence. What is wrong with this test?

9.7.6. Four entirely unrelated hypotheses are tested with four different samples. The following critical ratios were obtained: .90, 1.05, 1.35, .82. How can you test all four of these hypotheses simultaneously, using these critical ratios?

9.7.7. A sample of 100 Democrats yields 65 who are in favor of a certain policy.

a. Test the hypothesis that there are just as many Democrats opposed to the policy as there are in favor of it.

b. Find the .01 confidence interval for the proportion of Democrats in favor of the policy.

9.7.8. A sample of 225 plants from a forest yields 70 which are infected.

a. Test the hypothesis that 40 per cent of the plants are infected.

b. Find the .03 confidence interval for the percentage of infected plants.

9.7.9. How large a sample must be taken to ensure, at the .01 level of confidence, that the proportion of life-insurance policies for amounts greater than $10,000 has been estimated from the sample to within .02 of the true proportion?

9.8. Difference between Two Independent Normally Distributed Variates.

We state without proof[1] the following theorem.

Theorem 9.8.1. Let X be distributed according to $\phi(\mu_x, \sigma_x^2)$ and Y be distributed according to $\phi(\mu_y, \sigma_y^2)$. Then $X - Y$ is distributed according to $\phi(\mu_x - \mu_y, \sigma_x^2 + \sigma_y^2)$ if X and Y are chosen independently.

The reader should be able to prove for himself that

$$\frac{x - y - (\mu_x - \mu_y)}{\sqrt{\sigma_x^2 + \sigma_y^2}}$$

is distributed according to $\phi(0,1)$ and to see the way in which a hypothesis about the value of the difference $\mu_x - \mu_y$ can be tested with a member from each population. Also, he should be

[1] A proof is given in the Appendix, Sec. B.21.

able to show that

$$\text{prob } (x - y \pm b \sqrt{\sigma_x^2 + \sigma_y^2} \text{ includes } \mu_x - \mu_y) = \int_{-b}^{b} \phi(0,1) \, dx$$

Definition. The standard deviation of the sampling distribution of the difference between two variates is called the "standard error of the difference," abbreviated σ_{x-y}. As we have just seen, if X and Y are independent, $\sigma_{x-y}^2 = \sigma_x^2 + \sigma_y^2$.

Notice that X and Y can be any normally distributed variates whatsoever in Theorem 9.8.1. In particular they may be *means* of samples of size n_x and n_y respectively drawn from two normally distributed populations (see Theorem 9.5.2). Thus we have as a corollary that if m_x and m_y are the means of samples drawn from $N(\mu_x, \sigma_x^2)$ and $N(\mu_y, \sigma_y^2)$ respectively, then

$$f(m_x - m_y) = \phi \left(\mu_x - \mu_y, \frac{\sigma_x^2}{n_x} + \frac{\sigma_y^2}{n_y} \right)$$

from which we have

$$f \left[\frac{m_x - m_y - (\mu_x - \mu_y)}{\sqrt{(\sigma_x^2/n_x) + (\sigma_y^2/n_y)}} \right] = \phi(0,1)$$

and

$$\text{prob } [m_x - m_y \pm b \sqrt{(\sigma_x^2/n_x) + (\sigma_y^2/n_y)} \text{ includes } \mu_x - \mu_y]$$
$$= \int_{-b}^{b} \phi(0,1) \, dx$$

Thus we can test hypotheses about the value of $\mu_x - \mu_y$ and also find confidence intervals, if we know that the populations being sampled are normal and we know their variances.

We also state the following theorem without proof.

Theorem 9.8.2. Consider samples drawn independently and at random from two populations, each with finite mean and variance. The sampling distribution of the difference between the means $m_x - m_y$ will approach $N \left(\mu_x - \mu_y, \frac{\sigma_x^2}{n_x} + \frac{\sigma_y^2}{n_y} \right)$ as n_x and n_y approach infinity; more precisely,

$$\lim_{n_x, n_y \to \infty} \text{prob } (a < m_x - m_y < b) = \int_{a}^{b} \phi \left(\mu_x - \mu_y, \frac{\sigma_x^2}{n_x} + \frac{\sigma_y^2}{n_y} \right) dx$$

Corollary

$$\lim_{n_x, n_y \to \infty} \text{prob} \left[a < \frac{(m_x - m_y) - (\mu_x - \mu_y)}{\sqrt{\dfrac{\sigma_x^2}{n_x} + \dfrac{\sigma_y^2}{n_y}}} < b \right]$$

$$= \int_a^b \phi(0,1) \, dx$$

Corollary

$$\lim_{n_x, n_y \to \infty} \text{prob} \left[(m_x - m_y) \pm b \sqrt{\frac{\sigma_x^2}{n_x} + \frac{\sigma_y^2}{n_y}} \text{ includes } (\mu_x - \mu_y) \right]$$

$$= \int_{-b}^b \phi(0,1) \, dx$$

With large samples we can use the sample variances as estimates of the population variances and thus test hypotheses about the value of $\mu_x - \mu_y$, and also find confidence intervals.

An important special case of Theorem 9.8.2 arises when each of the two populations is dichotomous. By transforming the values into 0 and 1, as discussed in Sec. 9.7, we obtain

$$\lim_{n_x, n_y \to \infty} \text{prob} \, (a < p_x' - p_y' < b)$$

$$= \int_a^b \phi \left(p_x - p_y, \frac{p_x q_x}{n_x} + \frac{p_y q_y}{n_y} \right) dx$$

in which p_x' and p_y' are sample proportions. Also,

$$\lim_{n_x, n_y \to \infty} \text{prob} \left[a < \frac{p_x' - p_y' - (p_x - p_y)}{\sqrt{\dfrac{p_x q_x}{n_x} + \dfrac{p_y q_y}{n_y}}} < b \right] = \int_a^b \phi(0,1) \, dx$$

This corollary implies that with large samples we can test a hypothesis about the size of $p_x - p_y$, using p_x' and p_y' as estimates of the sizes of p_x and p_y respectively. In most cases our hypothesis will be that $p_x - p_y = 0$, that is, that $p_x = p_y$, in which case we can use $\dfrac{n_x p_x' + n_y p_y'}{n_x + n_y}$ as our estimate of p_x (and p_y).

We can also easily obtain

$$\lim_{n_x, n_y \to \infty} \text{prob} \left(p'_x - p'_y \pm b \sqrt{\frac{p_x q_x}{n_x} + \frac{p_y q_y}{n_y}} \text{ includes } p_x - p_y \right)$$
$$= \int_{-b}^{b} \phi(0,1) \, dx$$

which enables us to find confidence intervals, using p'_x and p'_y as estimates of p_x and p_y respectively.

EXERCISES

9.8.1. Suppose we plan to draw a member X at random from a population having the distribution $N(100, 100)$ and a member Y at random from a population having the distribution $N(110, 225)$. Find the probability that x will be
  a. greater than y
  b. at least 10 greater than y
9.8.2. Suppose we plan to draw a random sample of 9 from $N(100,25)$ and a random sample of 16 from $N(95,36)$. Call the mean of the first sample m_x and the mean of the second sample m_y. What is the probability that m_x will be
  a. greater than m_y?
  b. at least 2 greater than m_y?
9.8.3. Samples of 9 and 25 are drawn at random from populations $N(\mu_x,16)$ and $N(\mu_y,36)$ respectively. The sample means are $m_x = 10$ and $m_y = 20$, and the variances are 25 and 25 respectively.
  a. Test the hypothesis that $\mu_x = \mu_y$.
  b. Find the .05 confidence interval for $\mu_x - \mu_y$.
9.8.4. Random samples of 100 and 225 are drawn from two populations with unknown distributions. The sample means and variances are $m_x = 100$; $s_x^2 = 25$; $m_y = 99$; $s_y^2 = 9$.
  a. Test the hypothesis that $\mu_x = \mu_y$.
  b. Test the hypothesis that $\mu_x \geq \mu_y$.
  c. Find the .01 confidence interval for $\mu_x - \mu_y$.
  d. Test the hypothesis that $\mu_x = 105$.
  e. Find the .01 confidence interval for μ_x.
  f. Find the .01 confidence interval for μ_y.
9.8.5. Samples of 100 and 200 are drawn from two dichotomous populations. The respective sample proportions are $p'_x = .36$ and $p'_y = .45$.
  a. Test the hypothesis that $p_x - p_y = 0$.
  b. Test the hypothesis that $(p_y - p_x) \geq .15$.
  c. Find the .05 confidence interval for $p_x - p_y$.
  d. Find the .05 confidence interval for p_x.
9.8.6. Samples of 100 and 225 are drawn from two dichotomous populations. The respective sample proportions are $p'_x = .70$ and $p'_y = .65$.

a. Test the hypothesis that $p_x - p_y = 0$.

b. Test the hypothesis that $(p_y - p_x) \geq .02$.

c. Find the .05 confidence interval for $p_x - p_y$.

9.8.7. A manufacturer is faced with the problem of choosing between two machine designs, each claimed to result in greater precision than the other in turning out the manufacturer's product. An experimental model of each is built, and the products turned out by each are measured for deviations from exact specifications, the absolute value of each deviation being taken. The absolute deviations of 225 products produced by machine A yield a mean of .00412678 and variance of .00000036. The absolute deviations of 225 products produced by machine B yield a mean of .00453860 and variance of .00000025.

a. Does the manufacturer have good evidence on which to make a choice?

b. Within what limits can the difference in mean precision between A and B be said to lie at the .01 level of confidence?

c. What assumptions are made in regarding these samples as random?

9.8.8. Each of 800 persons seated in a large auditorium is given a simple paper-and-pencil attitude test. The papers are collected and a mimeographed article relevant to the attitude is handed each person. Two different articles, A and B, are handed out, each person receiving only one of the two. After reading the article, each person takes another attitude test. Of the 400 people reading A, 80 have "higher" attitude scores on the second test; of those reading B, 160 have "higher" scores.

a. Test the hypothesis that A and B are equally effective in raising attitude scores.

b. Find the .05 confidence interval for the difference between A and B in proportion of changes.

c. What assumptions are made in regarding these samples as random?

9.8.9. A vaccine is tested on 400 volunteers and found to be 80 per cent effective.

a. Find the .01 confidence interval for its effectiveness in the general population.

b. What assumption is involved in regarding the volunteers as a random sample?

9.8.10. Two different agricultural methods are compared for growing a certain crop. Each of 100 plots is treated by method A and each of 100 plots by method B. The mean yield for A is 55 units, with variance of 4; the mean yield for B is 50 units with variance of 9.

a. Test the hypothesis that the two mean yields differ only as an effect of random sampling.

b. Find the .05 confidence interval for the difference between the mean yields.

c. What assumption is involved in regarding the yields as random samples?

9.8.11. A physiological index of emotionality is taken under each of two experimental conditions, A and B, on each of 100 subjects. The mean and variance of the indices under condition A are 4.50 and 1.44 respectively. The mean and variance of the indices under condition B are 5.32 and 2.89 respectively. The mean and variance of the 100 differences between indices (one difference for each subject) are 0.82 and 1.21 respectively. What is the correct test to make of the hypothesis that the indices under the two conditions differ only by the effects of random sampling? Upon what theorem is the test based? Define the population sampled in making this test. Why is the other test that might be made with these data not valid?

9.9. Fitting a Normal Distribution to a Sample. In Sec. 5.6 we discussed fitting a binomial distribution and in Sec. 6.4 fitting a Poisson distribution. The principle of fitting a normal distribution is the same, that is, we construct a sample of the same size, having certain characteristics in common with our actual sample but having the desired kind of distribution, in this case a normal distribution (i.e., the discrete counterpart of a normal distribution).

The characteristics which our constructed sample will have in common with our actual sample are simply the same size, mean, and variance. First of all we must have our data grouped into class intervals (see Sec. 4.8), for reasons which will be obvious once the complete process has been described. Next, after calculating the mean and standard deviation of the sample, we find, with the aid of the tables for $N(0,1)$, the proportion of cases we should have for each class interval to obtain the discrete counterpart of a normal distribution. This process can best be explained by an example. Assume that a large number of observations have been made correct to the nearest tenth of a unit, and that the first two columns of the table on page 122 represent the result of grouping the data into class intervals. The interval limits are the "true" limits; for example, the observation 7.4 is assumed to include all values from 7.35 to 7.45. Thus the highest interval is assumed to include all true values from 7.25 to ∞. In the calculation of the mean m and the standard deviation s, all observations are treated as though they fell at the mid-points of the class intervals. The theoretical proportions are found by taking the number of standard deviations each class limit is from the sample mean. Calling the class limit x, this amounts to the transformation $y = (x - m)/s$. If the original observations have the distribution $N(m,s^2)$, then the transformed values have the distribution $N(0,1)$; therefore, by using the tables for $N(0,1)$ we can find what proportion of a normal distribution should lie within each of the class intervals. This computation has been carried out for the sample shown in the table, which has $m = 4.945$ and $s = 1.081$. For example,

Interval	Observed proportion	Theoretical proportion
7.25–∞	.01	.01
6.75–7.25	.03	.03
6.25–6.75	.08	.07
5.75–6.25	.11	.12
5.25–5.75	.16	.16
4.75–5.25	.21	.18
4.25–4.75	.14	.14
3.75–4.25	.12	.13
3.25–3.75	.07	.09
2.75–3.25	.04	.04
2.25–2.75	.03	.02
– ∞–2.25	.00	.01

the interval 6.25–6.75 becomes transformed into the interval $(6.25 - 4.945)/1.081$ to $(6.75 - 4.945)/1.081$, which is the interval 1.207–1.670. From the tables for $N(0,1)$ we find that the theoretical proportion for this interval is .07. As an exercise, the student should check this fit.

As in the case of the binomial or the Poisson, we may wish to raise the question of how "good" a fit this represents, but we must defer this question until the next chapter.

Chapter 10

CHI SQUARE

10.1. Definition of Chi Square. Consider a random sample of size n from a population having the distribution $N(0,1)$, that is, normally distributed with zero mean and unit variance. The sum of squares of values of members of the sample is called *chi square with n degrees of freedom*.

Definition. $\chi_n^2 \equiv \sum_{i=1}^{n} x_i^2$, with each x_i independently distributed according to $\phi(0,1)$.

We state without proof[1] that the distribution of χ_n^2 is given by

$$f(\chi_n^2) = \frac{(\chi^2)^{(n/2)-1} e^{-\chi^2/2}}{2^{(n/2)} \Gamma(n/2)}$$

in which $\Gamma(n/2) = [(n/2) - 1]!$ if n is even and $[(n/2) - 1]$ $[(n/2) - 2] \cdots \frac{1}{2} \sqrt{\pi}$ if n is odd. This function (Γ) is called the *gamma function*.

The sum of two independent χ^2's is itself distributed according to χ^2, since

$$\chi_{n_1}^2 + \chi_{n_2}^2 = \sum_{i=1}^{n_1} x_i^2 + \sum_{i=1}^{n_2} x_i^2 = \sum_{i=1}^{n_1+n_2} x_i^2 = \chi_{n_1+n_2}^2$$

and therefore[2] $f(\chi_{n_1}^2 + \chi_{n_2}^2) = f(\chi_{n_1+n_2}^2)$.

---

[1] A proof is given in the Appendix, Sec. B.22.
[2] This argument is not a proof, as it assumes that because the two χ^2's are independent the individual x_i's are also independent. A proof is given in the Appendix, Sec. B.22.

Frequency functions of χ_n^2 for $n = 1, 2, 6, 15$ are illustrated in Fig. 10.1.1.

We state without proof[1] that $\mu[\equiv E(\chi_n^2)] = n$ and

$$\sigma^2\{\equiv E[(\chi_n^2 - n)^2]\} = 2n$$

Further, the mode is $n - 2$, except for $n = 1$.

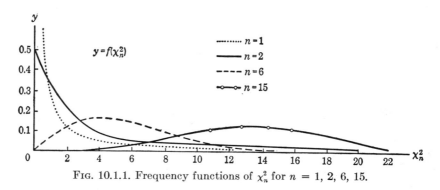

FIG. 10.1.1. Frequency functions of χ_n^2 for $n = 1, 2, 6, 15$.

10.2. Goodness of Fit When the Hypothetical Distribution Is Completely Specified.

Suppose we have a random sample of size n from a population with unknown distribution, and we wish to test the hypothesis that the population is distributed in a certain way, which we specify completely, that is, we not only hypothesize the functional form of the distribution (normal, binomial, Poisson, etc.) but we hypothesize also the values of all parameters. In order to test our hypothesis we need merely to compute, on the basis of our hypothesis, the expected frequencies (theoretical frequencies) for each of the possible values (or value categories, for example, class intervals) in the population and to compare these expected or theoretical frequencies with those actually obtained in the sample.

Let our sample values be tabulated into k groups, and let the frequencies in these groups be $f_{o1}, f_{o2}, \ldots, f_{ok}$ (f_o meaning observed frequency). On the basis of our hypothesis we then calculate the corresponding theoretical frequencies $f_{t1}, f_{t2}, \ldots,$

[1] Derivations of the mean and variance are given in the Appendix, Sec. B.22.

f_{tk}. We then form the statistic $\sum\limits_{i=1}^{k} \dfrac{(f_{oi} - f_{ti})^2}{f_{ti}}$. We state without proof the following theorem, first proved by K. Pearson.[1]

Theorem 10.2.1

$$\lim_{\text{as } n \to \infty} F\left[\sum_{i=1}^{k} \frac{(f_{oi} - f_{ti})^2}{f_{ti}} \right] = F(\chi^2_{k-1})$$

in which the symbols have the meanings[2] described above. In other words, as our sample size increases, the distribution of $\sum\limits_{i=1}^{k} \dfrac{(f_{oi} - f_{ti})^2}{f_{ti}}$ becomes a closer and closer approximation to the distribution of χ^2_{k-1}, *regardless of the distribution of the original population.* For this reason the statistic $\sum\limits_{i=1}^{k} \dfrac{(f_{oi} - f_{ti})^2}{f_{ti}}$ will be called χ^2, trusting that the context will make clear whether we are speaking of this statistic or of χ^2 as defined in the previous section.

When all the theoretical frequencies f_{ti} are at least 5 and $k \geq 5$, the approximation is sufficiently close for ordinary purposes. If $k < 5$ the f_{ti} should be 10 at least. Whenever some of the f_{ti} are too small, it is advisable to pool the smaller groups.

The hypothesis that our sample was drawn from a population with the distribution which we have specified can be tested in a manner analogous to that in which we have previously tested hypotheses. Note that, if our theoretical frequencies fit our sample exactly, χ^2 equals 0. The further our sample departs from expectation, the larger the value of χ^2 we obtain. We find a critical value C such that if the hypothesis is correct the probability (before the sample is drawn) that χ^2 will exceed C is only $p(.05, .02, \text{etc.})$. The critical value C for a given p is found by

---

[1] Proofs are given by Cramér (3) and Mood (9).

[2] This theorem means $\lim\limits_{\text{as } n \to \infty} \text{prob} \left[\sum\limits_{i=1}^{k} \dfrac{(f_{oi} - f_{ti})^2}{f_{ti}} \leq C \right] = \int_0^C f(\chi^2_{k-1}) \, d\chi^2.$

solving the following equation:

$$1 - p = \int_0^C f(\chi^2_{k-1}) \, d\chi^2$$

In other words, a value C is found such that p of the probability will lie in the interval C to ∞. Values of C have been tabulated in Appendix D for various values of $1 - p$ and for n (degrees of freedom) ≤ 30. If the number of degrees of freedom is greater than 30, the following theorem can be used:

Theorem 10.2.2. $\sqrt{2\chi^2_n}$ is approximately normally distributed with mean $\sqrt{2n - 1}$ and unit variance.

Corollary. $\sqrt{2\chi^2_n} - \sqrt{2n - 1}$ has approximately the distribution $N(0,1)$.

Examples. **1.** On each trial of a learning sequence, a monkey chooses one of two perceptually different objects. One is correct (filled with food); the other is incorrect. Of 500 trials, 300 are correct and 200 are incorrect. On the hypothesis that the monkey is responding at random on each trial we have theoretical frequencies of 250 and 250. Therefore, we have

$$\chi^2 = \sum_{i=1}^{2} \frac{(f_{oi} - f_{ti})^2}{f_{ti}} = \frac{2(50)^2}{250} = 20$$

Referring to the Appendix, we see that for $n = 1$ the probability of obtaining a value of χ^2 this large or larger is less than .005. Therefore we reject our hypothesis at the .005 level of confidence.

Notice that we could have tested our hypothesis in this case also by the critical ratio, for

$$\text{C.R.} = \frac{p' - p}{\sqrt{pq/n}} = \frac{\frac{3}{5} - \frac{1}{2}}{\sqrt{\frac{1}{2000}}} = +\sqrt{20}$$

It is not a coincidence that the C.R. is a square root of χ^2 for one degree of freedom. If our hypothesis were correct, the C.R. would have the distribution $N(0,1)$. Therefore, the square of the C.R. would, by definition, be χ^2 with one degree of freedom. This means that we could have computed χ^2_1, on the basis of our hypothesis, by computing the C.R. and squaring.

2. Suppose we have the hypothesis that variations A, B, C, and D in a certain kind of plant will be distributed in the ratio $6:4:3:1$. Of 200 plants observed, the respective frequencies are 90, 54, 44, 12. Each theoretical frequency is $200p_i$, where p_i is the probability, on the basis of our hypothesis, that a plant selected at random will be of variety i. We then have the accompanying table:

Variety	f_o	f_t	$\dfrac{(f_o - f_t)^2}{f_t}$
A	90	85.7	.216
B	54	57.1	.168
C	44	42.9	.028
D	12	14.3	.370
			.782

Since the probability of obtaining a χ_3^2 this large or larger is $>.80$, we must consider the agreement good.

If a second independent set of observations yields a χ_3^2 of 6.015, we can test both sets of observations together by taking the sum $\chi_3^2 + \chi_3^2 = 6.797 = \chi_6^2$. We observe from our table that the probability of a χ_6^2 of this size or larger is $>.30$. Thus the agreement is still acceptable. We could also have thrown our observations together and obtained a χ_3^2 based on a larger sample.

3. Suppose we have a sample of 670 observations whose distribution is given by the following table:

Value	Frequency	Value	Frequency
26	1	4	32
25	2	3	27
24	2	2	30
23	4	1	30
22	5	0	21
21	6	-1	18
20	5	-2	23
19	8	-3	17
18	10	-4	11
17	9	-5	13
16	12	-6	11
15	17	-7	15
14	15	-8	9
13	25	-9	8
12	22	-10	9
11	26	-11	5
10	31	-12	7
9	30	-13	3
8	25	-14	0
7	38	-15	4
6	33	-16	1
5	40		

Suppose we wish to test the hypothesis that our sample was drawn randomly from a population having the distribution $N(5,49)$. To do this we calculate f_{ti} in exactly the same way as described in Sec. 9.9, except that we use 5 as the mean and 49 as the variance in computing f_{ti} instead of the sample mean and variance. We then obtain the following table:

Interval	f_o	f_t
21.5–∞	14	6.10
18.5–21.5	19	11.86
15.5–18.5	31	26.80
12.5–15.5	57	50.59
9.5–12.5	79	79.60
6.5–9.5	93	104.32
3.5–6.5	105	111.49
0.5–3.5	87	104.32
−2.5–0.5	62	79.60
−5.5––2.5	41	50.59
−8.5––5.5	35	26.80
−11.5––8.5	22	11.86
−∞––11.5	15	6.10

χ^2_{12} calculated on the basis of the table is about 51, which allows us to reject our hypothesis at the .005 level of confidence. If the extreme theoretical frequencies had been less than 5, we should have combined the two extreme class intervals at each end and calculated χ^2_{10}. In this case, calculation of χ^2_{10} yields about 48, which still allows us to reject our hypothesis at the .005 level of confidence.

We can also make the χ^2 test by considering that if our sample were drawn from a population having the distribution $N(5,49)$ and if we transform each value x in our sample into y by the transformation $y = (x - 5)/7$, we should have a sample drawn from a population having the distribution $N(0,1)$. The sum of the squares of the y's therefore should be distributed as χ^2_{670}. As n is too large for our tables, we have to use the theorem that $\sqrt{2\chi^2_n} - \sqrt{2n - 1}$ has the distribution $N(0,1)$. This test actually yields $\chi^2_{670} = 876$, and $\sqrt{2\chi^2_{670}} - \sqrt{2(670) - 1} = 5.3$, a value which allows us to reject our hypothesis at the .001 level of confidence. Whereas our previous test is approximate, this test is exact, because by hypothesis $F\left(\sum_{i=1}^{670} y_i^2\right) = F(\chi^2_{670})$; furthermore, our latter test would be applicable even if the sample were small.

EXERCISES

10.2.1. Test the hypothesis that the following sample of IQ's is drawn at random from a population having the distribution $N(100, 100)$:

x (mid-point of interval)	Frequency
130	2
125	5
120	7
115	10
110	20
105	40
100	60
95	35
90	30
85	20
80	8
75	4
70	1

10.2.2. Test the hypothesis that the following sample is drawn at random from $N(50,2)$: 47, 47, 49, 50, 48, 55.

10.2.3. Test the hypothesis that the following sample is drawn at random from $N(10,1)$: 9.0, 9.4, 11.8, 10.1, 8.5.

10.2.4. According to theory, the progeny of a certain species are distributed among the three categories A, B, and C in the ratio $5:3:2$. Are the following 100 observations in accord with this theory?

Category	Frequency
A	50
B	49
C	10

10.2.5. Test the hypothesis that the following sample is drawn randomly from a population whose distribution is given by $f(x) = (x^2 + 2x + 1)/91$ when $x = 0, 1, 2, 3, 4, 5$:

x	Frequency
5	88
4	40
3	25
2	15
1	10
0	4

10.2.6. Test the hypothesis that the following critical ratios were all obtained by testing hypotheses that are correct: .20, 1.20, .61, −.20, .95.

10.2.7. Test the hypothesis that the following sample was drawn randomly from a population having a Poisson distribution with a mean of 2:

x	Frequency
3	25
2	30
1	20
0	15

10.2.8. A machine is constructed which, it is asserted, turns out digits "at random." The following data are obtained by taking 100 runs of 10 digits each and counting the number of 4's in each run:

x	Frequency
3	10
2	20
1	45
0	25

Are these data consistent with the assertion that digits are turned out "at random"? What are some other tests that could be made?

10.2.9. A product is marketed in two packages which are identical except for being of different colors, red and pink. The packages are mixed together thoroughly in a display and each customer serves himself. After 100 packages have been sold (this number having been determined in advance) it is found that 60 red and 40 pink packages have been sold.

a. Is this result consistent with the hypothesis that color makes no difference?

b. What does the assumption of random sampling mean in this case?

10.2.10. Flip a coin as "randomly" as you can 100 times; record the number of heads and tails and test the hypothesis that your flips are unbiased.

10.2.11. Toss a die 100 times and test your tosses for bias.

10.3. Goodness of Fit When the Hypothetical Distribution Is Incompletely Specified.
In many, if not most, applications we wish to test the hypothesis that our sample is drawn from a population having a certain form (that is, normal, binomial, Poisson, etc.), but we do not wish to include in our hypothesis specific parameter values. In order to compute theoretical frequencies for this case, we must estimate parameter values from

our sample. In so doing, however, we obviously tend to make our sum $\sum_{i=1}^{k} \frac{(f_{oi} - f_{ti})^2}{f_{ti}}$ smaller than it would be if we knew or hypothesized the parameter values. To compensate for this decrease in the value of χ^2 we must therefore decrease the number of degrees of freedom whereby we interpret χ^2. A remarkable theorem due to R. A. Fisher states that if we estimate parameters in such a way as to make χ^2 as small as possible, it is necessary only to reduce the number of degrees of freedom by one for each parameter estimated from the sample. Suppose that we estimate r parameters from our sample; then, with the same meanings for the symbols as in Theorem 10.2.1, we have the following theorem.

Theorem 10.3

$$\lim_{\substack{\text{as } n \to \infty}} F\left[\sum_{i=1}^{k} \frac{(f_{oi} - f_{ti})^2}{f_{ti}} \right] = F(\chi^2_{k-r-1})$$

Note that Theorem 10.2.1 is a special case of Theorem **10.3**, that is, the case in which we estimate no parameters from the sample $(r = 0)$.

We state without proof[1] that for a given sample the estimates of the mean and variance of a normal population which minimize χ^2 are the sample mean and variance. The estimate of the mean of a Poisson population which minimizes χ^2 is the sample mean.[1]

Examples. **1.** Suppose that we have the sample given in Example 3, Sec. 10.2, and we wish to test the hypothesis that our sample was drawn from a normal population. We compute the theoretical frequencies in exactly the same way as before, except that we now use the sample mean and variance as our estimates of μ and σ^2. The student can verify that χ^2 is about 7. This χ^2 is to be interpreted on the basis of $13 - 2 - 1 = 10$ degrees of freedom rather than $13 - 1 = 12$ as before, since we estimated two parameters in making our fit. We find that we cannot reject the hypothesis that our sample is drawn from a normal population, although we can reject the hypothesis that it was drawn from $N(5,49)$.

2. Suppose we have a sample of observations and we wish to test the hypothesis that our sample is randomly drawn from a population having a Poisson distribution. We need merely divide all possible values of a Poisson distribu-

[1] A proof is given by Cramér (3).

tion $(0, 1, 2, \ldots)$ into k groups and calculate the theoretical frequency for each group by using the Poisson expression $f(x) = e^{-\mu}\mu^x/x!$, using the sample mean as an estimate of μ. As we estimate only one parameter, we interpret this χ^2 according to $k - 2$ degrees of freedom.

EXERCISES

10.3.1. Test the goodness of fit of the example in Sec. 9.9, assuming the sample has
    a. 1,000 members
    b. 10,000 members

10.3.2. Test the hypothesis that the following sample of laboratory grades can be considered drawn randomly from a normal population:

x (mid-point)	Frequency
60	3
59	10
58	15
57	21
56	38
55	40
54	30
53	25
52	21
51	12
50	5

10.3.3. Are the following sample data on the incidence of incoming telephone calls during a 5-min period on each of 110 days (for one telephone) consistent with the hypothesis that the calls are individually and collectively at random?

Number of calls	Frequency
0	2
1	5
2	15
3	25
4	30
5	23
6	10

10.3.4. Test the goodness of fit in Exercise 6.4.2.

10.3.5. It is often assumed that errors of measurement are distributed normally. Is the following random sample of errors made in operating tracking instruments consistent with this assumption?

Error	Frequency
5	1
4	4
3	8
2	15
1	31
0	45
−1	22
−2	12
−3	10
−4	7
−5	5

10.3.6. Over a period of 10 years a random sample of 135 students winning competitive scholarships for undergraduate work is tabulated by dormitories. The number of students living in each dormitory during that time is also shown.

Dormitory	Number of students living in dormitory	Number winning scholarships
A	2,500	30
B	1,250	15
C	2,000	29
D	1,050	22
E	2,200	14
F	2,800	35

Are these data consistent with the hypothesis that the dormitory a student lives in has had no relation to whether he wins a scholarship?   Define carefully the population sampled and state the assumptions involved in making this test.

10.4. Test of Independence in a Contingency Table.   Suppose we are sampling a population each of whose members we classify in two ways instead of only one.   A table showing the two-way classification of a sample from such a population is called a *contingency table.*   Let the contingency table shown as Table 10.4.1

represent the distribution of a sample of 200 randomly drawn from a population in which each member has one of the values x_1 or x_2 and also one of the values y_1 or y_2. Now suppose that we are interested in the following problem. In the population

TABLE 10.4.1. CONTINGENCY TABLE SHOWING DISTRIBUTION OF SAMPLE OF 200 DRAWN FROM POPULATION IN WHICH EACH MEMBER HAS TWO VALUES

	x_1	x_2	$x_1 + x_2$
y_1	20	100	120
y_2	40	40	80
$y_1 + y_2$	60	140	200

sampled, are the two values independent of each other in the sense that, of those members having the value x_1, the distribution of members with respect to y is the same as the distribution with respect to y of those members having the value x_2 (and therefore the distribution with respect to y of the entire population)? For example, if in the population $f(x_1)$ were .56 [so that $f(x_2)$ would be .44] and $f(y_1)$ were .25 [so that $f(y_2)$ would be .75], then would .56 be divided between y_1 and y_2 in the ratio of 1 to

TABLE 10.4.2. THEORETICAL PROPORTIONS ON HYPOTHESIS THAT $f(x_1) = .56$, $f(y_1) = .25$, AND $f(x,y) = f(x)f(y)$

	x_1	x_2	$x_1 + x_2$
y_1	.14	.11	.25
y_2	.42	.33	.75
$y_1 + y_2$	.56	.44	1.00

3, as in the entire population? If this were the case, the population would have the distribution shown in Table 10.4.2. This table was obtained by dividing .56 and .44 each into two parts having the ratio $\frac{1}{3}$. Note that

$$f(x_1, y_1) = .14 = (.56)(.25) = f(x_1)f(y_1)$$

similarly for the other entries in the table. As a matter of fact, a general condition for independence is simply $f(x, y) = f(x)f(y)$. (Compare with the discussion in Sec. 2.3.)

It is possible to make a χ^2 test of the hypothesis that $f(x_1)$ and $f(y_1)$ have certain specified values and that x and y are independent by computing theoretical proportions (probabilities) as indicated above and multiplying each proportion by the size of the sample to obtain theoretical frequencies. A χ^2 computed in this way would have three degrees of freedom. In most situations, however, we wish to test the hypothesis of independence without including in our hypothesis a specification of the values of $f(x_1)$ and $f(y_1)$. By using the marginal totals in our sample divided

TABLE 10.4.3. THEORETICAL FREQUENCIES COMPUTED FROM MARGINAL TOTALS OF SAMPLE

	x_1	x_2	$x_1 + x_2$
y_1	36	84	120
y_2	24	56	80
$y_1 + y_2$	60	140	200

by the size of the sample as estimates of the parameters $f(x_1)$ and $f(y_1)$, we can apply Theorem 10.3 and thus make a χ^2 test with one degree of freedom. Following this procedure with our sample of 200 we obtain the theoretical frequencies shown in Table 10.4.3. We then have

$$\chi_1^2 = \sum_{i=1}^{4} \frac{(f_{oi} - f_{ti})^2}{f_{ti}} = 25.40$$

By our table we see that a χ_1^2 of this size is significant at the .005 level of confidence.

Each classification may be qualitative or quantitative or ordinal and may involve more than two values. In general, we have the sample shown in Table 10.4.4. The estimated independent marginal proportions (probabilities) are $\frac{n_{i\cdot}}{n}$ $(i = 1, 2, \ldots, r - 1)$ and $\frac{n_{\cdot j}}{n}$ $(i = 1, 2, \ldots, s - 1)$.

TABLE 10.4.4. SAMPLE CONTINGENCY TABLE WITH rs CELLS

	x_1	x_2	$\cdots$	x_s	$\sum_{j=1}^{s}$
y_1	n_{11}	n_{12}	$\cdots$	n_{1s}	$n_{1\cdot}$
y_2	n_{21}	n_{22}	$\cdots$	n_{2s}	$n_{2\cdot}$
$\vdots$	$\vdots$	$\vdots$	$\cdots$	$\vdots$	$\vdots$
y_r	n_{r1}	n_{r2}	$\cdots$	n_{rs}	$n_{r\cdot}$
$\sum_{i=1}^{r}$	$n_{\cdot1}$	$n_{\cdot2}$	$\cdots$	$n_{\cdot s}$	n

The theoretical probability for cell ij is simply $\left(\dfrac{n_{i\cdot}}{n}\right)\left(\dfrac{n_{\cdot j}}{n}\right)$. The theoretical frequency for cell ij is therefore

$$n\left(\frac{n_{i\cdot}}{n}\right)\left(\frac{n_{\cdot j}}{n}\right) = \frac{n_{i\cdot}n_{\cdot j}}{n}$$

As $(r-1)+(s-1) = r+s-2$, independent parameters have been estimated, and as there are rs cells in all, by Theorem 10.3 the number of degrees of freedom is

$$rs - (r+s-2) - 1 = rs - r - s + 1 = (r-1)(s-1)$$

Although a large value of χ^2 relative to the number of degrees of freedom provides strong evidence that the two variables are related, it does not indicate the degree of relationship. With a very large n, a contingency table may give a very large χ^2 even with only a slight difference in the distributions of the rows (or columns). (The student should be able to prove this as an exercise.) A quantitative estimate of the degree of relationship is $\chi^2/n(q-1)$ in which q is the smaller of the numbers r and s.

We state without proof that this measure of relationship can have values only between 0 and 1.

EXERCISES

10.4.1. A sample of 150 is drawn at random from all alumni of a large university. Each alumnus is classified as either professional or nonprofessional and also as either satisfied or not satisfied with his work. The following contingency table is obtained:

	Prof.	Nonprof.
Satis.	50	40
Not satis.	30	30

Test the hypothesis that
a. being professional has no relation to being satisfied.
b. there are as many nonprofessional alumni as professional, and as many satisfied as not satisfied alumni, and the two variables have no relation to each other.
c. among professional alumni there are three times as many who are satisfied as there are who are not satisfied, whereas among nonprofessional alumni there are as many not satisfied as there are who are satisfied.

10.4.2. In an experiment using the Rorschach ink blot test, each patient is classified as to whether his profile on the test gives a favorable prognosis for therapy and also as to whether he has been judged (by clinicians other than those using the test) to have a good chance of recovery. The obtained contingency table is shown:

	Unfav. prog. (Rorschach)	Fav. prog. (Rorschach)
Good chance	50	75
Not good chance	50	25

a. Test the hypothesis that the prognosis made from the Rorschach is unrelated to that made independently.
b. Estimate the degree of relationship.

10.4.3. In an experiment on the relation of types of figural after-effects to measures of rigidity in thinking, each of 200 subjects was tested on both variables, and the following contingency table was obtained:

Type of figural after-effect

		A	B	C	D
	X	14	25	14	17
Rigidity	Y	20	15	21	24
	Z	6	10	15	19

Test the hypothesis that rigidity is independent of type of figural after-effect.

10.4.4. Derive the following computational formula for a 2×2 contingency table, in which theoretical frequencies are estimated from marginal totals and the obtained frequencies are a, b, c, and d, with b and d located diagonally with respect to each other:

$$\chi_1^2 = \frac{(a+b+c+d)(ad-bc)^2}{(a+b)(c+d)(b+d)(a+c)}$$

10.4.5. Eighty specimens of a certain species were examined and tabulated with respect to presence or absence of characteristic A and presence or absence of characteristic B. The following table was obtained:

	A	$\bar{A}$
B	14	21
$\bar{B}$	16	29

If approximately the same proportions were to hold in a larger sample, how large would the sample have to be to obtain a χ^2 significant at the .01 level when the hypothesis of independence is tested?

10.5. Tests of Homogeneity. Let us suppose that we have s different samples, each member of each sample having one of r different values, y_1, y_2, . . . , y_r. We can then assemble our data into a table which is formally identical with that of Sec. 10.4. In this case, however, the marginal totals $n._j$ ($j = 1, 2,$ . . . , s) are determined in advance or, at any rate, have nothing to do with estimates of parameters.

We wish to test the hypothesis that all our samples are drawn from populations having the same distribution. We estimate this distribution (the distribution of y) from the marginal totals

n_i. $(i = 1, 2, \ldots, r)$, the last parameter estimated not being independent of the others. In other words, estimated $f(y_i) = n_i./n$. We then multiply the number in the sample to get each theoretical frequency, that is, the theoretical frequency

TABLE 10.5.1 FREQUENCY DISTRIBUTIONS OF s SAMPLES

Sample

	1	2	$\cdots$	s	
y_1	n_{11}	n_{12}	$\cdots$	n_{1s}	$n_1.$
y_2	n_{21}	n_{22}	$\cdots$	n_{2s}	$n_2.$
$\cdot$					
y_r	n_{r1}	n_{r2}	$\cdots$	n_{rs}	$n_r.$
$\sum_{i=1}^{r}$	$n._1$	$n._2$	$\cdots$	$n._s$	n

for y_i for sample j equals $(n_i./n)n._j$. Our theoretical frequencies, therefore, are the same numerically as in a test for independence. As in the test for independence,

$$\chi^2 = \sum_{i=1}^{rs} \frac{(f_{oi} - f_{ti})^2}{f_{ti}}$$

We state without proof[1] that, as before in the test for independence, the number of degrees of freedom is $(r - 1)(s - 1)$. This should seem reasonable, because if our theoretical frequencies were entirely hypothetical (rather than estimated) we could compute a χ^2 with $r - 1$ degrees of freedom for each sample. The sum of these χ^2's would be χ^2 with $s(r - 1)$ degrees of freedom. Since we estimated $r - 1$ independent parameters, we should then have, if Theorem 10.3 applied (actually a slight modification of this theorem is required),

$s(r - 1) - (r - 1) = (r - 1)(s - 1)$ degrees of freedom

[1] A proof is indicated by Cramér (3).

EXERCISES

10.5.1. A sample of 50 students has been drawn from each of five large secondary schools. Each member of each sample is given an intelligence test, and an IQ is obtained. The sample distributions are shown in the following table.

	School 1	2	3	4	5
110–	12	9	4	15	10
x 100–109	16	23	18	20	15
90–99	12	11	15	10	16
–89	10	7	13	5	9

Test the hypothesis that the samples are drawn from populations having the same distribution.

10.5.2. In a large community a sample of 50 Democrats and a sample of 50 Republicans have been drawn at random. Each member of each sample is asked whether he is for, against, or indifferent to a certain policy. The following table is obtained:

	Republican	Democrat
For...............	20	10
Against...........	15	30
Indifferent.........	15	10

Test the hypothesis that Democrats and Republicans in the community are homogeneous with respect to their potential replies to the question.

10.5.3. Subjects are divided into two "types" on the basis of a personality inventory and then tested on the Rorschach, each subject obtaining scores on form, color, movement, whole, and detail. There are 50 subjects in all. The following table is obtained, in which each entry is the sum of scores for subjects:

	Type A	Type B
Form...............	257	201
Color...............	31	50
Movement...........	108	183
Whole...............	300	252
Detail...............	354	272

Why would it be incorrect to compute chi square for this table? Can the table be modified in any way so as to justify a chi-square test of independence?

10.5.4. In an experiment on effects of diet on behavior, one group of 30 rats was run under conditions of vitamin B deficiency; another group of 30 was run under conditions of an adequate diet. Each rat was tabulated as showing or not showing each of the following three kinds of behavior: retracing, perseverating, giving up. The following table shows the number of rats in each group showing each of these kinds of behavior:

	Deficiency	Normal
Retracing..............	15	10
Perseverating..........	20	7
Giving up.............	12	3
None of these.........	8	16

Should chi square be used to test for homogeneity? Explain your answer.

10.5.5. Analyze the data of Exercise 10.3.6, considering the students from each dormitory as a sample and testing for homogeneity. Why is the value of χ^2 practically the same as that obtained previously, despite the much larger sample?

10.5.6. Inspection of a sample of 300 products yields 15 defectives. Test the hypothesis that the proportion of defectives being turned out is .04. Show the equivalence of the χ^2 test and the test based on the central-limit theorem for this type of situation (that is, a two-cell table).

10.6. Test for Variance of a Normal Population.

We state without proof[1] the following theorem.

Theorem 10.6. Consider a sample of size n drawn at random from a population having the distribution $N(\mu,\sigma^2)$. Then ns^2/σ^2 is distributed as χ^2_{n-1}, where s^2 is the sample variance.

To test the hypothesis that a given sample is drawn from a normally distributed population with variance c, we compute ns^2/c and use the tables for $f(\chi^2_{n-1})$.

Further, a confidence interval (at the p level) from σ^2_L (lower bound) to σ^2_U (upper bound) can be obtained by the following relations:

$\sigma^2_L = ns^2/d$, in which d is obtained by finding the value d for which $\int_d^\infty f(\chi^2_{n-1}) \, d\chi^2 = p/2$.

[1] A proof is given by Hoel (8).

$\sigma_{\bar{U}}^2 = ns^2/b$, in which b is obtained by finding the value b for which $\int_0^b f(\chi_{n-1}^2) \, d\chi^2 = p/2$.

The values of b and d are, of course, obtained from tables of $f(\chi_{n-1}^2)$. As an exercise the student should deduce these relations from Theorem 10.6.

EXERCISES

10.6.1. A sample of 10 is drawn at random from a normally distributed population. The sum of squared deviations from the mean is 50.

a. Test the hypothesis that the variance of the population is 5.

b. Find a .05 confidence interval for the population variance.

10.6.2. A sample of 20 is drawn at random from a normally distributed population. The sum of the values is 60; the sum of squares of the values is 200.

a. Test the hypothesis that the population variance is 3.

b. Find a .01 confidence interval for the population variance.

Chapter 11

"STUDENT'S" t DISTRIBUTIONS

11.1. Definition of t_n and the Distribution of t_n. In Chap. 9 we found satisfactory ways of testing hypotheses about (and finding confidence intervals for) means of populations in the following cases:

1. When the sample is large ("large" meaning greater than about 30).

2. When the sample is large or small, but from a *normal* population with *known* variance.

It would be highly desirable to find a satisfactory method for testing hypotheses about population means when the sample is small from a population with completely unknown distribution. Such a method has never been found and probably does not exist; however, a satisfactory method has been found for the case in which the sample is drawn from a *normal* population with unknown variance. We cannot use the variance of a small sample as an estimate of the population variance, as in the case of large samples, because the standard error of the sample variance is too large with small samples. We now describe a method which does not involve estimating the population variance, first found by W. S. Gosset, writing under the name "Student," and later proved rigorously by R. A. Fisher.

Let X be distributed according to $\phi(0,1)$ and Y be independently distributed according to $f(\chi_n^2)$. We define t_n as

$$t_n \equiv \frac{X}{\sqrt{Y/n}}$$

We state without proof[1] that the distribution of t_n is given by the following theorem.

[1] A proof is given in the Appendix, Sec. B.23.

143

Theorem 11.1

$$f(t_n) = \frac{\Gamma\left(\dfrac{n+1}{2}\right)}{\Gamma\left(\dfrac{n}{2}\right)\sqrt{n}\,\sqrt{\pi}} \left(1 + \frac{t^2}{n}\right)^{-\frac{n+1}{2}} \qquad -\infty < t < \infty$$

in which n is called "the number of degrees of freedom" and Γ means the gamma function as described in Sec. 10.1. Note that

$$f(t_n) = \frac{f(0)}{\left(1 + \dfrac{t^2}{n}\right)^{\frac{n+1}{2}}}$$

Since $(1 + t^2/n)^{(n+1)/2}$ has a minimum value for $t = 0$, $f(t_n)$ has a maximum value for $t = 0$; that is, $f(0)$ is the greatest density in the t_n distribution. Further, as $t^2 = (-t)^2$, and as t appears in $f(t_n)$ only as t^2, the t distributions are symmetrical about 0, as

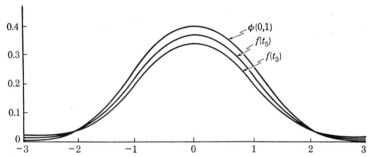

FIG. 11.1.1. The density functions $f(t_3)$ and $f(t_5)$, compared with $\phi(0,1)$. (*Reprinted from W. J. Dixon and F. J. Massey, Introduction to statistical analysis, McGraw-Hill, 1951, with permission of the authors and publishers.*)

illustrated in Fig. 11.1.1. This symmetry about 0 implies that for all values of n for which μ [that is, $E(t_n)$] exists, $\mu = 0$. For $n = 1$, μ does not exist.[1] The symmetry about 0 also implies that all existing odd moments about the mean are 0. We state without proof[2] that the variance σ^2 is equal to $n/(n - 2)$ for $n \geq 3$, and also that as n gets larger the distribution of t_n

[1] This statement means that $\displaystyle\int_0^\infty t_1 f(t_1)\, dt_1$ does not have a finite value, that is, that $\Sigma t_1 f(t_1)\, \Delta t_1$ does not approach a limit as Δt_1 approaches 0.

[2] A proof is given by Cramér (3).

approaches a normal distribution with 0 mean and unit variance, that is, $\lim_{\text{as } n \to \infty} f(t_n) = \phi(0,1)$.

Tables of the distribution of t_n for various sizes of n are given in Appendix D.

EXERCISES

11.1.1. An experimenter has tested a certain hypothesis with two independent samples. For one sample, the experiment was designed so that χ^2_{20} was appropriate, and the value obtained was 5. For the other sample, the critical ratio was the appropriate statistic, and the value obtained was 1.5. How can these two results be used simultaneously to test the hypothesis? Why does this test have a very low power, in fact so low that the experimenter should have considerable difficulty in explaining his results?

11.1.2. Using Theorems 10.6 and 11.1, find the distribution of $\dfrac{m - \mu}{s/\sqrt{n-1}}$, in which m and s are the sample mean and standard deviation and μ is the population mean, assuming that m and s are independently distributed and that the population sampled is normally distributed.

11.2. Testing Hypotheses about Population Means and Finding Confidence Intervals with Small Samples from Normal Populations with Unknown Variances.

Consider a sample of size n drawn from $N(\mu,\sigma^2)$. As we saw in Sec. 9.4, $\dfrac{m - \mu}{\sigma/\sqrt{n}}$ has the distribution $N(0,1)$. We state without proof[1] that s^2n/σ^2, in which s^2 is the sample variance, is independently distributed as χ^2_{n-1}. Therefore

$$\frac{(m - \mu)\sqrt{n}/\sigma}{\sqrt{(s^2 n)/\sigma^2(n - 1)}} = \frac{m - \mu}{s/\sqrt{n - 1}}$$

is distributed as t_{n-1}. As a corollary we have

$$\text{prob}\left(m + b \frac{s}{\sqrt{n - 1}} \text{ includes } \mu\right) = \int_{-b}^{b} f(t_{n-1})\, dt$$

We stated in Sec. 11.1 that the method which we would describe does not involve estimating the population variance.

---

[1] A proof is given by Mood (9). We had already stated in Theorem 10.6 that s^2n/σ^2 has the χ^2 distribution, but not that it is independent of $\dfrac{m - \mu}{\sigma/\sqrt{n}}$.

On the other hand, it is often stated that t is the ratio of a normally distributed variate to an unbiased estimate of its sampling error. It is true that $s^2/(n-1)$ is an unbiased[1] estimate of σ^2/n, the variance of $m - \mu$, and that therefore $s^2n/(n-1)$ is an unbiased estimate of the population variance σ^2. With small n, however, this estimate, though unbiased, is by no means a good estimate in the sense of tending to have a small sampling error, and in using t with small n we are not making the assumption that the denominator is a good estimate in this sense any more than we are assuming that with a small sample m is a good estimate (in this sense) of μ. With small n, both numerator and denominator of t tend to have large sampling errors, yet the distribution of the ratio is known just as exactly as with large n.

In Sec. 9.8 we considered the problem of testing the hypothesis that the mean of two populations have the same value (or differ by a specified amount). We found a way of making such a test (and of finding confidence intervals) with large samples. With small samples, however, we must make use of Theorem 11.2, which is given below.

The corollary to Theorem 9.8.1 states that if m_x and m_y are the means of samples drawn from $N(\mu_x, \sigma_x^2)$ and $N(\mu_y, \sigma_y^2)$ respectively, then

$$f(m_x - m_y) = \phi\left(\mu_x - \mu_y, \frac{\sigma_x^2}{n_x} + \frac{\sigma_y^2}{n_y}\right)$$

A special case is that in which $\sigma_x^2 = \sigma_y^2$, so that we have

$$f(m_x - m_y) = \phi\left(\mu_x - \mu_y, \frac{\sigma^2}{n_x} + \frac{\sigma^2}{n_y}\right)$$

in which σ^2 is the variance of each population. In this case

$$f\left[\frac{(m_x - m_y) - (\mu_x - \mu_y)}{\sqrt{\sigma^2/n_x + \sigma^2/n_y}}\right] = \phi(0,1)$$

Also, $(n_x s_x^2 + n_y s_y^2)/\sigma^2$ is distributed independently as $\chi_{n_x+n_y-2}^2$. Therefore, by Theorem 11.1 we have the following:

[1] A statistic z is an unbiased estimate of a parameter ξ if and only if $E(z) = \xi$.

Theorem 11.2

$$\frac{[(m_x - m_y) - (\mu_x - \mu_y)]/\sqrt{\sigma^2/n_x + \sigma^2/n_y}}{\sqrt{(n_x s_x^2 + n_y s_y^2)/\sigma^2(n_x + n_y - 2)}}$$

$$= \frac{[(m_x - m_y) - (\mu_x - \mu_y)]\sqrt{n_x + n_y - 2}}{\sqrt{n_x s_x^2 + n_y s_y^2}\sqrt{1/n_x + 1/n_y}}$$

is distributed as $t_{n_x + n_y - 2}$.

Corollary

$$\text{prob}\left[(m_x - m_y) \pm \frac{b\sqrt{n_x s_x^2 + n_y s_y^2}\sqrt{1/n_x + 1/n_y}}{\sqrt{n_x + n_y - 2}}\right.$$

$$\left. \text{includes } (\mu_x - \mu_y)\right] = \int_{-b}^{b} f(t_{n_x + n_y - 2})\, dt$$

We use these results in exactly the same way that we used the corresponding results in Sec. 9.8, whenever we have two small samples from normal populations and we are willing to assume that *the variances of the two populations are equal.* Of course we do not have to make this assumption; we have the alternative of including the hypothesis of equal variances in the hypothesis that we are testing. In this case, however, we have to remember that a significant result does not permit us to assert that the population means are not equal.

There is one fairly satisfactory way, however, to avoid making the assumption of equal variances. If the members of the sample are *paired at random* (which necessitates $n_x = n_y$ or else the discarding of some members of the larger sample at random), and in each pair one is subtracted from the other, we can use Theorem 9.8.1, which states that if X is distributed according to $\phi(\mu_x, \sigma_x^2)$ and Y is independently distributed according to $\phi(\mu_y, \sigma_y^2)$, then $f(x - y) = \phi(\mu_x - \mu_y, \sigma_{x-y}^2)$, in which

$$\sigma_{x-y}^2 = \sigma_x^2 + \sigma_y^2$$

Therefore $f(m_{x-y}) = \phi(\mu_x - \mu_y, \sigma_{x-y}^2/n)$, remembering that

$$m_{x-y} = m_x - m_y$$

Therefore

$$f\left[\frac{m_{x-y} - (\mu_x - \mu_y)}{\sqrt{\sigma^2_{x-y}/n}}\right] = \phi(0,1)$$

Furthermore, $f(s^2_{x-y}n/\sigma^2_{x-y}) = f(\chi^2_{n-1})$, in which s^2_{x-y} is the variance of the sample differences. Therefore

$$f\left[\frac{m_{x-y} - (\mu_x - \mu_y)}{s_{x-y}/\sqrt{n-1}}\right] = f(t_{n-1})$$

Corollary

$$\text{prob}\left[m_{x-y} \pm b \frac{s_{x-y}}{\sqrt{n-1}} \text{ includes } (\mu_x - \mu_y)\right] = \int_{-b}^{b} f(t_{n-1})\, dt$$

In many cases there is a certain obvious, nonrandom, pairing of our sample values. For example, suppose we have a sample of 7 reaction times under condition A and 7 reaction times under condition B, obtained on the same 7 individuals. In this case it seems obvious that we should pair the reaction times according to the individuals, as indicated in the accompanying table:

Individual	$RT(A)$	$RT(B)$	$RT(A) - RT(B)$
1	.245	.261	− .016
2	.280	.277	.003
3	.252	.260	− .008
4	.226	.240	− .014
5	.317	.327	− .010
6	.274	.270	.004
7	.260	.265	− .005

Even if we can assume that $RT(A)$ and $RT(B)$ are each normally distributed, we cannot thereby assume that $RT(A) - RT(B)$ will be normally distributed, because our theorem about the difference between two normally distributed variates (Theorem 9.8.1) holds only for *independent* variates, and there is every reason to consider $RT(A)$ and $RT(B)$ as nonindependent. If, however, we make the separate assumption that the difference

$RT(A) - RT(B)$ is normally distributed, then we can apply the t test exactly as described in the foregoing, in which σ^2_{x-y} is the variance of the population of differences and is not necessarily equal to $\sigma^2_x + \sigma^2_y$. If it is assumed that the difference is normally distributed, then it is not necessary to assume that the distribution of each of the variates is normal. In many cases in which the experimenter has a choice in the design of his experiment, the pairing method is considerably more precise for the same amount of data, as s^2_{x-y} is often considerably smaller than $s^2_x + s^2_y$. It is strictly incorrect, moreover, to match two samples by matching individuals or any other method and then treat the data as though they were independent samples. Such a treatment, besides violating an assumption, can result in the failure to obtain a significant difference between means when the correct analysis would have done so.

EXERCISES

11.2.1. The anxiety level of 10 students was measured by physiological indices before and after an examination. The following data show the results (units are arbitrary):

Student	Before	After
1	10	8
2	7	6
3	8	8
4	5	4
5	4	3
6	6	7
7	2	2
8	5	4
9	7	5
10	6	6

Test the hypothesis that the before and after scores can be considered drawn from populations having the same mean. What assumptions does your test make? Is it possible to make two t tests or only one in this case?

11.2.2. In a study using identical twins, one twin is given a drug and then an intelligence test while under the influence of the drug; the other twin is given an intelligence test under normal conditions. The data are as follows:

Pair	Twin A	Twin B (drug)
1	135	122
2	115	110
3	149	143
4	125	116
5	158	148
6	132	121

Test the hypothesis that the drug has no effect on intelligence-test score. What assumptions does your test make? Can you make one or two t tests with these data?

11.2.3. In a gasoline mileage contest, 10 cars of one make have a mean of 20 miles per gal and a variance of 36; a sample of 9 cars of a rival make have a mean of 30 and a variance of 32. Test the hypothesis that the two makes generally give equal mileages. What assumptions does your test make? Would it be possible to make two t tests or only one with the data obtained? Find the .05 confidence interval for the mileage given by the first make.

11.3. A Criterion for the Discarding of Exceptional Observations and the Testing of a Difference between the Mean of a Subsample and the Mean of the Sample.

In many sets of observations the experimenter or research worker is tempted to discard certain observations which lie so far from the mean that they appear to have come from a population other than that which he is interested in sampling. In some cases there may in addition be other reasons for suspecting these observations of being irrelevant to the sample. Yet there is always a danger in discarding such observations without a statistical criterion, for whether he intends to do so or not the research worker may be selecting his data in a way which biases the final conclusion.

A useful statistical criterion for the rejection of atypical observations, when sampling from a normal population, can be obtained from the following theorem, which we state without proof.[1]

Theorem 11.3.1. Consider a sample of size n drawn from $N(\mu,\sigma^2)$. Let $w \equiv (x_i - m)/s$, in which x_i is the value of the

---

[1] A proof is given by Cramér (3).

ith member of the sample and m and s are the sample mean and standard deviation respectively. Then

$$f\left(\frac{w\sqrt{n-2}}{\sqrt{n-1-w^2}}\right) = f(t_{n-2})$$

Caution must be exercised in the use of this theorem, because with a sample of size n ($n \geq 3$) the probability that at least one member of the sample will give a value of $w\sqrt{n-2}/\sqrt{n-1-w^2}$ which is significant (by the t tables) at the p level is, of course, greater than p, even if all members of the sample are actually drawn from the same population. Therefore, the level of confidence required for the discarding of an observation should be low.

A generalization of Theorem 11.3.1 is as follows:[1]

Theorem 11.3.2. Let m_k be the mean of k members of a sample of size n drawn from $N(\mu,\sigma^2)$, where $1 \leq k \leq n$. Let $w \equiv (m_k - m)/s$. Then

$$f\left[\frac{w\sqrt{k(n-2)}}{\sqrt{n-k-kw^2}}\right] = f(t_{n-2})$$

This theorem is appropriate for testing the significance of the difference between the mean of a subsample and the mean of the sample.

[1] A proof is given by Cramér (3).

Chapter 12

BIVARIATE DISTRIBUTIONS

12.1. Definition and Properties of Bivariate Distributions

Definition. A bivariate population is a population in which each member has two ordered values, that is, it is a class of ordered pairs $[(x,y), (X,Y)]$ such that the second member (X,Y) of each pair is a member[1] of a set and the first member of each pair is the ordered pair of values of that member of the set.

Definition. A bivariate frequency function is a class of ordered pairs $[f(x,y), (x,y)]$ such that the second member of each pair is a pair of values and the first member is the proportion (or proportion density) of the population having that pair of values.

Examples. 1. Suppose we plan to toss four ordinary dice, two red and two blue. The value of each toss is the ordered pair (x,y) such that x is the sum of the red faces turned up and y is the sum of the blue faces turned up. The fr.f. of the population of all possible ways (there are $6^4 = 1,296$ in all) in which the four dice can land is a bivariate fr.f., in which $f(2,2) = \frac{1}{1296}$, $f(3,2) = \frac{2}{1296}, f(3,3) = \frac{4}{1296}, f(7,7) = \frac{36}{1296}$, etc.

2. The distribution given by $f(x,y) = (x^2 + y)/32$ for $x = 0, 1, 2, 3$ and $y = 0, 1$ is a bivariate distribution. This distribution is given in Table 12.1.1, in which each entry is a proportion $f(x,y)$.

TABLE 12.1.1. DISCRETE BIVARIATE DISTRIBUTION

y	1	$\frac{1}{32}$	$\frac{2}{32}$	$\frac{5}{32}$	$\frac{10}{32}$
	0	0	$\frac{1}{32}$	$\frac{4}{32}$	$\frac{9}{32}$
		0	1	2	3
			x		

[1] The reason for using a pair of letters to denote a member will become apparent later in the discussion.

152

3. The continuous distribution given by $f(x,y) = 3x^2y + x$ for $0 \leq x \leq 1$ and $0 \leq y \leq 1$ is a bivariate distribution. The density at the point $(1,1)$, for example, is 4.

4. Suppose we have a population of size N, in which there are N_1 A's, N_2 B's, and $N_3 (= N - N_1 - N_2)$ C's. What is the fr.f. of the population of all possible samples of size n, the value of each sample being the pair (x,y) in which x is the number of A's and y is the number of B's? The student will recognize this as the hypergeometric case with two variables, and should be able to prove for himself that

$$f(x,y) = \frac{C_x^{N_1} C_y^{N_2} C_{n-x-y}^{N-N_1-N_2}}{C_n^N}$$

in which C_b^a is understood to be 0 if $b > a$ or $b < 0$.

5. Consider a population as described in Example 4. What is the fr.f. of all possible sequences of n draws, replacing each member after drawing it? The student can prove as an exercise that

$$f(x,y) = P_{x,y,n-x-y}^n \left(\frac{N_1}{N}\right)^x \left(\frac{N_2}{N}\right)^y \left(\frac{N-N_1-N_2}{N}\right)^{n-x-y}$$

in which $P_{x,y,n-x-y}^n$ is the number of discernibly different permutations of n objects of which x are of one kind, y are of a second kind, and $n - x - y$ are of a third kind. The student should also be able to prove that

$$P_{x,y,n-x-y}^n = \frac{n!}{x!y!(n-x-y)!}$$

Obviously $\displaystyle\sum_{\text{all } x,y} f(x,y) = 1$ for a discrete bivariate distribution.

Note that this summation can be performed by holding y constant and summing for all values of x, then taking another value of y and again summing, etc., until all pairs of values (x,y) have been taken. This process can be represented by the double summation $\displaystyle\sum_{\text{all } x}\sum_{\text{all } y} f(x,y)$.

For the continuous case, consider the probability spread out in the xy plane so that the probability density at a given point in the plane is $f(x,y)$. This means that the probability is spread so that

$$\lim_{\Delta x, \Delta y \to 0} \left(\frac{\text{prob in rectangle } \Delta xy}{\Delta x \, \Delta y}\right) = f(x,y)$$

This implies that to approximate the amount of probability in a given rectangle we can take the area, $\Delta x \, \Delta y$, times the density of any point within the rectangle, the approximation improving as we take smaller and smaller sizes of Δx and Δy. Suppose that we wish to find the probability in the rectangle $a \le x \le b$, $c \le y \le d$. We can divide this rectangle into n equal horizontal

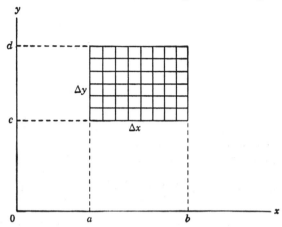

FIG. 12.1.1. The approximation $\displaystyle\sum_{j=1}^{m}\sum_{i=1}^{n} f(x_i,x_j)\,\Delta x\,\Delta y$ to probability $(a \le x \le b,$ $c \le y \le d)$, with each point in the xy plane having the density $f(x,y)$.

intervals each of length Δx and m equal vertical intervals each of length Δy and form the sum $\displaystyle\sum_{j=1}^{m}\sum_{i=1}^{n} f(x_i,y_j)\,\Delta x\,\Delta y$, in which x_i is any value of x in the ith horizontal interval and y_j is any value of y in the jth vertical interval. We then have

$$\lim_{\Delta x, \Delta y \to 0}\left(\sum_{j=1}^{m}\sum_{i=1}^{n} f(x_i,y_j)\,\Delta x\,\Delta y\right) = \text{prob}\ (a \le x \le b,\ c \le y \le d)$$

We abbreviate this limit as $\displaystyle\int_{c}^{d}\int_{a}^{b} f(x,y)\,dx\,dy$. In actually performing the integration, we integrate first with respect to x, treating y as though it were a constant, and then we integrate with respect to y. As an example, we have

$$\int_{c}^{d}\int_{a}^{b}(3x^2y + x)\,dx\,dy = \int_{c}^{d}\left(b^3y + \frac{b^2}{2} - a^3y - \frac{a^2}{2}\right)dy$$

$$= \frac{b^3d^2}{2} + \frac{b^2d}{2} - \frac{a^3d^2}{2} - \frac{a^2d}{2} - \frac{b^3c}{2} - \frac{b^2c}{2} + \frac{a^3c^2}{2} + \frac{a^2c}{2}$$

Obviously for any continuous fr.f. we have

$$\int_{R_y}\int_{R_x} f(x,y)\ dx\ dy\ =\ 1$$

in which R_x and R_y indicate the entire range of x and y respectively. Example 3 above was the continuous bivariate distribution given by $f(x,y) = 3x^2y + x$ for $0 \le x \le 1, 0 \le y \le 1$. The student will find that $\int_0^1\int_0^1 (3x^2y + x)\ dx\ dy\ =\ 1$.

In any bivariate distribution $f(x,y)$ the distribution of X is called the *marginal distribution of X* and that of Y is called the *marginal distribution of Y*. In the case of a discrete bivariate fr.f. the marginal distribution of X is obtained by summing $f(x,y)$ for all values of Y, holding the value of X constant, and doing this for each value of X. For example, suppose the X values are $x_1, x_2, \ldots, x_k$. Then $f(x_1) = \sum\limits_{\text{all } y} f(x_1,y)$; $f(x_2) = \sum\limits_{\text{all } y} f(x_2,y)$; $\ldots$; $f(x_k) = \sum\limits_{\text{all } y} f(x_k,y)$. The marginal distribution of Y is obtained analogously.

In the case of a continuous bivariate fr.f., the marginal distribution of X is obtained by integrating $f(x,y)$ on y, treating x as though it were a constant; that is,

$$f(x)\ =\ \int_{R_y} f(x,y)\ dy$$

Examples. **1.** Let a discrete bivariate distribution be given by

$$
\begin{array}{ll}
f(0,0) = .1 & f(1,0) = .1 \\
f(0,1) = .2 & f(1,1) = .1 \\
f(0,2) = .3 & f(1,2) = .2
\end{array}
$$

The marginal distribution of X is given by

$$f(0)\ =\ \sum_{y=0}^{2} f(0,y) = .6$$

$$f(1)\ =\ \sum_{y=0}^{2} f(1,y) = .4$$

The marginal distribution of Y is given by

$$f(0) = \sum_{x=0}^{1} f(x,0) = .2$$

$$f(1) = \sum_{x=0}^{1} f(x,1) = .3$$

$$f(2) = \sum_{x=0}^{1} f(x,2) = .5$$

2. The marginal distribution of X in the discrete bivariate distribution given as Example 1 of a bivariate distribution is simply $f(2) = \frac{1}{36}$; $f(3) = \frac{2}{36}$; $f(4) = \frac{3}{36}$; $f(5) = \frac{4}{36}$; $f(6) = \frac{5}{36}$; $f(7) = \frac{6}{36}$; $f(8) = \frac{5}{36}$; etc. (The student should obtain this as an exercise.)

3. Consider the bivariate distribution given by $f(x,y) = 3x^2y + x$ when $0 \leq x \leq 1; 0 \leq y \leq 1$. Then

$$f(x) = \int_0^1 (3x^2y + x)\, dy = \left(\frac{3x^2y^2}{2} + xy\right)\Big|_0^1 = \frac{3x^2}{2} + x$$

Note that

$$\int_0^1 f(x)\, dx = \int_0^1 \left(\frac{3x^2}{2} + x\right) dx = \left(\frac{x^3}{2} + \frac{x^2}{2}\right)\Big|_0^1 = 1$$

Similarly,

$$f(y) = \int_0^1 (3x^2y + x)\, dx = \left(x^3y + \frac{x^2}{2}\right)\Big|_0^1 = y + \frac{1}{2}$$

Note that

$$\int_0^1 f(y)\, dy = \int_0^1 \left(y + \frac{1}{2}\right) dy = \left(\frac{y^2}{2} + \frac{y}{2}\right)\Big|_0^1 = 1$$

For the marginal distributions, we have the usual moments and other parameters or statistics. We also have parameters and statistics depending upon the joint distribution. For example, we have the moments $E[(X - c_1)^{k_1}(Y - c_2)^{k_2}]$, in which c_1, c_2 are any constants and k_1, k_2 are any positive integers or 0 (note that when one of the k's is 0 we have a moment of one of the marginal distributions). In the discrete case a moment is $\sum_{\text{all } y} \sum_{\text{all } x} (x - c_1)^{k_1}(y - c_2)^{k_2}$; in the continuous case,

$$\int_{R_y} \int_{R_x} (x - c_1)^{k_1}(y - c_2)^{k_2}\, dx\, dy$$

EXERCISES

12.1.1. A bowl has 3 red, 2 white, and 1 black chip in it.

a. Find the distribution of the population consisting of all possible samples of 3 chips, each sample having as values the number of red chips and the number of white chips.

b. Find the marginal distribution of the number of red chips, also of the number of white chips.

c. If X is the number of red chips and Y is the number of white chips in a sample, find $E\{[X - E(X)][Y - E(Y)]\}$.

12.1.2. A bowl has 2 red, 1 white, and 2 black chips in it.

a. Find the distribution of all possible samples of 2 chips, each sample having as values the number of red chips and the number of white chips.

b. Find each of the marginal distributions.

c. If X is the number of red chips and Y the number of white chips in a sample, find $E\{[X - E(X)][Y - E(Y)]\}$.

12.1.3. Let $f(x,y) = (3x + y)/2$ when $0 \le x \le 1; 0 \le y \le 1$. Find

a. the proportion of the population such that $0 \le x \le .5$ and $0 \le y \le .5$

b. $E(X)$ and $E(Y)$

c. variances of X and Y

d. $E\{[X - E(X)][Y - E(Y)]\}$

12.2. Regression. Consider a bivariate distribution $f(x,y)$. Choose a particular value of X, say x_1. Now consider the set of probabilities (or probability densities) $f(x_1,y)$. It is convenient to treat this set of probabilities (or probability densities) as though it were itself a fr.f., which we can do easily enough if we make the sum (or integral) of the $f(x_1,y)$ equal to 1 by multiplying each $f(x_1,y)$ by a constant. Since

$$\sum_{\text{all } y} f(x_1,y) \left[\text{or } \int_{R_y} f(x_1,y) \, dy\right] = f(x_1)$$

the necessary constant is simply $1/f(x_1)$. We call the probability (or probability density) $f(x,y)/f(x)$ the *conditional* probability (or probability density) of y, given x. The conditional probability (or probability density) is written $f(y|x)$.

Definition. The conditional probability (or probability density) $f(y|x)$ is defined as $f(x,y)/f(x)$, that is $f(y|x) \equiv f(x,y)/f(x)$. The conditional fr.f. is the class of ordered pairs $[f(y|x),y]$.

Examples. 1. Consider the discrete bivariate distribution given by $f(x,y) = (x^2 + y)/32$ for $x = 0, 1, 2, 3$ and $y = 0, 1$ (Table 12.1.1). Since

$f(x) = \frac{1}{32}$ for $x = 0$,

$$f(y|0) = \frac{f(0,y)}{f(0)} = \frac{(0+y)/32}{1/32} = y$$

Thus $f(0|0) = 0$, $f(1|0) = 1$. Note that $\sum_{y=0}^{1} f(y|0) = 1$. Similarly,

$$f(y|1) = f(1,y)/f(1) = \frac{(1+y)/32}{3/32} = (1+y)/3$$

Thus $f(0|1) = \frac{1}{3}$; $f(1|1) = \frac{2}{3}$. Again note that $\sum_{y=0}^{1} f(y|1) = 1$. More generally,

$$f(y|x) = f(x,y)/f(x) = f(x,y) \Big/ \sum_{y=0}^{1} f(x,y) = \frac{(x^2+y)/32}{x^2/32 + (x^2+1)/32}$$

$$= \frac{(x^2+y)/32}{\frac{1}{32}(2x^2+1)} = \frac{x^2+y}{2x^2+1}$$

From the latter we obtain $f(y|0) = y$; $f(y|1) = (1+y)/3$, as above, also $f(y|2) = (4+y)/9$; $f(y|3) = (9+y)/19$. Note that

$$\sum_{y=0}^{1} \frac{x^2+y}{2x^2+1} = 1$$

2. Consider the continuous bivariate distribution given by $f(x,y) = 3x^2y + x$ for $0 \le x \le 1$ and $0 \le y \le 1$. We have

$$f(y|.5) = \frac{f(.5,y)}{\int_0^1 f(.5,\ y)\ dy} = \frac{.75y + .5}{\int_0^1 (.75y + .5)\ dy} = \frac{.75y + .5}{(.75y^2/2 + .5y)\ \Big|_0^1}$$

$$= \frac{.75y + .5}{1.75/2} = \frac{1.5y + 1}{1.75}$$

Note that

$$\int_0^1 \frac{1.5y + 1}{1.75}\ dy = \frac{1}{1.75}\left(\frac{1.5y^2}{2} + y\right)\Big|_0^1 = \frac{1}{1.75}\left(\frac{1.5}{2} + 1\right) = 1$$

More generally,

$$f(y|x) = \frac{f(x,y)}{\int_0^1 f(x,y)\ dy} = \frac{3x^2y + x}{\int_0^1 (3x^2y + x)\ dy} = \frac{3x^2y + x}{\left(\frac{3x^2y^2}{2} + xy\right)\Big|_0^1}$$

$$= \frac{3x^2y + x}{\frac{3x^2}{2} + x} = \frac{x(3xy + 1)}{x\left(\frac{3x}{2} + 1\right)} = \frac{6xy + 2}{3x + 2}$$

from which we obtain

$$f(y|.5) = \frac{6(.5)y + 2}{3(.5) + 2} = \frac{3y + 2}{3.50} = \frac{1.5y + 1}{1.75}$$

as above.   Note that

$$\int_0^1 \frac{6xy + 2}{3x + 2}\, dy = \frac{1}{3x + 2}\left(\frac{6xy^2}{2} + 2y\right)\Big|_0^1 = \frac{1}{3x + 2}(3x + 2) = 1$$

If the conditional distribution of Y is equal to the marginal distribution of Y for all values of X, then we say that Y is *independent* of X.

Definition. Y is independent of X if and only if $f(y|x) = f(y)$ for all values of X.

Note that, if $f(y|x) = f(y)$, then $\dfrac{f(x,y)}{f(x)} = f(y)$ and therefore $f(x,y) = f(x)f(y)$.   Further, if $f(x,y) = f(x)f(y)$, then

$$f(y|x) = f(y)$$

Therefore, a necessary and sufficient condition for the independence of Y is that $f(x,y) = f(x)f(y)$.   It can easily be shown that X is independent of Y if and only if Y is independent of X. Therefore, X and Y are independent if and only if

$$f(x,y) = f(x)f(y)$$

We can define moments and other statistics (or parameters) for conditional fr.f.'s in the same way as for other fr.f.'s.   It is useful in many applications to consider the way in which the mean (or some other measure of central tendency) of the conditional distribution of Y varies as X varies.   The curve which

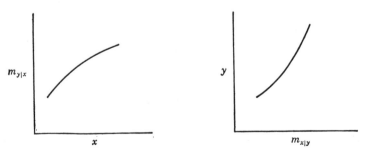

Fig. 12.2.1. Mean regression curves.

the mean (or other measure) describes is called a *regression* curve and is said to represent the *regression of Y on X*. The regression of X on Y is defined analogously. Letting $m_{y|x}$ and $m_{x|y}$ denote the means of the conditional distributions of Y and X respectively, the mean regression curves are illustrated in Fig. 12.2.1.

Examples. **1.** For the discrete bivariate distribution mentioned in Example 1 above, we have

$$m_{y|x} = \sum_{y=0}^{1} y f(y|x) = 0 f(0|x) + 1 f(1|x)$$

$$f(1|x) = \frac{x^2 + 1}{2x^2 + 1}$$

Thus

$$m_{y|0} = \frac{0 + 1}{0 + 1} = 1$$

$$m_{y|1} = \frac{1 + 1}{2 + 1} = \frac{2}{3}$$

$$m_{y|2} = \frac{4 + 1}{8 + 1} = \frac{5}{9}$$

$$m_{y|3} = \frac{9 + 1}{18 + 1} = \frac{10}{19}$$

Similarly,

$$m_{x|y} = \sum_{x=0}^{3} x f(x|y) \qquad \text{etc.}$$

2. For the continuous bivariate distribution mentioned in Example 2 above, we have

$$m_{y|x} = \int_0^1 y f(y|x)\, dy = \int_0^1 y \left(\frac{6xy + 2}{3x + 2} \right) dy$$

$$= \frac{1}{3x + 2} \int_0^1 (6xy^2 + 2y)\, dy = \frac{1}{3x + 2} (2xy^3 + y^2) \Big|_0^1$$

$$= \frac{1}{3x + 2} (2x + 1) = \frac{2x + 1}{3x + 2}$$

Thus

$$m_{y|0} = \tfrac{1}{2}$$
$$m_{y|.5} = 2/3.5 = \tfrac{4}{7} \qquad \text{etc.}$$

The student should plot this regression curve as an exercise.

Suppose that, knowing the value of X, we wish to estimate the value of Y. By using $m_{y|x}$ as our estimate of y for all values of

X we can minimize the mean of squares of "errors," defining "error" as the deviation of y from the estimation. This follows from the statement in Sec. 4.5 that for any distribution the second moment about a point c is a minimum when c is the mean. This important minimum property is summed up by saying that, of all curves that can be drawn in the xy plane, the mean regression curve minimizes the mean of squares of deviations from the curve, the deviations being measured along the y axis when the curve shows the regression of Y on X and along the x axis when the curve shows the regression of X on Y.

Examples. **1.** In Example 1 above, we found the four means defining the mean regression of Y on X. The mean squared deviation from $m_{y|0}$ in $f(y|0)$ is of course 0, since all the probability in this conditional distribution is concentrated at one point. The mean squared deviation from $m_{y|1}$ in $f(y|1)$ is

$$\sum_{y=0}^{1} (y - m_{y|1})^2 f(y|1) = \sum_{y=0}^{1} (y^2 - 2ym_{y|1} + m_{y|1}^2)f(y|1)$$

$$= m_{y|1}^2 f(0|1) + (1 - 2m_{y|1} + m_{y|1}^2)f(1|1) = (\tfrac{2}{3})^2(\tfrac{1}{3})$$
$$+ (1 - \tfrac{4}{3} + \tfrac{4}{9})(\tfrac{2}{3}) = \tfrac{4}{27} + \tfrac{2}{27} = \tfrac{2}{9}$$

The other two mean squared deviations are found analogously. The student can choose any point other than $m_{y|x}$ and verify for himself that the mean squared deviation from this point is larger than the mean squared deviation from $m_{y|x}$.

2. In Example 2 above, the mean squared deviation is given by the integral $\int_0^1 (y - m_{y|x})^2 f(y|x) \, dy$. For example,

$$\int_0^1 (y - m_{y|0})^2 f(y|0) \, dy = \int_0^1 (y - \tfrac{1}{2})^2 (1) \, dy = \int_0^1 (y^2 - y + \tfrac{1}{4}) \, dy$$
$$= (y^3/3 - y^2/2 + y/4) \Big|_0^1 = \tfrac{1}{3} - \tfrac{1}{2} + \tfrac{1}{4} = \tfrac{1}{12}$$

The student should have recognized that the mean squared deviation is simply the variance of the conditional distribution. For computational purposes, note that

$$\sum_{\text{all } y} (y - m_{y|x})^2 f(y|x) = \sum_{\text{all } y} (y^2 - 2ym_{y|x} + m_{y|x}^2)f(y|x)$$

$$= \sum y^2 f(y|x) - 2m_{y|x} \sum yf(y|x) + m_{y|x}^2 \sum f(y|x)$$

$$= \sum y^2 f(y|x) - 2m_{y|x}(m_{y|x}) + m_{y|x}^2(1) = \sum y^2 f(y|x) - m_{y|x}^2$$

Similarly,

$$\int_{R_y} (y - m_{y|x})^2 f(y|x)\, dy = \int_{R_y} (y^2 - 2m_{y|x}y + m_{y|x}^2) f(y|x)\, dy$$

$$= \int_{R_y} y^2 f(y|x)\, dy - 2m_{y|x} \int_{R_y} yf(y|x)\, dy + m_{y|x}^2 \int_{R_y} f(y|x)\, dy$$

$$= \int_{R_y} y^2 f(y|x)\, dy - m_{y|x}^2$$

This is basically the same computational theorem as that shown in Sec. 4.3. We have shown that

$$E[Y - E(Y)]^2 = E(Y^2) - [E(Y)]^2$$

for a conditional distribution.

EXERCISES

12.2.1. Let $f(x,y) = 3(x^2 + y^2)/2$ when $0 \leq x \leq 1; 0 \leq y \leq 1$. Find
a. $f(x)$ and $f(y)$
b. $f(y|x)$
c. $m_{y|x}$

12.2.2. Let $f(x,y) = x^2 + xy/12 + y^2$ when $0 \leq x \leq 1; 0 \leq y \leq 1$. Find
a. $f(x)$
b. $f(y|x)$
c. $m_{y|x}$

12.2.3. Let $f(x,y) = (x + 3x + y)/18$ when $x = 0, 1$ and $y = 0, 1, 2$. Find
a. $f(y)$
b. $f(y|x)$
c. $m_{y|x}$

12.3. Linear Regression. Of particular interest are those bivariate distributions in which the mean regression of Y on X is *linear*, that is, $m_{y|x} = ax + b$, in which a and b are constants. For these distributions a moment of considerable importance is the moment with $c_1 = E(X)$, $c_2 = E(Y)$, $k_1 = 1$, $k_2 = 1$, that is, the moment $E\{[X - E(X)][Y - E(Y)]\}$. This moment is called the *product moment* or the *covariance* (Cov). For computational purposes, note that

$$E\{[X - E(X)][Y - E(Y)]\}$$
$$= E[XY - YE(X) - XE(Y) + E(X)E(Y)]$$
$$= E(XY) - E(X)E(Y)$$

When X and Y are independent, $E(XY) = E(X)E(Y)$ (this should be proved as an exercise); thus $\text{Cov}_{xy} = 0$.

The ratio of the covariance to the geometric mean of the two variances is called the *product-moment correlation coefficient* (p-mcc); that is,

$$\text{p-mcc} \equiv \frac{\text{Cov}_{xy}}{\sqrt{\text{Var}_x \ \text{Var}_y}}$$

We denote the parameter p-mcc by ρ and the statistic p-mcc by r. The p-mcc is defined for all bivariate distributions, whether the mean regression is linear or not (but see below). The maximum value of the p-mcc is 1 and the minimum value is -1. An absolute value of 1 is obtained when and only when all points of the distribution lie on the mean regression line and the mean regression is linear. To show that the maximum absolute value is 1, we note that, as the square of any quantity is positive or zero,

$$E[\sigma_y(X - \mu_x) \pm \sigma_x(Y - \mu_y)]^2 \geq 0$$

Squaring, we obtain

$$E[\sigma_y^2(X - \mu_x)^2 \pm 2\sigma_x\sigma_y(X - \mu_x)(Y - \mu_y) + \sigma_x^2(Y - \mu_y)^2] \geq 0$$
$$\sigma_y^2 E(X - \mu_x)^2 \pm 2\sigma_x\sigma_y E[(X - \mu_x)(Y - \mu_y)]$$
$$+ \sigma_x^2 E(Y - \mu_y)^2 \geq 0$$
$$\sigma_y^2\sigma_x^2 \pm 2\sigma_x\sigma_y \, \text{Cov}_{xy} + \sigma_x^2\sigma_y^2 \geq 0$$
$$2\sigma_x^2\sigma_y^2 \geq \pm 2\sigma_x\sigma_y \, \text{Cov}_{xy}$$
$$\sigma_x\sigma_y \geq \pm \text{Cov}_{xy}$$
$$1 \geq \pm \frac{\text{Cov}_{xy}}{\sigma_x\sigma_y} \equiv \pm\rho$$

An analogous proof holds for r, the sample p-mcc.

If X and Y are independent, then p-mcc $= 0$, but the converse is not true, that is, p-mcc may be 0 even when X and Y are not independent, if the mean regression curve is not linear. An example of a bivariate distribution with p-mcc $= 0$ and with X and Y clearly not independent is given in Table 12.3.1.

The student can verify that p-mcc $= 0$ in this distribution, yet for no point (x,y) does $f(x,y) = f(x)f(y)$. In this distribution the mean regression of Y on X is nonlinear, as the student can verify. As a matter of fact, in all cases in which the mean regression is linear, the p-mcc is 0 if and only if X and Y are

TABLE 12.3.1. BIVARIATE DISTRIBUTION WITH p-mcc $= 0$ AND X AND Y NOT INDEPENDENT

y			
3	0	.3	0
2	.1	.2	.1
1	.1	.1	.1
	1	2	2
		x	

independent. The p-mcc is an adequate measure of relationship only if the mean regression curves are linear.

Examples. 1. Consider the discrete bivariate distribution given by the following table [entries are $f(x,y)$].

y			
3	$\frac{1}{16}$	$\frac{2}{16}$	$\frac{2}{16}$
2	$\frac{2}{16}$	$\frac{1}{16}$	0
1	$\frac{2}{16}$	$\frac{2}{16}$	0
0	$\frac{4}{16}$	0	0
	0	1	2
		x	

The covariance of the above distribution is obtained as follows:

$$E(XY) = \sum_{y=0}^{3} \sum_{x=0}^{2} xyf(x,y) = (1)(1)\frac{2}{16} + (1)(2)\frac{1}{16} + (1)(3)\frac{2}{16}$$

$$+ (2)(3)\frac{2}{16} = \frac{22}{16}$$

$$E(X) = (1)\frac{5}{16} + (2)\frac{2}{16} = \frac{9}{16}$$

$$E(Y) = (1)\frac{4}{16} + (2)\frac{3}{16} + (3)\frac{5}{16} = \frac{25}{16}$$

Therefore

$$\text{Cov}_{xy} = \frac{22}{16} - \left(\frac{9}{16}\right)\left(\frac{25}{16}\right) = \frac{127}{16^2}$$

Further,

$$\text{Var}_x = E(X^2) - [E(X)]^2 = (1)\frac{5}{16} + (4)\frac{2}{16} - \left(\frac{9}{16}\right)^2 = \frac{127}{16^2}$$

$$\text{Var}_y = (1)\frac{4}{16} + (4)\frac{3}{16} + (9)\frac{5}{16} - \left(\frac{25}{16}\right)^2 = \frac{351}{16^2}$$

Therefore

$$\rho = \frac{\text{Cov}_{xy}}{\sqrt{\text{Var}_x \text{Var}_y}} = \frac{127/16^2}{\frac{1}{16^2}\sqrt{(127)(351)}} = \sqrt{\frac{127}{351}} = .60$$

The student should verify that the mean regression of Y on X is linear, while the mean regression of X on Y is nonlinear. For this particular distribution, therefore, ρ is less suitable if we are interested in the mean regression of X on Y than if we are interested in the mean regression of Y on X.

2. Consider the distribution discussed in Example 2 in the three sets of examples given in Sec. 12.2. This is the distribution given by

$$f(x,y) = 3x^2y + x$$

for $0 \leq x \leq 1$ and $0 \leq y \leq 1$. We have

$$E(XY) = \int_0^1 \int_0^1 xyf(x,y)\,dx\,dy = \int_0^1 \int_0^1 (3x^3y^2 + x^2y)\,dx\,dy$$

$$= \int_0^1 \left(\frac{3y^2}{4} + \frac{y}{3}\right) dy = \left(\frac{y^3}{4} + \frac{y^2}{6}\right)\bigg|_0^1 = \frac{1}{4} + \frac{1}{6} = \frac{5}{12}$$

$$E(X) = \int_0^1 xf(x)\,dx = \int_0^1 x\left(\frac{3x^2}{2} + x\right) dx = \int_0^1 \left(\frac{3x^3}{2} + x^2\right) dx$$

$$= \left(\frac{3x^4}{8} + \frac{x^3}{3}\right)\bigg|_0^1 = \frac{3}{8} + \frac{1}{3} = \frac{17}{24}$$

$$E(Y) = \int_0^1 yf(y)\,dy = \int_0^1 y\left(y + \frac{1}{2}\right) dy = \left(\frac{y^3}{3} + \frac{y^2}{4}\right)\bigg|_0^1 = \frac{1}{3} + \frac{1}{4} = \frac{7}{12}$$

Therefore

$$\text{Cov}_{xy} = E(XY) - E(X)E(Y) = \frac{5}{12} - (\frac{17}{24})(\frac{7}{12}) = (120 - 119)/288$$

$$= \frac{1}{288}$$

Also

$$E(X^2) = \int_0^1 x^2f(x)\,dx = \int_0^1 \left(\frac{3x^4}{2} + x^3\right) dx = \left(\frac{3x^5}{10} + \frac{x^4}{4}\right)\bigg|_0^1 = \frac{3}{10} + \frac{1}{4} = \frac{11}{20}$$

$$\text{Var}_x = E(X^2) - [E(X)]^2 = \frac{11}{20} - \left(\frac{17}{24}\right)^2 = \frac{139}{(24^2)(5)}$$

Similarly,

$$E(Y^2) = \int_0^1 y^2 f(y)\, dy = \int_0^1 \left(y^3 + \frac{y^2}{2}\right) dy = \left(\frac{y^4}{4} + \frac{y^3}{6}\right)\Big|_0^1 = \frac{1}{4} + \frac{1}{6} = \frac{5}{12}$$

$$\therefore \operatorname{Var}_y = \frac{5}{12} - \left(\frac{7}{12}\right)^2 = \frac{60 - 49}{144} = \frac{11}{144}$$

$$\therefore \rho \equiv \frac{\operatorname{Cov}_{xy}}{\sqrt{\operatorname{Var}_x \operatorname{Var}_y}} = \frac{\frac{1}{2}88}{\sqrt{\frac{139}{(24^2)5}\frac{11}{12^2}}} = \frac{\frac{1}{2}88}{\frac{1}{288}\sqrt{\frac{1{,}529}{5}}} = \sqrt{\frac{5}{1{,}529}} = .06$$

We had found previously that $m_{y|x} = (2x + 1)/(3x + 2)$, which is non-linear. Thus for this distribution, if we are interested in the regression of Y on X, ρ is not the best measure of relationship; however, as the student can see by plotting $(2x + 1)/(3x + 2)$ for several points between 0 and 1, the approximation to linearity is quite good.

We state without proof[1] that in any bivariate population with linear mean regression, the constant $a = \rho(\sigma_y/\sigma_x)$ and the constant $b = \mu_y - \rho(\sigma_y/\sigma_x)\mu_x$, so that the mean regression equation becomes $m_{y|x} = \rho(\sigma_y/\sigma_x)(x - \mu_x) + \mu_y$. Note that the point (μ_x, μ_y) satisfies this equation, that is, the equation passes through this point.

It is customary in many applications to assume that in the bivariate population being sampled the mean regression of Y on X is linear. In accordance with this assumption, a prediction equation of the form $y_p = ax + b$ is found which predicts a value y_p for each value of X such that the total sum of squares of deviations $\sum_{i=1}^{n} (y_i - y_{pi})^2$ is minimized. We state without proof[1] that, for a sample of size n, this sum of squares is a minimum when

$$a = r\frac{s_y}{s_x} \qquad b = m_y - r\frac{s_y}{s_x} m_x$$

Therefore the prediction (regression) equation becomes

$$y_p = r\frac{s_y}{s_x}(x - m_x) + m_y$$

[1] A proof is given in the Appendix, Sec. B.25.

In this equation r is the sample p-mcc and m_x, m_y, s_x, s_y are the sample means and standard deviations respectively. Note that when $x = m_x$, $y_p = m_y$, that is, the point (m_x, m_y) lies on the prediction curve.

Note that

$$\sum (y_{pi} - y_i) = \sum y_{pi} - \sum y_i$$

$$= r \frac{s_y}{s_x} \sum x_i - nr \frac{s_y}{s_x} m_x + nm_y - nm_y = 0$$

Since the mean error is zero, the standard deviation of the errors can be taken as a measure of adequacy of prediction. The standard deviation of the errors is called the *standard error of estimate* (s_e), that is,

$$s_e^2 \equiv \frac{\sum\limits_{i=1}^{n} (y_{pi} - y_i)^2}{n}$$

The student can prove as an exercise that $s_e^2 = s_y^2(1 - r^2)$.

Example. Suppose we have drawn a sample of 100 from a bivariate population in which we assume the mean regression curves are linear. Our sample yields the following statistics:

$$m_x = 101.2 \qquad m_y = 53.7$$
$$s_x^2 = 6.25 \qquad s_y^2 = 4.00$$
$$\text{Cov}_{xy} = 3.50$$

Then
$$r = \frac{3.50}{\sqrt{25}} = .70$$

And
$$y_p = .70 \frac{4}{6.25} (x - 101.2) + 53.7$$
$$= .448x - 8.362$$

This regression equation can be used in the following way. Suppose we now observe the value of X for a new member (X, Y) from the same bivariate population. We can predict the value of Y by substituting the value of X in the above equation. The standard error of estimate in our example is $s_e = \sqrt{4.00(1 - .49)} = 1.43$.

EXERCISES

12.3.1. Find the regression of Y on X for the bivariate discrete distribution given by the following table:

		0	1	2
	5	$\frac{3}{18}$	$\frac{2}{18}$	$\frac{1}{18}$
y	4	$\frac{1}{18}$	$\frac{3}{18}$	$\frac{2}{18}$
	3	$\frac{1}{18}$	$\frac{1}{18}$	$\frac{4}{18}$

$$x$$

Is the regression linear?

12.3.2. In a study of the relationship between performance-on-the-job scores (Y) and selection-test scores (X), a sample of 400 pairs (X,Y) yields the following statistics:

$$m_x = 0 \qquad m_y = 10$$
$$s_x^2 = 25 \qquad s_y^2 = 9$$
$$r = .50$$

Find the linear regression of Y on X.

12.3.3. Find the regression of Y on X for the continuous bivariate distribution given by $f(x,y) = 2x/y$ for $0 \le x \le 1$, $1 \le y \le e$. Is the regression linear?

12.3.4. Prove that, for a bivariate population, $\sigma_{x+y}^2 = \sigma_x^2 + \sigma_y^2 + 2\rho\sigma_x\sigma_y$ and $\sigma_{x-y}^2 = \sigma_x^2 + \sigma_y^2 - 2\rho\sigma_x\sigma_y$.

12.3.5. Prove that, for a bivariate sample, $s_{x+y}^2 = s_x^2 + s_y^2 + 2rs_xs_y$ and $s_{x-y}^2 = s_x^2 + s_y^2 - 2rs_xs_y$.

12.3.6. Prove that linear transformations of x and y into w and z respectively do not change the size of the p-mcc; that is, that $r_{wz} = r_{xy}$ (and $\rho_{wz} = \rho_{xy}$).

12.4. The Correlation Ratio.

As we have seen, the p-mcc is an adequate measure of the relation between two variates only when the mean regression curves are linear. A measure of the relation which is adequate in some cases of nonlinear, as well as linear, regression is the *correlation ratio*.

Consider a regression curve $y_p = m_{y|x}$. A measure of how closely this curve fits all the points in the bivariate distribution is simply the variance of the errors, or $E[(y_p - Y)^2]$. In considering how adequate a fit this is, however, we should take into consideration the variance of Y itself, which we can do by dividing the variance of the errors (vertical deviations) by the variance of Y. This ratio gives the correlation ratio eta (η_{yx}), which is defined as follows.

Definition

$$\eta_{yx}^2 \equiv 1 - \frac{E[y_p - Y)^2]}{\sigma_y^2} \equiv 1 - \frac{\sigma_{y_p-y}^2}{\sigma_y^2}$$

in which $y_p = m_{y|x}$.

When the fit is perfect, that is, all the points lie on the regression curve $y_p = m_{y|x}$, then $\sigma_{y_p-y}^2 = 0$ and $\eta_{yx}^2 = 1$. When the points are scattered around the regression curve just as much as they are in the marginal distribution of y, we have $\sigma_{y_p-y}^2 = \sigma_y^2$ and $\eta_{yx}^2 = 0$.

For any bivariate distribution, $0 \le$ p-mcc$^2 \le \eta^2 \le 1$. Only when the mean regression curve is linear does p-mcc$^2 = \eta^2$.

EXERCISES

12.4.1. Find ρ and η_{yx} for the discrete bivariate distribution given by the following table:

	0	.3	0
2	0	.3	0
y 1	.1	.1	.1
0	.2	0	.2
	0	1	2
		x	

Why is η_{yx} so much larger than ρ?

12.4.2. Find ρ and η_{yx} for the following distribution.

	0	.1	.2
3	0	.1	.2
y 2	0	.2	.1
1	.3	.1	0
	0	1	2
		x	

Why are ρ and η_{yx} almost the same size?

12.4.3. Whereas $\rho_{xy} = \rho_{yx}$, is it true in general that $\eta_{yx} = \eta_{xy}$?

12.4.4. If in a discrete bivariate distribution there are only 2 values of X, why must $\rho = \eta_{yx}$?

12.5. The Sampling Distribution of r. Often we wish to test the hypothesis that in the population sampled the p-mcc ρ has a specified value, for example, 0. The sampling distribution of r depends not only upon the size of ρ, but also upon the form of the distribution of the population. We shall concern ourselves only with one particular form of bivariate distribution, called the *bivariate normal* distribution. This distribution is defined as a distribution given by a rule of the form

$$f(x,y) = ke^{-\frac{1}{2}[a_1(x-c_1)^2 - 2a_2(x-c_1)(y-c_2) + a_3(y-c_2)^2]}$$

in which k, a_1, a_2, a_3, c_1, and c_2 are constants, $k > 0$, $a_1 > 0$, $a_3 > 0$, and $a_1a_3 > a_2^2$.

We state without proof[1] that

$$\mu_x = c_1 \qquad\qquad \mu_y = c_2 \qquad\qquad k = \frac{\sqrt{a_1a_3 - a_2^2}}{2\pi}$$

$$\sigma_x^2 = \frac{a_3}{a_1a_3 - a_2^2} \qquad\qquad \sigma_y^2 = \frac{a_1}{a_1a_3 - a_2^2}$$

$$\text{Cov}_{xy} = -\frac{a_2}{a_1a_3 - a_2^2}$$

Therefore

$$\rho^2 \equiv \frac{\text{Cov}_{xy}^2}{\sigma_x^2\sigma_y^2} = \frac{a_2^2}{a_1a_3}$$

We can therefore write the bivariate normal distribution in the following form:

$$f(x,y) = \frac{1}{2\pi\sigma_x\sigma_y \sqrt{1 - \rho^2}} e^{-\frac{1}{2(1-\rho^2)}\left[\frac{(x-\mu_x)^2}{\sigma_x^2} - 2\frac{\rho}{\sigma_x\sigma_y}(x-\mu_x)(y-\mu_y) + \frac{(y-\mu_y)^2}{\sigma_y^2}\right]}$$

When the rule is written in this form, it is easily seen that $f(x,y)$ is a maximum at the point (μ_x,μ_y) (see Sec. 9.2). It can also be shown[2] that, if points of equal probability density are connected by a curve in the xy plane, the curve is an ellipse for any probability density between zero and the maximum $f(\mu_x,\mu_y)$. These ellipses of equal probability density are illustrated in Fig. 12.5.1. Many populations sampled in applications are believed to have approximately this distribution.

---

[1] Proofs are given by Cramér (3) and Wilks (12).
[2] A proof is given in the Appendix, Sec. B.26.

We also state without proof[1] that for a bivariate normal distribution the two marginal distributions are each normal and, further, all conditional distributions are normal.

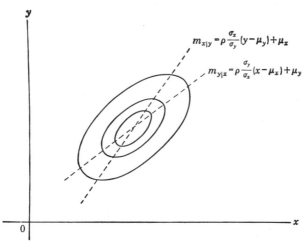

$$m_{x|y} = \rho \frac{\sigma_x}{\sigma_y}(y - \mu_y) + \mu_x$$

$$m_{y|x} = \rho \frac{\sigma_y}{\sigma_x}(x - \mu_x) + \mu_y$$

FIG. 12.5.1. Ellipses of equal probability density for a bivariate normal distribution, showing the mean regression lines.

The sampling distribution of r for a bivariate normal distribution is given by a complicated expression which we do not reproduce here; a remarkable property of this sampling distribution is that it depends only upon ρ and n. We state without proof[2] that the transformed variate $z \equiv \frac{1}{2} \log_e \frac{1 + r}{1 - r}$ is distributed approximately according to $\phi \left(\frac{1}{2} \log_e \frac{1 + \rho}{1 - \rho}, \frac{1}{n - 3} \right)$, in which ρ is the population p-mcc and n is the size of the sample. Remembering that $\log 1 = 0$, note that when $\rho = 0$ the approximate distribution of z is normal with mean 0 and variance $1/(n - 3)$.*

Corollary. Let $\xi \equiv \frac{1}{2} \log_e \frac{1 + \rho}{1 - \rho}$. Then $\frac{z - \xi}{\sqrt{1/(n - 3)}}$ is distributed approximately according to $\phi(0, 1)$.

---

[1] A proof is given in the Appendix, Sec. B.26.
[2] A proof is given by Cramér (3).
* When $\rho = 0$, r is also approximately normally distributed, with mean 0 and variance $1/(n - 1)$.)

Corollary

$$\text{prob}\left(z \pm b \sqrt{\frac{1}{n-3}} \text{ includes } \xi\right) = \int_{-b}^{b} \phi(0,1) \, dx$$

Corollary. Consider two samples of sizes n_1 and n_2 respectively, each drawn independently from normal bivariate populations. Then $f(z_1 - z_2)$ is approximately

$$\phi\left(\xi_1 - \xi_2, \frac{1}{n_1 - 3} + \frac{1}{n_2 - 3}\right)$$

Therefore $\dfrac{(z_1 - z_2) - (\xi_1 - \xi_2)}{\sqrt{\dfrac{1}{n_1 - 3} + \dfrac{1}{n_2 - 3}}}$ is distributed approximately according to $\phi(0,1)$.

Tables of the r-to-z transformation and the z-to-r transformation can be found in Appendix C. With these tables and the above corollaries and theorems, the student should be able to test hypotheses about ρ and $\rho_1 - \rho_2$ and find confidence intervals for ρ when samples from bivariate normal populations are available.

Examples. **1.** A sample of 84 from a bivariate population assumed to be approximately normal yields an r of .70.

a. Is it reasonable to suppose that $\rho = 0$? If ρ were 0 the distribution of z would be approximately $N(0,\frac{1}{81})$. Transforming r to z, we obtain $z = .87$ for $r = .70$ (from the Appendix). Then C.R. $= \dfrac{z - 0}{\sqrt{\frac{1}{81}}} = \dfrac{.87}{\frac{1}{9}} = 7.8$. The hypothesis is highly untenable ($p < .001$).

b. Is it reasonable to suppose that $\rho = .30$? We transform ρ to ξ, obtaining $\xi = .31$ for $\rho = .30$. Then C.R. $= \dfrac{z - \xi_H}{\sqrt{\frac{1}{81}}} = \dfrac{.87 - .31}{\frac{1}{9}} = 5.0$. Therefore we can also reject the hypothesis that $\rho = .30$ at the .001 level of confidence.

c. What is the .01 confidence interval for ρ? To find this interval we first find a confidence interval for ξ and then transform the two end values of ξ into ρ. The confidence interval for ξ is .87 $\pm$ 2.58($\frac{1}{9}$) or .58 to 1.15. The confidence interval for ρ is therefore .52 to .82. Note that r is *not* at the mid-point of the confidence interval for ρ.

2. A sample of 53 is drawn from each of two supposedly normal bivariate populations. The sample r's are $r_1 = .80$ and $r_2 = .50$. Is $\rho_1 = \rho_2$? To test this hypothesis, we take

$$\text{C.R.} = \frac{(z_1 - z_2) - (\xi_1 - \xi_2)_H}{\sqrt{\frac{1}{50} + \frac{1}{50}}} = \frac{(z_1 - z_2) - 0}{\sqrt{\frac{2}{50}}} = \frac{1.10 - .55}{\sqrt{\frac{1}{25}}} = \frac{.55}{\frac{1}{5}} = 2.75$$

Thus we can reject this hypothesis at the .01 level of confidence.

12.6. The Scatter Plot. A simple device of great usefulness in the understanding of bivariate distributions and in the interpretation of measures of relation is the *scatter plot*. A scatter plot is made by placing a mark in the xy plane for each member of the sample, locating the mark at the value of that member. Suppose, for example, that the X values (or class intervals) are $x_1, x_2, \ldots, x_r$ and the Y values are $y_1, y_2, \ldots, y_s$. A scatter plot made by placing a dot at the point (x_i, y_i) for each member

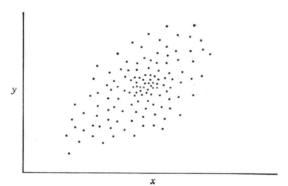

Fig. 12.6.1. A scatter plot, in which the mean regression curves are approximately linear.

(X_i, Y_i) might look like Fig. 12.6.1. We can tell at a glance from this scatter plot that the mean regression curves are at least approximately linear, and therefore we are justified in using the p-mcc as a measure of relationship. The research worker should not rely on the numerical value of r, however, but should build up a set of visual associations of scatter plots with the corresponding numerical values of r, because the relationship is not a simple one. The formula $s_e^2 = s_y^2(1 - r^2)$ indicates that the variance about the linear regression curve is $1 - r^2$ of the variance of Y. Values of s_e^2 for a few values of r are shown in the following table:

r	s_e^2
.10	$.99s_y^2$
.20	$.96s_y^2$
.40	$.84s_y^2$
.80	$.36s_y^2$
.90	$.19s_y^2$

Thus the difference between r's of .80 and .90 is much greater than that between .10 and .20 in terms of reduction in s_e^2. *The square of r gives the proportion by which s_y^2 is reduced in obtaining s_e^2.*

Since the variance is more difficult to interpret than the standard deviation, it is often convenient to think in terms of s_e rather than s_e^2. Values of s_e for a few values of r are given in the following table:

r	s_e
.10	$.99s_y$
.20	$.98s_y$
.40	$.92s_y$
.80	$.60s_y$
.90	$.44s_y$
.99	$.14s_y$

Since $s_e = s_y[1 - (1 - \sqrt{1 - r^2})]$, the proportion by which s_y is reduced in obtaining s_e is $1 - \sqrt{1 - r^2}$. As

$$\sin x = \sqrt{1 - \cos^2 x}$$

a table of trigonometric functions is convenient for finding $\sqrt{1 - r^2}$ or $1 - \sqrt{1 - r^2}$.

As indicated in Sec. 12.5, if r is used to test a hypothesis about ρ, then it is necessary that the sample be drawn from a normal bivariate distribution. As stated in Sec. 12.5, the marginal distributions of a normal bivariate distribution are themselves normal; therefore, each of the sample marginal distributions should be examined for approximate normality and tested, if sufficiently large, by the χ^2 test. If the mean regression is linear and each of the marginal distributions appears to be approximately normal, it is probably fairly safe to assume that the population sampled is a normal bivariate distribution, and to test hypotheses about ρ.

Frequently r is interpreted in terms of the adequacy of prediction, that is, in terms of the standard error of estimate s_e. Obviously to state a single figure for the adequacy of prediction assumes that the variance of errors is equal from one value of X to another. Since in a normal bivariate distribution all conditional distributions of Y have the same variance $[\sigma_y(1 - \rho^2)]$* and since the mean regression of Y on X is linear, it follows that with a normal bivariate distribution the assumption of equality of variance of errors is satisfied.

The interpretation of s_e depends in part upon the form of the distribution of errors. If the distribution of errors is normal, the table of $N(0,1)$ can be used in statements about what proportions of errors fall within certain limits. For any sample the distribution of errors should be found and examined for normality before statements of this kind are made. In any normal bivariate distribution, the distribution of errors (that is, deviations from the mean regression curve) is normal.

12.7. Computation of r. For computational purposes, note that the following sums from a bivariate sample provide all the information needed to calculate r: n, Σx, Σy, Σx^2, Σy^2, Σxy. First we calculate m_x, m_y, s_x, and s_y. Then we obtain

$$\text{Cov}_{xy} \equiv \frac{\Sigma(x - m_x)(y - m_y)}{n} = \frac{\Sigma xy}{n} - \frac{m_x \Sigma y}{n} - \frac{m_y \Sigma x}{n}$$

$$+ \frac{n m_x m_y}{n} = \frac{\Sigma xy}{n} - m_x m_y - m_y m_x + m_x m_y = \frac{\Sigma xy}{n} - m_x m_y$$

Next we find $r = \text{Cov}/s_x s_y$. Since we usually want to calculate m_x, m_y, s_x, and s_y anyway, the order indicated is usually the most efficient. If for any reason we want to obtain r directly, or to check our calculation, note that

* The property of equal variances of conditional distributions is called *homoscedasticity*.

$$\frac{\Sigma xy}{n} - m_x m_y = \frac{n\Sigma xy - \Sigma x \Sigma y}{n^2}$$

and

$$s_x s_y = \sqrt{\left(\frac{\Sigma x^2}{n} - \frac{(\Sigma x)^2}{n^2}\right)\left(\frac{\Sigma y^2}{n} - \frac{(\Sigma y)^2}{n^2}\right)}$$

$$= \frac{1}{n^2}\sqrt{\left[n\sum x^2 - \left(\sum x\right)^2\right]\left[n\sum y^2 - \left(\sum y\right)^2\right]}$$

Therefore

$$r = \frac{n\Sigma xy - \Sigma x \Sigma y}{\sqrt{[n\Sigma x^2 - (\Sigma x)^2][n\Sigma y^2 - (\Sigma y)^2]}}$$

If the size of the bivariate sample is extremely large, it may be convenient to divide each of the marginal distributions into class intervals, considering each score as falling at the mid-point of the interval, as described in Sec. 4.8. It may further be convenient to transform each value by a linear transformation; the student was asked to prove (Exercise 12.3.6) that the transformed variates yield an r equal to that of the original variates.

EXERCISES

12.7.1. In a study of the relation of scores on an aptitude test to productivity (in a factory) after three months of training, the 200 pairs of scores shown in the accompanying table were obtained by testing 200 randomly selected applicants and later measuring their productivity.

    a. On the basis of criteria available to the student, is one justified in considering r a measure of the relationship?

    b. Compute r.

    c. Find the linear mean regression of Y on X.

    d. Find the linear mean regression of X on Y.

    e. If a new applicant has an aptitude score of 43, what would you predict his productivity would be after three months of training?

    f. On the basis of criteria available to the student, is one justified in testing hypotheses about ρ? Make the computations necessary to justify your answer.

    g. Test the hypothesis that $\rho = 0$.

    h. Find the .05 confidence interval for ρ.

    i. What would you expect the mean error to be in predicting a large number of productivities? Within what interval would about 50 per cent of the errors lie? Would the error tend to vary systematically with x?

Applicant	Aptitude score (X)	Productivity (Y)	Applicant	Aptitude score (X)	Productivity (Y)
1	9	23	51	37	50
2	17	35	52	36	50
3	20	29	53	33	52
4	19	33	54	36	51
5	22	39	55	35	49
6	20	43	56	37	51
7	23	32	57	34	54
8	26	36	58	33	55
9	25	39	59	36	55
10	24	43	60	35	57
11	23	46	61	35	56
12	27	45	62	33	59
13	25	44	63	35	62
14	25	51	64	37	71
15	23	49	65	41	41
16	27	56	66	40	42
17	31	25	67	40	45
18	30	41	68	38	46
19	32	40	69	39	44
20	28	42	70	42	45
21	31	39	71	40	52
22	30	41	72	41	49
23	29	46	73	39	51
24	30	47	74	42	50
25	32	47	75	40	50
26	31	45	76	38	51
27	32	47	77	41	48
28	28	43	78	40	52
29	29	45	79	42	50
30	31	51	80	39	51
31	30	51	81	41	51
32	32	50	82	39	52
33	31	54	83	40	49
34	29	56	84	42	49
35	30	57	85	42	51
36	33	36	86	40	50
37	35	41	87	41	55
38	35	40	88	39	53
39	34	41	89	41	55
40	35	39	90	40	56
41	37	44	91	40	55
42	36	47	92	38	53
43	37	47	93	41	56
44	33	45	94	42	55
45	35	43	95	39	54
46	37	45	96	40	54
47	36	46	97	41	55
48	34	46	98	41	61
49	36	51	99	39	59
50	35	49	100	42	58

Applicant	Aptitude score (X)	Produc- tivity (Y)	Applicant	Aptitude score (X)	Produc- tivity (Y)
101	40	70	151	49	59
102	45	36	152	51	61
103	44	46	153	51	62
104	46	45	154	49	60
105	46	45	155	52	60
106	44	44	156	50	59
107	45	51	157	48	58
108	45	51	158	48	60
109	47	49	159	50	58
110	45	52	160	49	61
111	44	50	161	51	66
112	43	51	162	48	65
113	43	48	163	52	64
114	45	50	164	50	63
115	44	53	165	50	58
116	46	55	166	51	71
117	45	54	167	49	68
118	47	54	168	55	44
119	45	55	169	57	51
120	46	57	170	54	48
121	45	55	171	54	57
122	43	53	172	53	55
123	46	54	173	55	59
124	45	53	174	56	61
125	47	55	175	55	58
126	45	53	176	53	59
127	47	56	177	57	60
128	47	56	178	54	60
129	46	55	179	54	65
130	44	54	180	56	64
131	47	59	181	55	64
132	43	62	182	54	71
133	46	60	183	53	68
134	46	59	184	56	73
135	45	61	185	60	49
136	47	58	186	58	57
137	44	60	187	61	60
138	46	63	188	60	65
139	45	66	189	59	64
140	45	64	190	59	64
141	43	64	191	60	70
142	50	41	192	62	73
143	49	45	193	67	66
144	51	44	194	64	69
145	51	51	195	65	59
146	48	49	196	64	71
147	50	49	197	71	65
148	50	54	198	68	73
149	52	57	199	74	67
150	50	55	200	73	78

j. What would you expect the mean error to be in predicting a large number of productivities if the X scores were not available [but $E(Y)$ were known]? What would the standard deviation of the errors be?

k. What is the probability that a predicted productivity, using the regression equation, will have an error of $+10$, that is, be 10 points higher than the actual productivity? State clearly the assumptions involved.

l. Discuss the problem of random sampling in this case.

12.7.2. A clinician is interested in whether three measures of neuroticism, X, Y, and Z, are interrelated. He secures the three measures on each of 50 patients and thus obtains 150 pairs of measures, there being 3 for each patient: (X,Y), (X,Z), and (Y,Z). He then computes r for these 150 pairs and finds that he can reject the hypothesis that $\rho = 0$. Why is his test invalid?

12.7.3. If the standard error of estimating Y from X is the same regardless of the value of X and if $\rho \neq 0$ and the mean regression of Y on X is linear, how would ρ of a subpopulation with a smaller range of X compare with ρ for the entire population? For example, if the mean regression of academic averages on intelligence-test scores is linear and if $\rho \neq 0$ and the standard error of estimate is constant, would you expect $|\rho|$ to be higher for a very heterogeneous group of students or a relatively homogeneous group of students with respect to intelligence-test scores?

12.7.4. The "reliability" of a measure is sometimes defined by obtaining the same measure (that is, using the same or equivalent measuring procedures) at two different times on each member of a large group and then finding r for the paired measures. If the second measure tends to be larger than the first measure by a constant amount, will this discrepancy have any effect on the size of r? If $r = 1$, what has remained constant in the two sets of measurements?

12.7.5. A rather famous argument in psychology arose when investigations showed that under certain conditions the reliabilities of maze performance scores were quite low. Psychologist A maintained that these low reliabilities cast doubt on all results which had been reported using maze scores. Psychologist B maintained that certain results, which had been shown to be statistically significant, were valid from a statistical point of view despite the possibly low reliabilities of the measures used. Who was right? (*Hint:* Consider the case of having been able to reject the hypothesis that two sets of measures were drawn randomly from populations having the same mean.)

12.7.6. Try to derive a method of finding confidence intervals for $\rho_1 - \rho_2$, on the basis of the theorem and corollaries in Sec. 12.5. What is the difficulty?

Chapter 13

F DISTRIBUTIONS AND THE

ANALYSIS OF VARIANCE

13.1. Definition of F. Let X be distributed as χ_m^2 and Y be independently distributed as χ_n^2; then $F_{m,n}$ is defined as $\dfrac{X/m}{Y/n}$. In other words, $F_{m,n}$ is the ratio of two independent variates each distributed as chi square, each divided by its number of degrees of freedom. Note that $F_{m,n}$ is always positive.

13.2. Distribution of F. We state without proof[1] that the distribution of $F_{m,n}$ is given by

$$f(F_{m,n}) = \frac{\Gamma\left(\dfrac{m+n}{2}\right)}{\Gamma\left(\dfrac{m}{2}\right)\Gamma\left(\dfrac{n}{2}\right)} \left(\frac{m}{n}\right)^{m/2} F_{m,n}^{(m/2)-1}\left(1 + \frac{m}{n}F_{m,n}\right)^{-(m+n)/2}$$

A typical F density function is illustrated in Fig. 13.2.1.

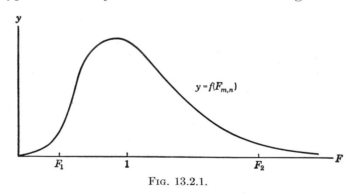

Fig. 13.2.1.

---

[1] A proof is given in the Appendix, Sec. B.24.

180

Let F_1 and F_2 be constants such that $F_1 < 1 < F_2$.   Note that $F_{m,n} = 1/F_{n,m}$; therefore, if $F_{m,n} < F_1$, $F_{n,m} > 1/F_1$ and vice versa.   Thus prob $(F_{m,n} < F_1) = $ prob $(F_{n,m} > 1/F_1)$.   Therefore,

prob $(F_{m,n} < F_1)$ or $(F_{m,n} > F_2)$

$$= \text{prob}\left(F_{n,m} > \frac{1}{F_1}\right) + \text{prob}\,(F_{m,n} > F_2)$$

Tables of F_p such that

$$\int_0^{F_p} f(F_{m,n})\,dF_{m,n} = 1 - p$$

for $1 - p = .90, .95, .975, .99, .995$, and for various values of m and n are given in the Appendix; thus the table of F_p gives the values $1/F_1$ and F_2 for the probabilities usually wanted.   Note that for small p, both F_2 and $1/F_1$ are greater than 1.   It is convenient, therefore, to compute $F_{m,n}$ or $F_{n,m}$, whichever is greater than 1, and then see whether the computed F is greater than F_p, using the same p in either case.   When this procedure is used, any hypothesis rejected because F is greater than F_p must be rejected at the $2p$ level of confidence, as a two-tailed test has been used.   By deciding beforehand which F to compute, a one-tailed test can be made.

13.3. The Ratio of Unbiased Estimates of Two Population Variances.   Let two random samples of sizes n_1 and n_2 respectively be drawn from $N(\mu_1, \sigma_1^2)$ and $N(\mu_2, \sigma_2^2)$.   By Theorem 10.6 the two statistics $n_1 s_1^2 / \sigma_1^2$ and $n_2 s_2^2 / \sigma_2^2$ are independently distributed as $\chi^2_{n_1-1}$ and $\chi^2_{n_2-1}$ respectively.   Therefore, by definition

$$\frac{\dfrac{n_1 s_1^2 / \sigma_1^2}{n_1 - 1}}{\dfrac{n_2 s_2^2 / \sigma_2^2}{n_2 - 1}} \equiv F_{n_1-1,\,n_2-1}$$

Note that this ratio can be written $\dfrac{n_1 s_1^2/(n_1 - 1)}{n_2 s_2^2/(n_2 - 1)} \dfrac{\sigma_2^2}{\sigma_1^2}$.   As we have stated earlier,[1] $n s^2/(n - 1)$ is an unbiased estimate of σ^2.

[1] A proof is given in the Appendix, Sec. B.20.

Thus the ratio of two independent unbiased estimates of population variances, multiplied by the inverse ratio of the variances which have been estimated, is distributed as F_{n_1-1, n_2-1}.

13.4. The Special Case $\sigma_1^2 = \sigma_2^2$. In the very important case that the two population variances are equal, the ratio of the unbiased variance estimates alone (multiplied by one) is distributed as F_{n_1-1, n_2-1}. This case arises when, for example, two independent samples are drawn from the same population.

EXERCISES

13.4.1. A sample of 17 drawn at random from $N(0,14)$ yields a standard deviation of 5. A sample of 10 drawn at random from $N(5,10)$ yields a standard deviation of 4.

 a. Compute F.

 b. Is this value reasonable?

 c. Would there be any point in computing F under these conditions?

13.4.2. A sample of 10 drawn at random from $N(0,6)$ yields a standard deviation of 3. A sample of 10 drawn at random from $N(4,10)$ yields a standard deviation of 2. Compute F. How would you interpret this value of F?

13.4.3. A sample of 25 drawn randomly from $N(\mu_1, \sigma_1^2)$ has a variance of 40. A sample of 49 drawn randomly from $N(\mu_2, \sigma_2^2)$ has a variance of 15. Test the hypothesis that

 a. $\sigma_1^2 = \sigma_2^2$

 b. $2\sigma_1^2 = \sigma_2^2$

 c. $\sigma_1^2 \leq \sigma_2^2$

13.4.4. In the use of certain precision instruments, the mean error can always be made zero by proper calibration; therefore, the critical measure of the adequacy of such an instrument is the variability of the errors made. In a comparison of two different instruments, 25 measurements were taken with instrument A and 35 with instrument B (all by the same operator) and the error of each measurement was found by a more accurate and precise (but also more laborious) procedure. The errors of instrument A had a variance of 30; those of B had a variance of 20. Assuming the population of errors to be normally distributed, test the hypothesis that

 a. the variances of errors of A and B are equal.

 b. the variance of A is twice that of B.

 c. the variance of A is no more than that of B.

What does the assumption of random sampling mean in this application? What are some of the experimental procedures that would violate this assumption? Exactly what populations have been sampled and what, from a statistical point of view, should be the scope of the conclusions drawn?

13.4.5. Two methods of manufacturing a certain product have been proposed and set up experimentally. How can the hypothesis that the two methods result in equal variabilities in the product be tested? List the assumptions involved in making the test.

13.5. The Special Case $\mu_1 = \mu_2; \sigma_1^2 = \sigma_2^2$. When not only the population variances but also the population means are equal (and the populations are normal), *three* independent estimates of the population variance can be obtained from two samples of the same size n. Two of these are $s_1^2 n/(n-1)$ and $s_2^2 n/(n-1)$, as before. The third is obtained from Theorem 9.5.2, that the mean m of a sample of size n drawn from $N(\mu, \sigma^2)$ will be normally distributed with mean μ and variance σ^2/n. Thus m_1 and m_2, the means of the two samples, can be considered a sample of two from $N(\mu, \sigma^2/n)$. Thus an unbiased estimate of σ^2/n is the variance of the two sample means s_m^2 times $2/(2-1) = 2$. Thus an unbiased estimate of σ^2 is $2ns_m^2$. We state without proof[1] that this estimate is independent of the two others, that is, that $f\left(2ns_m^2, s_1^2 \dfrac{n}{n-1}\right) = f(2ns_m^2)f\left(s_1^2 \dfrac{n}{n-1}\right)$, etc. Furthermore, the ratio of $2ns_m^2$ to either $s_1^2 \dfrac{n}{n-1}$ or $s_2^2 \dfrac{n}{n-1}$ is distributed as $F_{1,n-1}$. This follows from Theorem 10.6, for by that theorem $\dfrac{2s_m^2}{\sigma^2/n}$ is distributed as χ_1^2; therefore,

$$\frac{\dfrac{2s_m^2}{\sigma^2/n}}{\dfrac{s_1^2 n/(n-1)}{\sigma^2}} = \frac{2ns_m^2}{s_1^2 n/(n-1)}$$

is distributed as $F_{1,n-1}$.

Since in this special case $\sigma_1^2 = \sigma_2^2$, a better estimate of σ^2 can be obtained by combining $s_1^2 n/(n-1)$ and $s_2^2 n/(n-1)$ into a single estimate, which is the arithmetic mean of the two, $(s_1^2 + s_2^2)n/2(n-1)$. It can be shown that $\dfrac{2ns_m^2}{(s_1^2 + s_2^2)n/2(n-1)}$ is distributed as $F_{1,2n-2}$.

[1] Proofs are given by Cramér (3) and Wilks (12).

Note that

$$2ns_m^2 = 2n \frac{\left(m_1 - \dfrac{m_1 + m_2}{2}\right)^2 + \left(m_2 - \dfrac{m_1 + m_2}{2}\right)^2}{2}$$

$$= \frac{n(m_1 - m_2)^2}{2}$$

Therefore

$$\frac{2ns_m^2}{(s_1^2 + s_2^2)n/2(n-1)} = \frac{(m_1 - m_2)^2}{(s_1^2 + s_2^2)/(n-1)}$$

$$= \left(\frac{m_1 - m_2}{\sqrt{(s_1^2 + s_2^2)/(n-1)}}\right)^2 = t_{2n-2}^2$$

(See Chap. 11.) Thus, in this special case, $F = t^2$. As a matter of fact, it follows from the definitions of t and F that t_n^2 is distributed as $F_{1,n}$. This relation is indicated in the tables in Appendix D, as the entry for $F_{1,n}$ for a given confidence level (one-tailed test) is the square of t_n for that same confidence level (two-tailed test).

If we wish to use F to test the hypothesis that two populations have equal means by drawing samples of size n, we can decide beforehand to compute $F_{1,n}$ instead of $F_{n,1}$, and thus use a one-tailed test. The reasonableness of this becomes apparent when we consider that a significantly large value of $F_{n,1}$ would be difficult to interpret; about the only interpretation would be that some error in procedure was entering in to tend to make the difference between the two means smaller than it would ordinarily be under conditions of random sampling.

EXERCISES

13.5.1. A sample of 9 drawn from $N(0,\sigma^2)$ yields a mean of 1 and a variance of 8. Another sample of 9 drawn from the same population yields a mean of 3 and a variance of 7.

  a. Compute F, using as numerator the estimate based on the two means.

  b. How would you interpret this value of F?

  c. Compute t and compare this value with that for F.

  d. If F had been "significantly" large, what conclusion, if any, would you have drawn?

13.5.2. A sample of 20 drawn from $N(\mu_1,\sigma_1^2)$ yields a mean of 5 and a variance of 30. A sample of 20 drawn from $N(\mu_2,\sigma_2^2)$ yields a mean of 8 and a variance of 25. Test the hypothesis that

a. $\sigma_1^2 = \sigma_2^2$.

b. $\mu_1 = \mu_2$. Does your test presuppose that $\sigma_1^2 = \sigma_2^2$? If so, does your first test give you confidence that this is true?

c. $\mu_1 = \mu_2$, using t. Compare with F.

13.5.3. A controversy arose as to whether two different sets of skulls, found a short distance apart, came from the same prehistoric racial stock. The cephalic index of each skull was found. Outline the steps and assumptions involved in comparing the mean cephalic indices.

13.6. The Case of Several Groups. Let a sample of size r be drawn at random from each of k populations, each having the same normal distribution. Then one estimate of σ^2 is

$$\frac{\sum_{i=1}^{k} s_i^2 \dfrac{r}{r-1}}{k}$$

the mean of the k estimates; another estimate is obtained from the variance of the means, s_m^2, and is $\dfrac{rk}{k-1} s_m^2$ $\left(\text{since } \dfrac{k}{k-1} s_m^2 \text{ is}\right.$ an unbiased estimate of σ^2/r). We state without proof[1] that these two estimates are independent and that their ratio

$$\frac{\dfrac{rk}{k-1} s_m^2}{\dfrac{\sum_{i=1}^{k} s_i^2 \dfrac{r}{r-1}}{k}}$$

is distributed as $F_{k-1,rk-k}$.

When $F_{k-1,rk-k}$ is computed from k samples from k different normally distributed populations and is significantly large, we can reject the hypothesis that the populations all have the same mean and variance. Ordinarily we are more interested in differences between means than in differences between variances. To conclude from a significant value of $F_{k-1,rk-k}$ that the population means are different implies the assumption that the population

[1] Proofs are given by Cramér (3) and Wilks (12).

variances are equal. This is the assumption of *homogeneity of variance*. We can test for homogeneity by making use of the following theorem:

Theorem 13.6. Let $\hat{s}_1^2$, $\hat{s}_2^2$, . . . , $\hat{s}_k^2$ represent independent unbiased estimates of the population variance derived from k samples, each of size r, drawn at random from normal populations having the same variance. Let

$$\hat{s}^2 \equiv \frac{\sum_{i=1}^{k} \hat{s}_i^2}{k} \quad \text{and} \quad D \equiv \frac{3kr}{3kr + k + 1}$$

Then $H \equiv 2.3026 \, Dr \left(k \log_{10} \hat{s}^2 - \sum_{i=1}^{k} \log_{10} \hat{s}_i^2 \right)$ is distributed approximately as χ_{k-1}^2.

When H is significantly large (as given by tables of χ_{k-1}^2) the hypothesis of homogeneity of variance must be rejected. When H is small, the hypothesis has not, of course, been proved, but somewhat greater confidence can be placed in the conclusion, in case a significant F is obtained, that the population means differ, that is, somewhat greater confidence than in the absence of the H test.

If we are willing to assume normality and homogeneity of variance and we have obtained a significant value of F, then we can reject the hypothesis that the population means are equal. This does not mean, however, that we can conclude that *all* the means are different; it may be that the difference between a single pair of means is responsible for the large value of F. It has been customary, after finding a significant value of F, to test the difference between any two means by the t test. Strictly speaking, this procedure is invalid, as some of the probabilities given in the t tables will be spuriously small, because more than one comparison is involved and the comparisons are interdependent in a way that makes the exact computation of probabilities for t, following F, a hopelessly complicated and laborious procedure. For practical purposes, it is probably safe to set some significance level for F and the same significance level for t; then, if F is significant at the level set, compute t's and interpret them simply as to whether they do or do not reach the level set.   In other words, if the .05 level has been set, a value of 3.2 for t with 15 degrees of freedom should be interpreted as significant at the .05 level, not the .01 level indicated in the t tables.   This procedure can by no means be rigorously justified, and if an important decision must be made on the basis of a statistical test, a wise procedure is to gather additional data for any comparison which has yielded a significant value of t, following F.

In making the t test after F, a somewhat more powerful test can be made by using the assumption of homogeneity and taking

$$t = \frac{m_1 - m_2}{\sqrt{2 \sum_{i=1}^{k} \frac{s^2_i}{k(r-1)}}}$$

with $rk - k$ degrees of freedom instead of

$$t = \frac{m_1 - m_2}{\sqrt{(s^2_1 + s^2_2)/(r-1)}}$$

with $2r - 2$ degrees of freedom.

When F has a value which does not meet our requirement of significance, it will ordinarily be inappropriate to make any t tests.   However, when it has been decided beforehand that a particular comparison is of special importance, then that comparison, by means of t, should be made.   If more than one such comparison is to be made, the same problem of spuriously low levels of confidence is encountered as that discussed previously, and the same caution should be exercised.

A procedure which allows one to compare individual means and which avoids the pitfalls of t after F has been given by John W. Tukey.[1]   In outlining the procedure, the justification of which is far beyond the scope of this book, we shall take as an

---

[1] John W. Tukey, Comparing individual means in the analysis of variance, *Biometrics*, vol. 5, pp. 99–114, 1949.   Tukey discusses this procedure for the more complex case of a Latin-square design.

example the following hypothetical data:

Population sampled (sample size 12)	Sample mean	Sample variance
A	22	15
B	31	13
C	18	16
D	26	14
E	23	17
F	32	16
G	22	12

Step 1.   Choose a level of significance.
For our example we choose .05.

Step 2.   Calculate the difference which would have been significant if there were but two samples.

Making use of the assumption of homogeneity of variance, the estimated standard deviation (of the sampling distribution) of a single mean $\hat{\sigma}_m$ is $\sqrt{\sum_{i=1}^{k} s_i^2/k(r-1)} = \sqrt{103/7(11)} = 1.1566.$

We set $t[= (m_1 - m_2)/\sqrt{2\hat{\sigma}_m^2}]$ equal to 1.99, which is significant at the .05 level for 77 degrees of freedom, and solve for $m_1 - m_2$, obtaining 3.25.

Step 3.   Arrange the means in order and consider any gap larger than the value found in Step 2 as a group boundary.

The seven means in order are 18, 22, 22, 23, 26, 31, and 32, and the differences $22 - 18 = 4$ and $31 - 26 = 5$ exceed 3.25, so that we have divided the populations sampled into three groups: 18 (*C*) by itself; 22 (*A*), 22 (*G*), 23 (*E*), and 26 (*D*) together; and 31 (*B*) and 32 (*F*) together.

If no group contains more than two means, the process terminates.

Step 4.   In each group of 3 or more means, find the grand mean M, the most straggling mean m (that is, the mean differing most from the mean of the means in its group), and the difference of these two divided by $\hat{\sigma}_m$.   Convert this ratio into a statistic having approximately the distribution $N(0,1)$ by taking

$$\frac{\dfrac{m - M}{\hat{\sigma}_m} - \dfrac{6}{5}\log_{10} k'}{3(1/4 + 1/n)} \qquad (k' > 3 \text{ means in the group})$$

or

$$\frac{\dfrac{m - M}{\hat{\sigma}_m} - \dfrac{1}{2}}{3(1/4 + 1/n)} \qquad (3 \text{ means in the group})$$

in which n is the number of degrees of freedom on which $\hat{\sigma}_m$ is based. Separate off any straggling mean for which this ratio is significant at the chosen significance level using tables of $N(0,1)$.

In our example, we have only one group of 3 or more means, the group 22 (A), 22 (G), 23 (E), and 26 (D). The mean of these 4 means is 23.25, and the most straggling mean is 26. Thus $(m - M)/\hat{\sigma}_m = (26 - 23.25)/1.1566 = 2.37766$. Further, $\log_{10} 4 = .60206$. The ratio is thus

$$\frac{2.37766 - (\%)(.60206)}{3(\frac{1}{4} + \frac{1}{77})} = 2.10$$

As the .05 level for $N(0,1)$ is 1.96, we separate 26 (D) from the other members of the group.

Step 5. If Step 4 changed any group, repeat the process until no further means are separated in the old groups. The means separated off from one side of a group form a subgroup. If there are any subgroups of 3 or more when no more means are being separated from groups, apply the same process (Steps 4 and 5) to the subgroups.

In our example our old group has been reduced to 3 means, and of these the most straggling mean is 23, which differs from the mean 22.33 by only .67, yielding a ratio

$$\frac{(.67/1.1566) - (\%) \log_{10} 3}{.78896} = .01$$

which of course is not significant.

Step 6. Calculate the sum of squares of deviations from the group mean and the corresponding mean square for each group or subgroup of 3 or more resulting from Steps 4 and 5. Using

$\hat{\sigma}_m^2$ as the denominator, calculate the variance ratios and apply the F test.

We have one group of 3 or more, and calculating F for the means, using $\hat{\sigma}_m^2 = 1.34$ as denominator (77 degrees of freedom) and the variance of the 3 means, $\frac{2}{9}$, times $\frac{4}{3}$, as numerator (3 degrees of freedom), we obtain $F = (\frac{8}{27})/1.34$, which is less than 1 and therefore not significantly large (nor is the reciprocal, 4.52, significantly large for 77 and 3 degrees of freedom respectively). (Note that both numerator and denominator are, by hypothesis, estimates of the variance of the sampling distribution of the mean. To obtain estimates of the variance of the population we would multiply numerator and denominator by 12, leaving the ratio and the numbers of degrees of freedom unchanged.)

The procedure described allows us to make the following assertions, each at the .05 level of confidence:

Population C has the lowest mean of the populations sampled.

Each of the populations A, D, E, and G has a mean which is lower than the mean of B and also lower than the mean of F.

Population D has a higher mean than at least one of the populations A, G, and E.

EXERCISES

13.6.1. Six independent random samples of size 10 are drawn from a normally distributed population. The means and variances of the six samples are shown in the following table:

Sample	Mean	Variance
1	100	9
2	98	7
3	102	8
4	101	8
5	99	9
6	101	8

a. Compute F.

b. Is this value reasonable?

c. If F had turned out to be "significantly" large, what would your conclusion be?

13.6.2. A teacher divided a class of 60 students at random into 4 groups of 15 each and gave each group a different objective examination (testing all groups simultaneously). The means and variances of the four groups were as follows:

Group	Mean	Variance
1	74	30
2	80	25
3	78	33
4	70	28

Is there any evidence that the four tests differ in difficulty? Define the populations sampled as precisely as you can. Discuss the problem of random sampling. Why was it important to test the students simultaneously?

13.6.3. Eight stocks were selected by each of 5 methods and the increase (or decrease) over a period of 6 months was noted for each stock. The means and variances of the increases for each method are shown in the following table:

Method	Mean	Variance
A	0	4
B	4	15
C	−3	6
D	1	7
E	0	1

Is there any evidence that the 5 methods differ in the mean increase yielded? Define the populations sampled as precisely as you can and discuss the problem of random sampling.

13.7. The Partition of a Sample into k Groups.

Let us now approach F in a way that is superficially different from (but actually equivalent to) that in the preceding chapters. Suppose that we draw a sample of n at random from a normally distributed population, and that we have chosen n so that it is divisible by the integer k, that is, $n = rk$, where r is some integer. We can decide beforehand to divide the sample arbitrarily into k groups of r each, thus:

$$
\begin{array}{cccc}
1 & 2 & \ldots & k \\
X_{11} & X_{12} & \ldots & X_{1k} \\
X_{21} & X_{22} & \ldots & X_{2k} \\
\cdot & \cdot & \cdot\cdot\cdot & \cdot \\
\cdot & \cdot & \cdot\cdot\cdot & \cdot \\
\cdot & \cdot & \cdot\cdot\cdot & \cdot \\
X_{r1} & X_{r2} & \ldots & X_{rk}
\end{array}
$$

Now it can be shown that the total sum of squares of deviations from the mean m of the total sample, which is $\sum_{j=1}^{k} \sum_{i=1}^{r} (x_{ij} - m)^2$, can be split into two parts, S_b and S_w, such that S_b is the sum of squares of deviations of the group means, $m_{\cdot j}$, from the mean m, weighted by a factor r, as there are r members in each group, that is, $\sum_{j=1}^{k} r(m_{\cdot j} - m)^2$, and S_w is the sum of squares of deviations of the x's from their respective group means, that is,

$$
\sum_{i=1}^{r} (x_{i1} - m_{\cdot 1})^2 + \sum_{i=1}^{r} (x_{i2} - m_{\cdot 2})^2 + \cdots
$$

$$
+ \sum_{i=1}^{r} (x_{ik} - m_{\cdot k})^2 \equiv \sum_{j=1}^{k} \sum_{i=1}^{r} (x_{ij} - m_{\cdot j})^2
$$

The subscript b indicates that the sum of squares arises from variation between groups, w indicates that it arises from variation within groups. In other words, we have the following:

$$
\overset{S}{\sum_{j=1}^{k} \sum_{i=1}^{r} (x_{ij} - m)^2} = \overset{S_b}{\sum_{j=1}^{k} r(m_{\cdot j} - m)^2} + \overset{S_w}{\sum_{j=1}^{k} \sum_{i=1}^{r} (x_{ij} - m_{\cdot j})^2}
$$

A proof of this is as follows:

$$
\sum_{j=1}^{k} \sum_{i=1}^{r} (x_{ij} - m)^2 = \sum_{j} \sum_{i} (x_{ij} - m_{\cdot j} + m_{\cdot j} - m)^2
$$

$$
= \sum_{j} \sum_{i} (x_{ij} - m_{\cdot j})^2 + 2 \sum_{j} \sum_{i} (x_{ij} - m_{\cdot j})(m_{\cdot j} - m)
$$

$$
+ \sum_{j} \sum_{i} (m_{\cdot j} - m)^2
$$

But the middle term, when expanded, gives

$$2 \left(\sum \sum x_{ij} m_{\cdot j} - \sum \sum m_{\cdot j}^2 - \sum \sum m x_{ij} + \sum \sum m m_{\cdot j} \right)$$

$$= 2 \left(\sum_j m_{\cdot j} \sum_i x_{ij} - \sum_j r m_{\cdot j}^2 - m \sum \sum x_{ij} + m \sum r m_{\cdot j} \right)$$

$$= 2 \left(\sum_j m_{\cdot j} r m_{\cdot j} - \sum_j r m_{\cdot j}^2 - mrkm + mrkm \right) = 0$$

Further, $\sum \sum (m_{\cdot j} - m)^2 = \sum_j r(m_{\cdot j} - m)^2$. Thus our theorem
is proved.

Corresponding to this division of S into S_b and S_w is a division
of the degrees of freedom.   There are $n - 1$ degrees of freedom
in all (the size of the sample minus the number of constants computed from the sample and used in the computation of the sum
of squares, there being only one such constant, the mean).   The
number of degrees of freedom corresponding to S_w is $n - k$ (the
number of deviations n minus the number of computed constants used, the k group means), and that corresponding to S_b is
$k - 1$ (the number of deviations minus the number of computed constants used, the one general mean).   Note that
$n - 1 = (n - k) + (k - 1)$.

By dividing each sum of squares by its corresponding number
of degrees of freedom, we obtain three estimates of the population variance σ^2.   Thus we have the following table:

	Sum of squares	d.f.	Estimate of Var
Between groups.....	$S_b = r \sum_{j=1}^{k} (m_{\cdot j} - m)^2$	$k - 1$	$S_b/(k - 1)$
Within groups......	$S_w = \sum_{j=1}^{k} \sum_{i=1}^{r} (x_{ij} - m_{\cdot j})^2$	$n - k$	$S_w/(n - k)$
Total...........	$S = \sum_{j=1}^{k} \sum_{i=1}^{r} (x_{ij} - m)^2$	$n - 1$	$S/(n - 1)$

We state without proof[1] that $S_b/(k-1)$ and $S_w/(n-k)$ are independent estimates [though neither is independent of $S/(n-1)$], that is

$$f\left[\frac{S_b}{(k-1)}, \frac{S_w}{(n-k)}\right] = f\left[\frac{S_b}{(k-1)}\right]f\left[\frac{S_w}{(n-k)}\right]$$

and that $\dfrac{S_b/(k-1)}{S_w/(n-k)}$ is distributed as $F_{k-1,n-k}$.

The reader may already have realized that to partition arbitrarily a sample of n, drawn from $N(\mu,\sigma^2)$, into k groups of r each is equivalent to drawing k samples of r each from that same population. In fact, as far as the sample *values* are concerned, it is equivalent to drawing a sample of size r from each of k populations, each normally distributed with the same mean and variance. This, however, is the case discussed in Sec. 13.6; therefore $S_b/(k-1)$ should be equal to $rks_m^2/(k-1)$ and $S_w/(n-k)$

should be equal to $\dfrac{\sum\limits_{j=1}^{k} s_{\cdot j}^2}{k} \dfrac{r}{r-1}$. This follows from the fact that

$$S_b = r\sum_{j=1}^{k}(m_{\cdot j} - m)^2 = rk\frac{\sum\limits_{j=1}^{k}(m_{\cdot j} - m)^2}{k} = rks_m^2$$

and

$$S_w = \sum\sum(x_{ij} - m_{\cdot j})^2 = \sum_{j=1}^{k} r\frac{\sum\limits_{i=1}^{r}(x_{ij} - m_{\cdot j})^2}{r} = r\sum_{j=1}^{k}s_{\cdot j}^2$$

The reader may wonder why we have introduced the notion of partitioning a sample; the reason will be apparent in the remaining section.

13.8. The Double Partition of a Sample. Suppose that, as in Sec. 13.7, we draw a sample of $n(=rk)$ from $N(\mu,\sigma^2)$. Instead of a single partition as before, we now divide our sample not only into k groups of r each, but also into r groups of k each:

[1] Proofs are given by Cramér (3) and Wilks (12).

$$
\begin{array}{ccccc}
 & 1 & 2 & \cdots & k \\
1 & X_{11} & X_{12} & \cdots & X_{1k} \\
2 & X_{21} & X_{22} & \cdots & X_{2k} \\
 & \cdot & \cdot & \cdots & \cdot \\
 & \cdot & \cdot & \cdots & \cdot \\
 & \cdot & \cdot & \cdots & \cdot \\
r & X_{r1} & X_{r2} & \cdots & X_{rk}
\end{array}
$$

Whereas in our table in Sec. 13.7 the first subscript merely numbered the members of a given column, it now indicates membership in a certain row.

It can be shown (the student should show this as an exercise) that the total sum of squares of deviations from the mean m, which as before is $\Sigma\Sigma(x_{ij} - m)^2$, can be split into three parts, as follows:

$$
\overset{S}{\Sigma\Sigma (x_{ij} - m)^2} = r \overset{S_c}{\underset{j}{\Sigma} (m_{.j} - m)^2} + k \overset{S_r}{\underset{i}{\Sigma} (m_{i.} - m)^2}
$$

$$
+ \overset{S_{c \cdot r}}{\Sigma\Sigma (x_{ij} - m_{i.} - m_{.j} + m)^2}
$$

The number of degrees of freedom associated with $S_{o \cdot r}$ is $rk - r - k - 1$ or $(r - 1)(k - 1)$, which is the product of the degrees of freedom for rows and for columns respectively. We obtain four estimates of σ^2, and we state without proof[1] that $S_c/(k - 1)$, $S_r/(r - 1)$, and $S_{c \cdot r}/(k - 1)(r - 1)$ are independent of each other. These estimates are shown in the following table:

	Sum of squares	d.f.	Estimate of σ^2
Columns.......	$S_c = r \sum_j (m_{.j} - m)^2$	$k - 1$	$S_c/(k - 1)$
Rows.........	$S_r = k \sum_i (m_{i.} - m)^2$	$r - 1$	$S_r/(r - 1)$
Columns × rows interaction	$S_{c \cdot r} = \Sigma\Sigma(x_{ij} - m_{i.} - m_{.j} + m)^2$	$(k - 1)(r - 1)$	$S_{c \cdot r}/(k - 1)(r - 1)$
Total........	$S = \Sigma\Sigma(x_{ij} - m)^2$	$rk - 1$	$S/(rk - 1)$

[1] Proofs are given by Cramér (3) and Wilks (12).

Let us consider the columns × rows interaction. If the variation between rows, from column to column, were identical, this interaction sum of squares would be zero. For example, the following table gives a zero interaction sum of squares:

	1	2	3
1	4	3	1
2	6	5	3
3	2	1	−1
4	3	2	0

The difference between any two rows is constant from column to column; similarly, the difference between any two columns is constant from row to row. If this were not so, there would be a nonzero interaction sum of squares. The interaction, therefore, arises from the variation in row differences from column to column, or in column differences from row to row. In trying to understand the interaction sum of squares it is helpful to consider x_{ij} as the general mean m plus a deviation d_{ij}, to consider $m_{i.}$ as m plus a deviation $d_{i.}$, and to consider $m_{.j}$ as m plus a deviation $d_{.j}$. Then $\Sigma\Sigma(x_{ij} - m_{i.} - m_{.j} + m)^2$ becomes $\Sigma\Sigma(d_{ij} - d_{i.} - d_{.j})^2$ and we see that the interaction sum of squares is the sum of squares which would remain if we first subtracted the general mean from each entry in the table and also from each of the column and row means and then subtracted from each entry (which now would be a deviation from the general mean) the deviations of its column and row means.

The interaction sum of squares can also be written $\Sigma\Sigma(x_{ij} - d_{i.} - d_{.j} - m)^2$, which shows that it is the sum of squares of deviations from m which would remain if we "corrected" each x_{ij} by subtracting from it its column mean's deviation from m and its row mean's deviation from m.

We state without proof[1] that the ratio of any pair of our three

[1] Proofs are given by Cramér (3) and Wilks (12).

independent estimates of σ^2 is distributed as $F_{a,b}$, in which a is the number of degrees of freedom for the estimate in the numerator and b is the number of degrees of freedom for the estimate in the denominator.

Obviously there is no point in arbitrarily partitioning a sample and then making F tests; significant results would only make us suspicious of the randomness of our partitions. Applications arise when partitions are determined in advance by the design of an experiment. For example, suppose we want to compare an intellectual performance under normal conditions with that under the influence of a drug. If we plan to use 16 subjects in the experiment, there is an obvious and predetermined way of doubly partitioning the 32 observations, into drugs (two columns) and subjects (16 rows).[1]   We then obtain the following table:

	d.f.	Estimate of σ^2
Columns (drug vs. no drug)...........	1	S_c
Rows (subjects)....................	15	$S_r/15$
Interaction.......................	15	$S_{c \cdot r}/15$

If the drug has no effect, if there are no differences between subjects (except chance fluctuations), and if there is no systematic experimental error, then the ratio of *any* two of the estimates should be distributed as F. Note, however, that it is the first hypothesis that we are primarily interested in testing. The second hypothesis is one which we can be reasonably sure in advance will not hold, and we want our test of the first hypothesis to be valid regardless of whether there are differences between subjects or not. The interaction estimate is based on the variation within drug conditions after variation due to subjects has been taken out; therefore, this is the estimate which we should use as denominator in F. Suppose the following estimates were actually obtained:

---

[1] In this discussion we ignore the problem of order of conditions (drug and then no drug, or vice versa).

	Sum of squares	d.f.	Estimate of σ^2
Columns............	10.125	1	10.125
Rows..............	346.875	15	23.125
Interaction.........	19.875	15	1.325
Total............	376.875	31	

The comparison in which we are most interested yields $F_{1,15} = 10.125/1.325 = 7.64$, which is significant at less than the .025 level (one-tailed test).

The interaction estimate in the above example can be better understood if we consider an analysis of the same data by means of t. The following table shows the data by subjects, a difference column, and the calculation of a paired t.

Subject	No drug	Drug	No drug − drug
1	56	57	−1
2	52	50	2
3	51	53	−2
4	46	45	1
5	53	53	0
6	47	44	3
7	52	50	2
8	49	48	1
9	50	51	−1
10	57	55	2
11	51	50	1
12	53	49	4
13	50	47	3
14	45	45	0
15	49	47	2
16	53	52	1
Total			18

Mean difference $= {}^{18}\!/_{16}$
Variance of differences $= {}^{159}\!/_{64}$

$$t = \frac{{}^{18}\!/_{16}}{\sqrt{s^2/15}} = \frac{{}^{18}\!/_{16}}{\sqrt{159/(64)(15)}} = 2.764 \qquad p < .02$$

The hypothesis we have tested by t is that the 16 differences are drawn at random from a normal population with zero mean. Note, however, that $t^2 = 7.64 = F$. Our paired t test is the exact equivalent of our F test using the interaction estimate as denominator. The interaction estimate, therefore, can be considered as derived, just as the denominator of t, from variation in individuals in differences between drug and no drug. The student should answer for himself the following question: why, in this example, is a two-tailed t test the equivalent of a one-tailed F test?

If we had had more than two drug conditions, we would have used the interaction estimate, as before, in the denominator of F. Caution, however, would need to be exercised in drawing any conclusion about the population of scores under different drug conditions from which our subjects' scores could be considered a random sample, the reason being that with more than two columns the number of degrees of freedom associated with the interaction estimate (when the same subjects are used in each column) becomes spuriously large. This becomes obvious when we consider the case of two subjects and 20 conditions. The interaction estimate would be associated with 19 degrees of freedom, whereas only two subjects were actually used! A significant F would not allow us to draw an inference about people in general, although, depending upon the design of the experiment, we might be able to infer something about these two particular subjects.

Whenever an interaction estimate is used for the denominator of F, it is important that one of the variables be random (as in the preceding example, in which the subject variable is random, that is, subjects are randomly selected from some population); otherwise, F is difficult to interpret. For example, if instead of 16 subjects we had had 16 psychological tests, using the same subject for each test, our F test would imply that we were considering the 16 test differences as a random sample from this one subject's population of test differences, an interpretation which would rarely be appropriate. If each difference were based upon a different test *and* a different subject, we would have confounded a random variable with a nonrandom one, and although a significant $\bar{F}$ would allow us to reject the hypothesis that differences based on the 16 tests (assigning subjects randomly to tests and equating numbers of subjects on different tests) are normally distributed with mean zero, we could not claim that differences for any one of the tests have a nonzero mean.

A sample of size n can often be partitioned into equal groups in more than two ways; in fact, if $n = p_1^{n_1} p_2^{n_2} \cdots p_k^{n_k}$, in which each p_i is a prime integer (an integer greater than 1 which is not the product of any two integers other than itself and 1) and each n_i is an integer, then the sample can be partitioned into equal groups in Σn_i ways. This multiple partitioning results in a complex breakdown of the sum of squares, with higher-order interactions, but we shall not pursue this topic further. The student is referred to the references by Edwards (14), Fisher (5,6), Lindquist (16,17), McNemar (18), Rider (19), Snedecor (20), and, on a more advanced level, Mood (9).

There is one comment, however, which needs to be made about a common procedure called *pooling*. In some cases in which the logically correct denominator of F (for a given comparison) is an estimate based on interaction, the comparison desired is preceded by a comparison of the interaction estimate with an appropriate higher-order interaction estimate (using the first interaction estimate as numerator). If this latter comparison yields a nonsignificant F, the two sums of squares are combined to yield a "more reliable" estimate (with degrees of freedom equal to the sum of the two numbers of degrees of freedom), and this "more reliable" estimate is used as denominator in making the desired comparison. Although pointed out by Wilks (12) and other mathematicians, it is sometimes overlooked in applications that, when a pooled estimate is made, the hypothesis tested is no longer the same; it is being assumed that the first interaction is zero. A nonsignificant F does not prove this assumption, any more than any other failure to reject a hypothesis thereby proves it. If the numbers of degrees of freedom are small, there could be an appreciable interaction in the population and yet a nonsignificant F from the sample. Although pooling is no doubt useful in certain applications, it is very questionable in some psychological experimentation in which it has often been employed. Almost any statistically minded psychologist would disapprove of a paired t test made by pooling 20 differences on each of three subjects to obtain either 38 or 57 additional degrees of freedom (depending upon whether the 19 degrees of freedom or trials were eliminated or not), justified by the argument that an F test failed to show individual differences (in the mean differences) among the three subjects, yet this procedure is mathematically *identical* with pooling if an analysis of variance were performed on the same data. The fact that pooling is not found in the literature using paired t leads one to suspect that pooling in the analysis of variance has sometimes been employed without full awareness of the assumptions involved. It is good to keep in mind always the population about which an inference is desired and to remember that one can never have more degrees of freedom than one has independent observations from this population. In the example cited, we certainly do not have more than three independent observations from the population of differences of people from which the three subjects can be considered a random sample; if we are interested in drawing a conclusion about these three subjects themselves, we might under certain circumstances be justified in considering our 60 differences as a random sample, but if we are interested in generalizing to a larger population of people, no amount of statistical juggling can give us more than 2 degrees of freedom.

13.9. Computation of Sums of Squares. As an exercise the student should derive the following computational formulas for S, S_b, and S_w, in which $n = rk$:

$$S = \frac{1}{n}\left[n\sum\sum x_{ij}^2 - \left(\sum\sum x_{ij}\right)^2\right]$$

$$S_b = \frac{1}{n}\left[k\sum_j\left(\sum_i x_{ij}\right)^2 - \left(\sum\sum x_{ij}\right)^2\right]$$

$$S_w = \frac{1}{r}\left[r\sum\sum x_{ij}^2 - \sum_j\left(\sum_i x_{ij}\right)^2\right]$$

Thus for the case of a partition into k groups, three sums need to be computed: the sum of scores $\Sigma\Sigma x_{ij}$, the sum of squares of scores $\Sigma\Sigma x_{ij}^2$, and the sum of squares of group sums $\sum_j\left(\sum_i x_{ij}\right)^2$.

The following computational formulas can be derived for the case of double partitionings:

$$S = \frac{1}{n}\left[n\sum\sum x_{ij}^2 - \left(\sum\sum x_{ij}\right)^2\right]$$

$$S_c = \frac{1}{n}\left[k\sum_j\left(\sum_i x_{ij}\right)^2 - \left(\sum\sum x_{ij}\right)^2\right]$$

$$S_r = \frac{1}{n}\left[r\sum_i\left(\sum_j x_{ij}\right)^2 - \left(\sum\sum x_{ij}\right)^2\right]$$

$$S_{c\cdot r} = S - S_c - S_r$$

Thus in the case of double partitioning there are two sums of squares of group sums (one for column sums and one for row sums) to be computed.

EXERCISES

13.9.1. The following table gives the mean yield for each of 4 varieties of corn on each of 5 blocks of land, randomly selected from a large area. The means are all based upon comparable sets of small plots within each block.

	Variety			
	1	2	3	4
a	7	6	6	7
b	10	8	7	9
c	6	3	5	7
d	4	3	3	3
e	8	5	5	6

(Block)

a. Test the hypothesis that the varieties differ in mean yield only by random sampling. If you reject this hypothesis, try to state precisely the assumptions, statistical and otherwise, that you are making.

b. Test the hypothesis that the blocks differ in mean yield only by random sampling. If you reject this hypothesis, state your assumptions as precisely as possible.

c. Test the hypothesis that the varieties differ only by random sampling, treating the data as 5 random samples, ignoring the classification by blocks. Why does this analysis give a result different from that obtained in *a*?

d. If instead of blocks of land, randomly selected, we had methods of fertilization, with the same numerical table of data, why would the analysis you have made be inappropriate?

13.9.2. A large room is filled with thousands of small boxes. Each box contains five cards, in order, each card having a number written on it. In half the boxes the number on the first card is distributed approximately normally with mean 1 and variance 1; the number on the second card is distributed approximately normally with mean 2 and variance 1, . . . , the number on the fifth card is distributed approximately normally with mean 5 and variance 1. In the other half of the boxes, the means are reversed, that is, the number on the first card is normally distributed with mean 5 and variance 1, etc. Explain as fully as you can why someone not knowing the distributions cannot test the hypothesis that the numbers on the five orders have the same mean by taking a random sample of five boxes and making an analysis of variance, using the following format:

Order of card

	First	Second	Third	Fourth	Fifth
1					
2					
Box 3					
4					
5					

Sum of squares	d.f.	Estimate of Var.	F
Orders...............	4	O	O/I
Boxes................	4	B	B/I
Interaction............	16	I	

In particular, show that if this analysis were planned, the probability of rejecting the hypothesis of equal means (for orders) at the .01 level of confidence is greater than .01.

Chapter 14

NONPARAMETRIC STATISTICS

14.1. Definition. The sampling distribution of a statistic usually depends upon the form of the distribution of the population. For example, the sample mean will be distributed normally only if the population is normally distributed, although as the size of the sample increases the sampling distribution of the mean approaches normality as a limiting form. Some statistics have sampling distributions depending considerably upon the form of the population distribution even for large samples. In many applications, little is known about the population distributions and it is desirable to make as few assumptions about their forms and parameters as possible. Of particular interest, therefore, are statistics not involving any assumptions at all other than random sampling; methods employing these statistics are called *nonparametric* or *distribution-free* methods. In our discussion of finite populations we were using these methods, and certain uses of chi square which we have discussed also fall into the nonparametric category, though only for large samples.

It is usually inefficient to use these methods when justifiable assumptions about the form and/or parameters of the population sampled can be made, as nonparametric methods are less powerful than tests utilizing assumptions when the assumptions are in fact correct.

14.2. The Sign Test. One of the simplest nonparametric methods can be used in testing the hypothesis that equal proportions of a population lie above and below a certain point c. Consider drawing a random sample from such a population and discarding all members having the value c; the probability that exactly r of the N remaining members will have values less than

c is $C_r^N(\frac{1}{2})^N$, and the probability that at most r members will

have values less than c is $\sum_{i=0}^{r} C_r^N(\frac{1}{2})^N$. For a discussion of how

to use these probabilities in making tests of significance and finding confidence intervals the student is referred to Chaps. 3 and 5. Tables of critical values of r (two-tailed test) for $N = 1 - 90$ and for confidence levels .01, .05, .10, and .25 are given in Appendix D.

Of particular interest is the special case in which the population sampled is a population of pairs, the value of each pair being either plus or minus depending upon which is greater (that is, $c = 0$; hence the name "sign test"). This situation arises, for example, when two sets of observations are made at different times or under different experimental conditions, each member of the first set being paired with one and only one member of the second set, or when two groups of subjects are matched in pairs, or when plots of ground, industrial products, etc., are matched in pairs. If c is taken as a number other than 0 (the value of each pair being the difference between the two), the assumption must be made that the values are quantitative, not merely ordinal.[1]

14.3. The Run Test. In many applications a sequence of n observations is made, each observation resulting in one or the other of two values, a or b. If each of the observed events is independent of all others, then all possible permutations of the a's and b's are equally probable. If, on the other hand, there is a systematic trend in the sequence, certain permutations will be highly improbable. The number of *runs* is one indication of the presence or absence of trend (or other lack of independence) in the sequence. A run is a sequence of like observations which cannot be extended by including an observation on either side. For example, the sequence

$$\underline{a\ a}\ b\ \underline{a}\ b\ \underline{a\ a\ a}\ b\ b\ \underline{a}\ b\ b\ \underline{a}\ b\ b\ \underline{a}$$

contains 11 runs, 6 being a runs (underlined) and 5 being b runs.

[1] More complete discussions of the sign test are given by W. J. Dixon and A. M. Mood, The statistical sign test, *Journal of the American Statistical Association*, vol. 41, pp. 557–566, 1946; and by Dixon and Massey (13).

The probability (assuming independence) of obtaining r runs with n_1 a's and n_2 b's is given by a complicated expression which we do not reproduce here.[1]   Too large or too small sizes of r enable one to reject the hypothesis of independence.   Tables of significance are given in the Appendix for n_1, $n_2 \leq 20$, level of confidence $= .05$ (two-tailed test).   For n_1 and n_2 each greater than 20 the number of runs is approximately normally distributed with mean $2n_1n_2/(n_1 + n_2) + 1$ and variance $2n_1n_2(2n_1n_2 - n_1 - n_2)/(n_1 + n_2)^2(n_1 + n_2 - 1)$.

In making the run test the observations can be ordered into a sequence by means of any principle with respect to which a test of mutual independence of observations is desired.   For example, in production processes it is important to watch for any change in the product with respect to time.   Further, any principle of dichotomizing which is logically independent of the ordering principle can be chosen; for example, products can be dichotomized according to whether on a certain measure they exceed a certain amount, whether they exceed the median of the total sequence, etc.

14.4. Tolerance Limits.   In many applications, especially in controlling the quality of an industrial product, it is useful to find two numbers, L_1 and L_2, between which it can be asserted, at any desired level of confidence, that a given proportion of the population lies.   There are various ways of choosing L_1 and L_2; one particularly simple way is to take the lowest and highest values, respectively, in the sample.   It can be shown[2] that if the population sampled has a continuous distribution, then no matter what its form or parameters, the probability density of z, the proportion of the population lying between the extreme values of the sample, is given by

$$f(z) = n(n - 1)z^{n-2}(1 - z)$$

in which n is the size of the sample.   Thus z and n alone determine the density of z.   To find what sample size will enable us to assert, at the p level of confidence, that proportion P (at least) of the population lies between L_1 and L_2, the extreme values of

[1] This expression and its derivation are given by Hoel (8).
[2] A proof is given by Hoel (8).

the sample, we need to find the value of n satisfying the equation

$$\int_P^1 f(z)\, dz = 1 - p$$

The integral is

$$\int_P^1 n(n-1)z^{n-2}(1-z)\, dz = n(n-1)\left(\frac{z^{n-1}}{n-1} - \frac{z^n}{n}\right)\Big|_P^1$$

$$= n(n-1)\left(\frac{1}{n-1} - \frac{1}{n} - \frac{P^{n-1}}{n-1} + \frac{P^n}{n}\right)$$

$$= 1 - nP^{n-1} + P^n(n-1)$$

The resulting equation,

$$nP^{n-1} - P^n(n-1) = p$$

is laborious to solve; a close approximation is given by

$$n \cong \frac{1}{4}\chi_p^2 \frac{1+P}{1-P} + \frac{1}{2}$$

in which χ_p^2 is the value of chi square for 4 degrees of freedom for which prob $(\chi^2 > \chi_p^2) = p$.

For example, to find the size sample which we need in order to be confident, at the .01 level, that .95 of the population lies between the extreme values of the sample, we take

$$n \cong \frac{1}{4}\chi_{.01}^2 \frac{1+.95}{1-.95} + \frac{1}{2} = \frac{1}{4}(13.3)\frac{1.95}{.05} + \frac{1}{2} = 130.175$$

The sample size required is therefore 130, the integer nearest to the solution.

14.5. Order Statistics. The method of finding tolerance limits, described in Sec. 14.4, is an example of the use of what are known as *order statistics*. Consider drawing a random sample of size n from any continuously distributed population; if the members of the sample are ranked according to size, they are order statistics. In the following discussion x_1 will denote the value of the smallest member of the sample, x_2 the value of the second smallest, . . . , x_n the value of the largest. In Sec. 14.4 an application was made of the known distribution of z, the proportion of the population lying between x_n and x_1.

It can be shown[1] that the expected proportion of the population smaller than x_i is $i/(n + 1)$. Thus the expected proportion lying between x_i and x_{i+1} (two successively ordered observations) is $\dfrac{i + 1}{n + 1} - \dfrac{i}{n + 1} = \dfrac{1}{n + 1}$. In other words, the n order statistics tend to divide the population into $n + 1$ equal parts, regardless of the distribution of the population. The two extreme values, x_1 and x_n, tend to include

$$\frac{n + 1}{n + 1} - \frac{2}{n + 1} = \frac{n - 1}{n + 1}$$

of the population.

The way in which the n order statistics tend to divide the population is illustrated in Fig. 14.5.1.

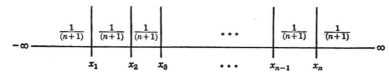

Fig. 14.5.1. Division of a population into $n + 1$ equal proportions by n order statistics.

14.6. Confidence Intervals for Percentile Points. Consider drawing at random a sample of size n from any continuously distributed population. If ξ_p is the value below which the proportion p of the population lies [that is, ξ_p is defined by $F(\xi_p) \equiv p$], then the probability that exactly i members of the sample will have values less than ξ_p is $C_i^n p^i(1 - p)^{n-i}$. Now consider the probability that x_r, the rth order statistic, exceeds ξ_p. This can happen if x_r exceeds ξ_p but x_{r-1} does not (and thus exactly $r - 1$ members have values less than ξ_p) or if x_{r-1} also exceeds ξ_p but x_{r-2} does not (and thus exactly $r - 2$ members have values < ξ_p), . . . , or if all members of the sample exceed ξ_p. These events are exclusive of each other, therefore the probability that $x_r > \xi_p$ is $\displaystyle\sum_{i=0}^{r-1} C_i^n p^i(1 - p)^{n-i}$. In a similar way it

[1] A proof is given by Mood (9).

can easily be shown that prob $(x_s < \xi_p) = \sum_{i=s}^{n} C_i^n p^i (1-p)^{n-i}$.

The probability that in the same sample either $x_r > \xi_p$ or $x_s < \xi_p$ is prob $(x_r > \xi_p)$ + prob $(x_s < \xi_p)$ − prob $(x_r > \xi_p$ and $x_s < \xi_p)$. If s is taken greater than r, then prob $(x_r > \xi_p$ and $x_s < \xi_p) = 0$. We have then

$$\text{prob } (x_r < \xi_p < x_s) = \text{prob (neither } x_r > \xi_p \text{ nor } x_s < \xi_p)$$
$$= 1 - \text{prob } (x_r > \xi_p \text{ or } x_s < \xi_p)$$
$$= 1 - \sum_{i=0}^{r-1} C_i^n p^i (1-p)^{n-i}$$
$$- \sum_{i=s}^{n} C_i^n p^i (1-p)^{n-i}$$
$$= \sum_{i=r}^{s-1} C_i^n p^i (1-p)^{n-i}$$

Thus we can find confidence intervals for ξ_p at the $1 - q$ level of confidence by finding values of r and s for which

$$\sum_{i=r}^{s-1} C_i^n p^i (1-p)^{n-i} = q$$

For example, a .05 confidence interval for $\xi_{.20}$ can be obtained from a sample of size 20 by finding values of r and s such that

$$\sum_{i=r}^{s-1} C_i^n (\tfrac{1}{5})^i (\tfrac{4}{5})^{n-i} = .95.$$

The tables for the sign test can be used for finding confidence intervals for the median $\xi_{.50}$.

A confidence interval with one bound only can of course be found by making use of either x_r or x_s alone. The derivations are left to the student.

It should also be mentioned that point estimates of ξ_p can be made by using the x_i's as estimates of the $i/(n + 1)$ points and interpolating linearly.

14.7. Wilcoxon's Matched-pairs Signed-ranks Test.[1] When a population of paired observations is being sampled, and when

[1] The derivation of this test is given by Frank Wilcoxon, Individual comparisons by ranking methods, *Biometrics Bulletin*, vol. 1, pp. 80–82, 1945.

the differences between pairs can be considered quantitative, then a somewhat more powerful test of the hypothesis that the differences are *symmetrically* distributed about zero can be made than by using the sign test described in Sec. 14.2. If the differences are ranked according to absolute size, the sum of ranks for positive differences should tend to equal the sum of ranks for negative differences, if the hypothesis is true. If either sum is smaller than a certain critical value, the hypothesis can be rejected. Tables of significance values for the smaller sum of ranks for 6 to 25 differences and for the .05, .02, and .01 levels of confidence (two-tailed test) are given in Appendix D. The p values must be halved for a one-tailed test. For more than 25 differences each sum of ranks is approximately normally distributed with mean $N(N + 1)/4$ and variance $N(N + 1)(2N + 1)/24$, in which N is the number of differences.[1]

EXERCISES

14.7.1. How many television tubes must be tested to determine limits within which it can be asserted at the .05 level of confidence that 99 per cent of the tube lifetimes lie?

14.7.2. An individual who claimed to have extrasensory powers of perception maintained that the reason she did not score significantly more "hits" (correct naming of cards) then chance was that she would receive correctly for several times, then incorrectly for several times, etc.; that is, that her ESP powers "came and went in spurts." In an experiment she scored the following sequence of hits and misses:

H H H M H H H M M M M H H H M M M M H H H H M M M H H H H M M
H H H M M M

Do these data support her claim; if they do, at what level of confidence?

14.7.3. In an experiment on cognitive processes, each of 12 subjects was classified according to whether a rather complex contingency table yielded a positive or negative relationship. There were 10 negative and 2 positive relationships found. Is there evidence of a preponderance of negative relationships in the population sampled?

14.7.4. In an experiment using identical twins, one member of each pair was tested under one set of conditions (A) and the other member was tested under another set of conditions (B). The datum recorded was the number of

[1] A further discussion of nonparametric methods, as well as a good bibliography, is given by Lincoln E. Moses, Non-parametric statistics for psychological research, *Psychological Bulletin*, vol. 49, pp. 122–143, 1952.

seconds it took the subject to solve a certain problem, and the following results
were obtained:

Twin pair	A	B
1	80	39
2	21	16
3	74	90
4	53	32
5	128	62
6	5	45
7	60	15
8	25	33
9	111	91
10	54	42
11	64	81
12	42	18
13	73	79
14	92	36
15	40	41

Make two nonparametric and one classical test with these data, explaining
the hypothesis tested and assumptions involved in each case.

14.7.5. A machine which is claimed to turn out digits "at random" gives
the following sequence: 4 0 2 8 3 9 7 1 2 2 9 6 4 0 6 3 5 1 8 0 7 3 8 1 2 4 3 3 6 4.
Test this sequence for "randomness" considering it as a sequence of

a. odds and evens (considering zero even)
b. numbers greater or not greater than 2
c. primes and nonprimes (2, 3, 5, and 7 are primes)

REFERENCES

1. Courant, R.: *Differential and integral calculus*, vol. I, 2d ed., New York, Nordeman, 1937. A rigorous and clear presentation of the calculus.
2. Courant, R., and H. Robbins: *What is mathematics?* New York, Oxford, 1941. A semipopular but precise introduction to mathematics, including calculus.
3. Cramér, H.: *Mathematical methods of statistics*, Princeton, N.J., Princeton University Press, 1946. A self-contained but advanced coverage of mathematical statistics.
4. Feller, W.: *An introduction to probability theory and its applications*, vol. I, New York, Wiley, 1950. A mathematical treatment of the discrete case.
5. Fisher, R. A.: *Statistical methods for research workers*, 1st to 10th eds., Edinburgh, Oliver & Boyd, 1925–1946; 11th ed., New York, Hafner, 1950. A classic.
6. Fisher, R. A.: *The design of experiments*, 1st to 5th eds., Edinburgh, Oliver & Boyd, 1935–1949; 6th ed., New York, Hafner, 1951. Another classic, with special attention to the analysis of variance and covariance.
7. Fry, T. C.: *Probability and its engineering uses*, New York, Van Nostrand, 1928.
8. Hoel, P. G.: *Introduction to mathematical statistics*, New York, Wiley, 1947. A mathematical treatment requiring knowledge of elementary calculus.
9. Mood, A. M.: *Introduction to the theory of statistics*, New York, McGraw-Hill, 1950. A mathematical treatment at an intermediate level, requiring a solid background in elementary calculus.
10. Peters, C. C., and W. R. Van Voorhis: *Statistical procedures and their mathematical bases*, New York, McGraw-Hill, 1940. A detailed presentation of the mathematical derivations underlying many commonly used statistics.
11. Uspensky, J. V.: *Introduction to mathematical probability*, New York, McGraw-Hill, 1937. A mathematical treatment requiring a considerable mathematical background.
12. Wilks, S. S.: *Mathematical statistics*, Princeton, N.J., Princeton University Press, 1944. An advanced mathematical treatment, one of the classics in the field.

The following texts, written at a simpler mathematical level, present and explain numerous statistical techniques, with applications to special fields:

13. Dixon, W. J., and F. J. Massey, Jr.: *Introduction to statistical analysis*, New York, McGraw-Hill, 1951.

14. Edwards, A. L.: *Experimental design in psychological research*, New York, Rinehart, 1950.
15. Guilford, J. P.: *Fundamental statistics in psychology and education*, 2d ed., New York, McGraw-Hill, 1950.
16. Lindquist, E. F.: *Statistical analysis in educational research*, Boston, Houghton Mifflin, 1940.
17. Linquist, E. F.: *Design and analysis of experiments in psychology and education*, Boston, Houghton Mifflin, 1953.
18. McNemar, Q.: *Psychological statistics*, New York, Wiley, 1949.
19. Rider, P.: *An introduction to modern statistical methods*, New York, Wiley, 1939.
20. Snedecor, G. W.: *Statistical methods*, 4th ed., Ames, Iowa, Iowa State College Press, 1946.

APPENDIX

Appendix A

SOME HINTS ON HOW TO ASK
QUESTIONS OF MATHEMATICAL
STATISTICIANS

In modern mathematics only the abstract structural properties of objects (or sets of objects) are of any real concern; what the objects *are* is largely irrelevant. Mathematical statistics is no exception; what the members of a population (or sample) *are* is of no importance whatever. When any problem is stated in concrete terms, that is, in terms of what objects actually are, it is necessary to abstract from the concrete situation the essential structural properties before the problem can be handled mathematically (in the following discussion, this kind of abstracting will be referred to as "structuring"). To most mathematicians a problem becomes really interesting only when (but not necessarily when) it is structured. Unless a mathematician is interested in applications, he is not particularly interested in structuring nor has he been especially trained in this process. It is true that many problems of pure mathematics have grown out of concrete situations or concrete ways of thinking—this is especially true of the theory of probability—and in mathematical terminology one finds remnants of this origin ("slope, rate, neighborhood, braid, knot, blanket, game, Monte Carlo method"), but when one recognizes that in modern mathematics even the term "point" has lost its intuitive geometrical meaning, it is apparent how far the process of structuring has gone.

A mistake that is often made in consulting a mathematician is in telling him what the members of a population (or sample) are (that is, telling him what observations one has made or is going to make) and leaving the entire burden of structuring to him. Even this mistake might seldom be fatal if only relevant information were given; unfortunately, the irrelevant as well as the relevant is often included, and some of the relevant is omitted. The mathematician may be so overwhelmed by the complexities and technical jargon of the special field that he either gives up or gives misleading advice, particularly if he cannot make his own questions understood.

Although there are a few statisticians who are trained in a number of fields—or who at least understand the language of those fields—and who are interested in applications, there is only one practicable solution to the problem of statistical consultation, and that is for the research worker himself to master enough of the concepts and language of mathematical statistics to perform most of the structuring himself and to state his problems in mathematical or at least semi-mathematical language.   The following series of questions is intended to help structure a research problem in statistical terms:

1. How can a population be defined such that the answer to the research problem will lie in the form and/or parameters of the distribution of the population?   In general there will be more than one way of defining the population unless the problem itself is unusually precisely specified.   For example, if a psychologist is interested in whether a given procedure *A* results in more change in a certain direction than a given procedure *B*, he may structure the problem into two populations (changes with procedure *A* and changes with procedure *B*) or one population (pairs of changes, with method *A* and with method *B*), and which of these is more suitable depends upon several quite complicated considerations.

2. How can a random sample be drawn from the population?   The answer to this question will of course often influence the answer to the first, as some populations are much more readily sampled than others.   Although the first condition for randomness—that each member of the population have equal probability of being drawn—is frequently violated, it can very often be plausibly argued that whatever bias is introduced is completely irrelevant to the problem being studied.   The violation of the second condition—that each member be drawn independently—is usually more serious, because the violation of this condition usually results in a spuriously low estimation of the sampling error and consequently assertions are made at a spuriously low level of confidence.   The violation of the assumption of independence accounts for a large proportion of statistical errors to be found in the literature.

3. What statistics will make possible a relevant inference about the form or parameters of the population, and what are the sampling distributions of these statistics?   The answers to these questions are mutually interdependent upon the answers to the first two.   In attempting to answer them the question of what assumptions can be made about the distribution of the population will usually arise.   It is with the last questions that one has reached the point that it may be necessary, and perfectly appropriate, to ask a statistician—in *his* language.   He knows about the sampling distributions of many statistics, where to find tables of them if available, and how to make approximations if tables are not available.   He may be able to derive the distribution of a statistic, if it is not already known.   By structuring the problem himself, the research worker can be prepared to give the statistician the information he needs in order to be of any aid to the research worker.

Appendix B

MATHEMATICAL APPENDIX

B.1. Limit of a Sequence. The student will recognize intuitively that the infinite sequence

$$1, \tfrac{1}{2}, \tfrac{1}{3}, \ldots , \frac{1}{n}, \ldots$$

approaches 0 as a limit, even though no member of the sequence is exactly 0. By saying that 0 is the limit, we seem to mean that in some sense the terms of the sequence get closer and closer to 0 as n gets larger and larger. There is a certain vagueness in this statement, however; interpreted literally it does not provide a sufficient criterion for asserting that a sequence approaches 0 as a limit. For example, the terms of the sequence

$$1 + .01, \tfrac{1}{2} + .01, \ldots , \frac{1}{n} + .01, \ldots$$

also get closer and closer to 0, because each term is smaller than the preceding one; yet we would say intuitively (and correctly) that the limit of this sequence is not 0, but .01. The same argument would apply if we substituted any number, even a very small one, for .01; for example, the sequence with the general term $1/n + .00001$ would approach .00001, not 0, as a limit.

By "closer and closer" then, we must mean closer than any definite quantity that we can assign in advance, that is, closer than .01 or .00001 or even 10^{-100}. This statement gives us the clue to a precise definition. By the statement that an infinite sequence approaches 0 as a limit, we mean that no matter how small a number ϵ we choose in advance, the terms of the sequence eventually get closer than ϵ to the limit 0. Even this statement is not quite right, because we can produce a sequence that might be said to satisfy it and yet does not have 0 as its limit, for example, the sequence

$$1, \tfrac{1}{2}, 1, \tfrac{1}{3}, 1, \tfrac{1}{4}, \ldots , 1, \tfrac{1}{100}, \ldots$$

We can pick as small an ϵ as we like and some of the terms eventually get smaller than ϵ, but every other term is the number 1. Therefore, we must insist in our definition that *all* the terms eventually get closer than ϵ to 0, and by "eventually" we must mean beyond some definite place in the sequence. In other words, to say that a sequence

$$a_1, a_2, \ldots, a_n, \ldots$$

approaches 0 as a limit means that for any ϵ, no matter how small, there exists some term a_N, such that any term beyond a_N, that is, any term a_n with $n > N$, will differ from 0 by less than ϵ in absolute value. We can easily prove that the sequence with $a_n = 1/n$ approaches 0, as follows: no matter what the size of ϵ, we can find an N greater than $1/|\epsilon|$, implying $1/N < |\epsilon|$; but if $n > N$, then $1/n < 1/N$, thus $1/n < |\epsilon|$; therefore $1/n \to 0$ ("approaches zero").

The same arguments apply to any limit other than 0, and thus we arrive at the following general definition:

The sequence $a_1, a_2, \ldots, a_n, \ldots$ has the limit L (or converges to the limit L) if and only if for any positive ϵ, no matter how small, there exists a term a_N (that is, a number N), such that for all $n > N$, $|a_n - L| < \epsilon$.

If we did not put absolute value marks around $a_n - L$, any sequence all of whose terms beyond a certain point are less than L would meet our definition, as $a_n - L$ would be negative and therefore less than the quantity ϵ.

We shall now accept the consequences of our definition whether those consequences satisfy our intuition or not. One consequence is that the sequence

$$0, 0, 0, \ldots, 0, \ldots$$

has the limit 0, as $|0 - 0| < \epsilon$.

B.2. Limit of a Series. An infinite sequence of additions of numbers is called an *infinite series;* that is,

$$a_1 + a_2 + \cdots + a_n + \cdots$$

in which a_n is the nth term in the sequence of additions is an infinite series. An example is the *harmonic series*

$$1 + \tfrac{1}{2} + \tfrac{1}{3} + \cdots + \frac{1}{n} + \cdots$$

An infinite series is said to *converge to a limit L* if and only if the sequence of partial sums

$$a_1, a_1 + a_2, \ldots, \sum_{i=1}^{n} a_i, \ldots$$

approaches L as a limit. Surprisingly enough, a series can be nonconvergent even though the terms of the series approach 0; for example, the harmonic series is nonconvergent. To prove this, consider that we can divide the series into the following segments:

$$1$$
$$\tfrac{1}{2}$$
$$\tfrac{1}{3} + \tfrac{1}{4}$$
$$\tfrac{1}{5} + \tfrac{1}{6} + \tfrac{1}{7} + \tfrac{1}{8}$$

.

.

.

$$1/(2^m + 1) + 1/(2^m + 2) + \cdots + 1/(2^{m+1})$$

.

.

Note that there are $2^{m+1} - 2^m = 2^m(2 - 1) = 2^m$ terms in each segment (after the first two) and that the smallest of these terms is $1/2^{m+1}$; therefore, the sum of each segment is at least $2^m(1/2^{m+1}) = \tfrac{1}{2}$. As there are infinitely many such segments (we can take m as large as we like), it is evident that the sum increases without limit.

It is important to think of an infinite series as a sequence of additions rather than the sum of an infinite class,[1] because the order in which the terms are added is sometimes crucial. The alternating harmonic series,

$$1 - \tfrac{1}{2} + \tfrac{1}{3} - \tfrac{1}{4} + \cdots + (-1)^{n+1}\frac{1}{n} + \cdots$$

converges to log 2. By rearranging terms, however, we can obtain a series converging to any number whatsoever, or we can obtain a divergent series.

Not all nonconvergent series tend to infinity; for example the series

$$1 - 1 + 1 - 1 + \cdots + (-1)^{n+1} + \cdots$$

[1] Of course from a purely formal point of view the term "sum of an infinite class" has no meaning anyway except the operational meaning given by specifying an order of additions; however, many of the "paradoxes" of mathematics have resulted from this unfortunate terminology. For example, consider the following one: take any positive series converging to .01; cover the rational points on the interval 0–1 in order, using the usual triangular ordering and covering each point by placing over it a line segment equal in length to the corresponding term in the series. Let the rational point lie at the center of each covering segment; then we have the "paradox" of covering all members of a set of points which are *dense* on the interval 0–1, each with a finite line segment, with the sum of line segments only .01. The trouble lies in the word "all"; we should say only that we can cover as many as we like—which does not imply that we can cover any dense set at all. The conceptual difficulties associated with the notion of infinite classes, and operations performed with them, lie at the basis of controversies about the foundations of mathematics; these controversies entail interesting psychological issues.

has the sequence of partial sums

$$1, 0, 1, 0, \ldots$$

which approaches no limit but never gets larger than 1.

An excellent introduction to series can be found in Courant's *Differential and integral calculus* (1).

B.3. Continuous Functions. We have already in the body of the text defined a function as a class of ordered pairs, such that if any two pairs have the same second member they must have the same first member (though the converse does not hold). When we say y is a function of x we mean that for every value of x (for which the function is defined) there is one and only one value of y (first member). Functions can be given by rules like $y = x^2$ for $-\infty < x < \infty$ or like

$$y = \begin{cases} 0 \text{ if } x \text{ is } 0 \\ x \text{ if } x \text{ is a rational number} \\ 1/x \text{ if } x \text{ is an irrational number} \end{cases}$$

A rational number is one that is equal to the ratio of two integers; for example, $17\!/\!32$ is rational. An irrational number is one that cannot be so represented, for example, $\sqrt{2}, \pi$, and e. Both rational and irrational numbers are *dense* on the number axis, that is, any finite interval contains infinitely many of each; thus the function just described would be very hard to visualize. Consider, for example, trying to graph it; our graph would look something like Fig. B.3.1. It may appear from this figure that for each value of x there are two, not one, values of y. This results from the density of both rational and irrational numbers; actually corresponding to each point on the x axis there is only one point on the y axis; for example above the point 2, which is rational, only the point on the straight line "counts" as part of the function. Functions like this do not behave in the way we naïvely think functions ought to, which is to let y change *continuously* from one value to another as x changes continuously. The intuitive concept of continuity, like the intuitive concept of limit, is vague. By "continuous" we seem to mean that there are no jumps in y as the value of x changes. By using the limit concept we can make this notion of "no jumps" precise as follows:

Definition. A function f is a continuous function of x at the point $x = x_1$ if and only if f is defined for x_1 and for every positive number ϵ, no matter how small, a positive number δ can be found such that if $|x - x_1| < \delta$ then $|f(x) - f(x_1)| < \epsilon$.

This definition means that we can restrict $f(x)$ to a preassigned interval around $f(x_1)$ that is as small as we wish to make it by restricting x to a small enough interval around x_1.

Definition. A function f is a continuous function of x in the interval $a \leq x \leq b$ if and only if f is continuous at every point in this interval.

In the following discussion we shall be concerned only with continuous functions; in fact, we shall for the most part be concerned only with a special subclass of these functions, those that are differentiable (see Sec. B.5). In advanced mathematics discontinuous functions are of great importance.

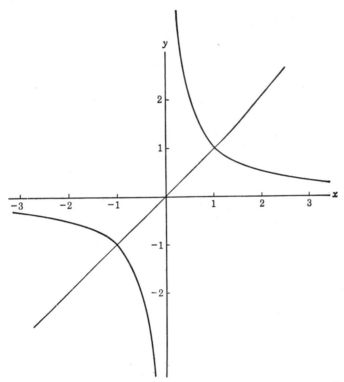

FIG. B.3.1. An attempted graph of the function given by the rule

$$y = \begin{cases} 0 \text{ if } x \text{ is } 0 \\ x \text{ if } x \text{ is rational} \\ 1/x \text{ if } x \text{ is irrational} \end{cases}$$

B.4. The Definite Integral. Consider any function f continuous in the interval $a \leq x \leq b$. As an aid in the following discussion we shall represent f by Fig. B.4.1, although our discussion will hold for any continuous function whatsoever, including those which dip below the x axis.

Consider the interval a–b divided into n intervals, each of length Δx. Within each interval i take any value x_i and form the sum

$$f(x_1) \, \Delta x + f(x_2) \, \Delta x + \cdots + f(x_n) \, \Delta x \equiv \sum_{i=1}^{n} f(x_i) \, \Delta x$$

Now consider the sequence

$$\sum_{i=1}^{1} f(x_i)\, \Delta x, \quad \sum_{i=1}^{2} f(x_i)\, \Delta x, \quad \ldots, \quad \sum_{i=1}^{n} f(x_i)\, \Delta x, \quad \ldots$$

It can be proved that for any continuous f this infinite sequence approaches a limit. As a matter of fact, a limit is approached even if the intervals are not equal (for a given n); it is necessary only that the longest interval Δx in each division approach 0 as n approaches infinity. A proof of this important theorem can be found in any rigorous textbook of the calculus, for example, Courant's *Calculus* (1).

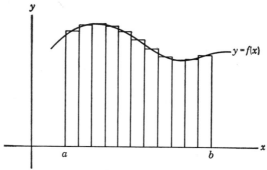

FIG. B.4.1. Area under a continuous curve approximated by rectangles.

The limit approached by this sequence is called the *definite integral of the function f in the interval* $a \le x \le b$ and is written with the sign $\int$; that is,

$$\int_a^b f(x)\, dx \equiv \lim_{\substack{n \to \infty \\ \Delta x \to 0}} \sum_{i=1}^{n} f(x_i)\, \Delta x$$

The symbol dx is used to indicate that $\Delta x \to 0$.

Note that if we use our intuitive concept of the area under the curve in Fig. B.4.1, the sum $\sum_{i=1}^{n} f(x_i)\, \Delta x$ is an approximation to that area, which tends to get better and better as $n \to \infty$ and $\Delta x \to 0$, because the "corners" which get included in the calculation get smaller and smaller. The limit $\int_a^b f(x)\, dx$ can therefore be used as a definition of the area under the curve, as it satisfies our intuitive concept of area.

B.5. The Derivative. If $f(x)$ changes continuously from $f(a)$ to $f(b)$ as x changes from a to b, we might take the ratio $\dfrac{f(b) - f(a)}{b - a}$ as a kind of "average" rate of change of $f(x)$ in this interval. However, this average rate might be very different from the average rates of change of much smaller segments of the interval a–b.   For example, Fig. B.5.1 shows a continuous function which has an "average" rate of change of 0 for the interval a–b; yet for the small segment c–d the function is changing rapidly in one direction and for the segment e–b it is changing rapidly in the other direction.   For this particular function, we might take a large number of small intervals each of length Δx, within each of which the rate of change is almost constant (in which case the curve could be approximated within each interval by a straight line), so that the "average" rate as defined previously would give adequate information about each segment.   This would be not only laborious but also imprecise; further, it would be necessary to study each function in detail in order to segment it properly.

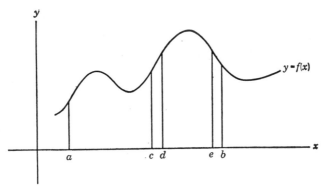

FIG. B.5.1. A continuous function.

A solution of the rate-of-change problem is achieved by considering the rate of change *at a point*.   Let $\Delta x \equiv x - k$ and form the ratio $\dfrac{f(x) - f(k)}{\Delta x}$.   Now keeping k fixed, let x approach k in any manner whatsoever, so that Δx approaches 0, through positive or negative values; $f(x)$ will of course approach $f(k)$, as we are assuming that the function is continuous at the point k.   If the ratio $\dfrac{f(x) - f(k)}{\Delta x}$ approaches a limit L, regardless of the manner in which Δx approaches 0, then L is called the *derivative of f with respect to x at the point k.* To say that $\dfrac{f(x) - f(k)}{\Delta x}$ approaches L as Δx approaches 0 means that for any positive number ϵ a positive number δ exists such that if $|\Delta x - 0| < \delta$ (excluding the case $\Delta x = 0$) then $\left| \dfrac{f(x) - f(k)}{\Delta x} - L \right| < \epsilon$.

The derivative is abbreviated $\dfrac{df}{dx}$ or $\dfrac{d}{dx} f(x)$ or $f'(x)$ or $\dfrac{dy}{dx}$ [if $y = f(x)$] or sometimes simply $D_x f$ or $D_x f(x)$.

By using the definition and the four-step rule given in the text, the student should try to prove the following theorems as exercises.

Theorem B.5.1. $\dfrac{d}{dx} c = 0.$ (The derivative of a constant is zero.)

Theorem B.5.2. $\dfrac{d}{dx} x = 1.$ (The derivative of a variable with respect to itself is one.)

Theorem B.5.3. $\dfrac{d}{dx} cf(x) = c\dfrac{d}{dx} f(x).$ (The derivative of a constant times a function is equal to the constant times the derivative of the function.) Note that this theorem is a special case of Theorem B.5.5. Note also the special case $\dfrac{d}{dx} cx = c.$

Theorem B.5.4. $\dfrac{d}{dx} [f(x) + g(x)] = \dfrac{d}{dx} f(x) + \dfrac{d}{dx} g(x).$ (The derivative of the sum of two functions is the sum of the derivatives.)

Theorem B.5.5. $\dfrac{d}{dx} [f(x)g(x)] = f(x)\dfrac{d}{dx} g(x) + g(x)\dfrac{d}{dx} f(x).$ (The derivative of a product of two functions is the first function times the derivative of the second plus the second times the derivative of the first.)

Theorem B.5.6. $\dfrac{d}{dx} [f(x)]^c = c[f(x)]^{c-1}\dfrac{d}{dx} f(x),$ in which c is any constant.

Note the special case $\dfrac{d}{dx} x^c = cx^{c-1}.$

Theorem B.5.7. $\dfrac{d}{dx}\left[\dfrac{f(x)}{g(x)}\right] = \dfrac{g(x)\dfrac{d}{dx} f(x) - f(x)\dfrac{d}{dx} g(x)}{[g(x)]^2}.$

Proofs of the following theorems are more difficult, but they can be found in almost any calculus textbook.

Theorem B.5.8. $\dfrac{d}{dx} \log f(x) = \dfrac{1}{f(x)}\dfrac{d}{dx} f(x).$ Note the special case $\dfrac{d}{dx} \log cx = \dfrac{1}{cx} c = \dfrac{1}{x}.$

Theorem B.5.9. $\dfrac{d}{dx} e^{f(x)} = e^{f(x)}\dfrac{d}{dx} f(x).$ Note the special case $\dfrac{d}{dx} e^{cx} = ce^{cx}.$

Many other theorems can be found in any calculus textbook; in fact, the process of differentiation has been reduced to a purely mechanical calculation for all, or almost all, functions encountered in applications. In courses in the calculus the student usually gets sufficient practice so that he can differentiate about as rapidly as he can do simple arithmetic.

The derivative is itself a function and, in the case of almost all functions encountered in applications, can itself be differentiated, so that we obtain the derivative of a derivative. For example, if $f(x) = x^2$, then $\dfrac{d}{dx} f(x) = 2x$, and $\dfrac{d}{dx}\left[\dfrac{d}{dx} f(x)\right] = \dfrac{d}{dx} 2x = 2.$ The second derivative is abbreviated $\dfrac{d^2}{dx^2} f(x)$ or

$f''(x)$, etc.　Similarly, we can usually obtain $\dfrac{d^3}{dx^3} f(x)$, . . . , $\dfrac{d^n}{dx^n} f(x)$.　In the

example $f(x) = x^2$, $\dfrac{d^2}{dx^2} f(x) = 2$ and $\dfrac{d^n}{dx^n} f(x) = 0$ for $n \geq 3$.

Whereas the first derivative is the rate of change of $f(x)$ with respect to x, the second derivative is the rate of change of the rate of change.　For example, consider the increasing volume of a spherical balloon as air is blown into it. What is the rate of change of the volume as a function of the radius?　The

volume V is given by the formula $V = \frac{4}{3} \pi R^3$.　Therefore, $\dfrac{dV}{dR} = 4\pi R^2$, which

implies that a given increase in R is accompanied by a much larger increase in V when R is large than when R is small.　The rate of the rate of increase is $8\pi R$; that is, not only is the volume increasing at an increasing rate, but the increase in the rate is itself increasing with R.　On the other hand, the rate of increase in the rate of increase in the rate of increase in V is the third derivative, the constant 8π; this third derivative does not change with R.

If air is being blown into the balloon at the rate of k units per second, we can

write V as a function of the time t in seconds; $V = kt$.　Then $\dfrac{dV}{dt} = k$; that is,

the rate of increase of V with respect to time is a constant, as is intuitively evident since air is being blown in at a constant rate.

If an object moves in a straight line so that we can write its distance from the point of origin as a function of the time of travel, that is, $D = f(t)$, in

which D is distance and t is the time in some appropriate units, then $\dfrac{dD}{dt}$ is the

instantaneous velocity of the object.　For example, if $D = ct^2$, then $\dfrac{dD}{dt} = 2ct$,

and the velocity at the time $t = 5$ is $10c$.　The second derivative, $\dfrac{d^2D}{dt^2}$, is the

acceleration, that is, the rate of change of the velocity.

A geometrical interpretation of the derivative is suggested by considering the linear function $y = ax + b$.　The reader will recall that the slope of a straight line is defined as the tangent of the angle formed with the x axis, as illustrated in Fig. B.5.2.　The tangent of α is the ratio of b to b/a; thus the tangent is a.　Note, however, that the derivative is also a, for $\Delta y/\Delta x$ is equal to a for every size Δx taken from any point x_1; therefore $\lim\limits_{\Delta x \to 0} \Delta y/\Delta x = a$.

Thus the derivative is the slope of the straight line.　Now consider the curve given by $y = f(x)$, illustrated in Fig. B.5.3.　The slope of this curve at the point P is the slope of the tangent at that point, and the tangent is defined as the limiting position of the secant PQ as Q approaches P.　Note, however, that PQ is the hypotenuse of the right triangle whose sides are Δy and Δx. Thus, the slope of the tangent is $\lim\limits_{\Delta x \to 0} \Delta y/\Delta x$, which is the derivative.　Thus

the derivative at a given point, if it exists, is the slope of a curve at that point.

Suppose that in a given interval of the x axis $f(x)$ rises to a maximum point and then decreases.　When $f(x)$ is increasing the derivative is positive; when

$f(x)$ is decreasing the derivative is negative. At the maximum point $f(x)$ is neither increasing nor decreasing; therefore, if the derivative exists at the maximum point, it must have the value zero. This is intuitively evident from the geometrical interpretation, for the slope at the maximum is zero unless the maximum is a "sharp point" on the curve, in which case the derivative at that

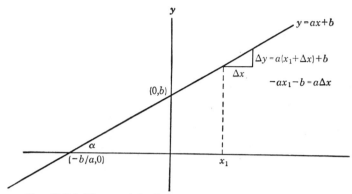

FIG. B.5.2. The straight line $y = ax + b$, with slope tan α.

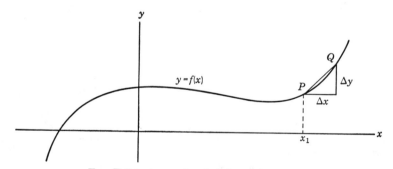

FIG. B.5.3. Approximated slope of a curve.

point does not exist. We can also prove this assertion by the following argument. If $f(x)$ is a maximum at the point k, then $f(x) - f(k)$ will be negative for all $x \neq k$, and $\dfrac{f(x) - f(k)}{\Delta x}$ will be positive or negative as Δx is negative or positive. Therefore, $\lim\limits_{\Delta x \to 0} \dfrac{f(x) - f(k)}{\Delta x}$ cannot be positive if Δx approaches 0 through positive values and cannot be negative if Δx approaches 0 through negative values. Therefore, if the limit (derivative) exists, it must be 0.

Figure B.5.4 illustrates a maximum point of each kind; the derivative at x_1 is 0 and the derivative at x_2 does not exist.

A similar argument holds for minimum values of $f(x)$, that is, the derivative at a minimum is 0, if it exists.   Note that minima and maxima are defined in terms of their neighborhoods (nearby values); for example, both $f(x_5)$ and $f(x_4)$ are minima, although $f(x_5) < f(x_4)$ and both are larger than values of $f(x)$ on the left side of the figure.

We have said that if $f(k)$ is a maximum or minimum and if $f'(k)$ exists, then $f'(k) = 0$.   On the other hand, it is not true that if $f'(k) = 0$ then $f(k)$ is necessarily a maximum or minimum.   For example, in Fig. B.5.4 $f'(x_3) = 0$, yet $f(x_3)$ is neither a maximum nor a minimum.

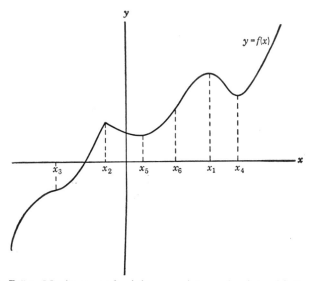

FIG. B.5.4. Maximum and minimum points, and points of inflection.

To find the maximum and minimum values of $f(x)$ we need merely differentiate, set $f'(x) = 0$, solve for the values of x satisfying this equation, and then examine $f(x)$ in the neighborhood of each solution to see whether the solution gives a maximum, a minimum, or neither.   For example, consider the function given by $f(x) = x^3/3 - x^2 - 3x + 3$.   Then $f'(x) = x^2 - 2x - 3$. Solving $x^2 - 2x - 3 = 0$ we obtain 3 and -1 as solutions.   Now compare $f(3)$ with $f(3 + \Delta)$ and $f(3 - \Delta)$, where Δ is small and positive.

$$f(3) = 9 - 9 - 9 + 3 = -6$$

$$f(3 + \Delta) = \frac{27 + 27\Delta + 9\Delta^2 + \Delta^3}{3} - (9 + 6\Delta + \Delta^2) - (9 + 3\Delta) + 3$$

$$= -6 + 2\Delta^2 + \Delta^3/3 > f(3) \qquad \text{as } \Delta > 0$$

$$f(3 - \Delta) = \frac{27 - 27\Delta + 9\Delta^2 + \Delta^3}{3} - (9 - 6\Delta + \Delta^2) - (9 - 3\Delta) + 3$$

$$= -6 + 2\Delta^2 - \Delta^3/3 > f(3) \qquad \text{for } \Delta < 1$$

Therefore, $f(3)$ is a minimum.   Similarly,

$$f(-1) = -\tfrac{1}{3} - 1 + 3 + 3 = 4\tfrac{2}{3}$$

$$f(-1 + \Delta) = \frac{-1 + 3\Delta - 3\Delta^2 + \Delta^3}{3} - (1 - 2\Delta + \Delta^2) + (3 - 3\Delta) + 3$$

$$= 4\tfrac{2}{3} - 2\Delta^2 + \Delta^3/3 < f(-1) \qquad \text{for } \Delta < 1$$

$$f(-1 - \Delta) = \frac{-1 - 3\Delta - 3\Delta^2 - \Delta^3}{3} - (1 + 2\Delta + \Delta^2) + (3 + 3\Delta) + 3$$

$$= 4\tfrac{2}{3} - 2\Delta^2 - \Delta^3/3 < f(-1)$$

Therefore $f(-1)$ is a maximum.

We could have saved a considerable amount of computation by considering that if a function changes from increasing to decreasing the derivative is changing from positive to negative and is therefore decreasing; thus the second derivative must be negative in this neighborhood.   Similarly, if the function changes from decreasing to increasing the second derivative must be positive. These arguments can be extended; if the first derivative at a given point is 0 and the second derivative is positive, then the first derivative is at that point changing from negative to positive (instead of, for example, merely decreasing to 0 and then increasing again, for then we would have to the left of the point a negative second derivative and on the right a positive second derivative), and the value of the function at that point is a minimum.   Similarly, if $f'(k) = 0$ and $f''(k) < 0$, then $f(k)$ is a maximum.

In the preceding example, $f''(x) = 2x - 2$; therefore, $f''(3) = 4$ and since $f'(3) = 0$, $f(3)$ is a minimum, as we found from our laborious computation. Also, $f''(-1) = -4$, and since $f'(-1) = 0$, $f(-1)$ is a maximum.

Note that if $f'(k) = 0$ and $f''(k) = 0$ we have a point on the curve such as $f(x_5)$ in Fig. B.5.4.   Any point k such that $f''(k) = 0$ is called a *point of inflection*.   If k is a point of inflection, it is not, of course, necessarily true that $f'(k) = 0$.   The point x_6 in Fig. B.5.4 is a point of inflection, but in this case the first derivative changes from increasing to decreasing but remains positive throughout.

B.6. Primitive Functions.   Consider any differentiable function f and its derivative f'.   The function f is called a *primitive function* of f'.   We say "a" rather than "the" because f' is always the derivative of more than one function.   In fact, any derivative has infinitely many primitive functions; let $h(x) \equiv f(x) + c$; then if f' is the derivative of f it is also the derivative of h, as $c' = 0$.

The differentiable function f is itself the derivative of some function; as a matter of fact, any continuous function has a primitive function and therefore infinitely many.   Let G be any function such that $G'(x) = f(x)$; then let $H(x) \equiv G(x) + c$; then $H'(x) = f(x)$ also, that is, any two functions differing only by a constant have the same primitive function.   The converse is also true; any two primitive functions of the same function must differ only by a constant.   Let $G'(x) = H'(x)$.   Then let $U(x) \equiv G(x) - H(x)$.   Then $U'(x) = G'(x) - H'(x) = 0$, that is, the rate of change of U with respect to x

is everywhere zero; this can happen, however, only if $G(x)$ and $H(x)$ differ only by a constant.

B.7. Indefinite Integrals. Consider any function f that is continuous over the range $-\infty < x < \infty$. We know already that the definite integral $\int_a^b f(x)\, dx$ exists, where $a \le b$. Note, however, that this integral exists for all values of b, letting b range over the same values as x. This means that the value of $\int_a^b f(x)\, dx$ depends upon (is a function of) b, considered as a variable. Substituting t for b (as the letter b ordinarily stands for a constant), we have $\int_a^t f(x)\, dx$, where $a \le t$. Obviously it makes no difference what letter we use for the variable following the integral sign, that is, we can write

$$\int_a^t f(x)\, dx = \int_a^t f(y)\, dy$$

meaning that if f remains the same the integrals have the same value. For example, $\int_a^t x^2\, dx = \int_a^t y^2\, dy$; $\int_a^t (1/z)\, dz = \int_a^t (1/w)\, dw$. If this is not clear the student should expand the integrals into the original limit notation and satisfy himself that our equations hold.

It is convenient in defining the indefinite integral of $f(x)$ to use the notation $\int_a^x f(u)\, du$ and to abbreviate this expression by $F(x)$; that is, $F(x) \equiv \int_a^x f(u)\, du$.

B.8. Fundamental Theorem of the Calculus. The fundamental theorem of the calculus states that the derivative of the indefinite integral

$$F(x) \left[\equiv \int_a^x f(u)\, du \right]$$

is equal to the value of $f(u)$ at the point x, that is, $F'(x) = f(x)$.

If we remember that $F(x)$ is the area under the curve $y = f(u)$ between the limits a and x, as represented in Fig. B.8.1, this theorem is intuitively plausible, for it states that the rate of change of the area at the point x is simply $f(x)$, the height of the curve.

Let M and m be respectively the maximum and minimum values of $f(u)$ in the interval between x and $x + \Delta u$. Then the area $F(x + \Delta u) - F(x)$ lies between $M \Delta u$ and $m \Delta u$, that is,

$$m \Delta u \le F(x + \Delta u) - F(x) \le M \Delta u$$

Therefore

$$m \le \frac{F(x + \Delta u) - F(x)}{\Delta u} \le M$$

Therefore

$$\lim_{\Delta u \to 0} m \le \lim_{\Delta u \to 0} \frac{F(x + \Delta u) - F(x)}{\Delta u} \le \lim_{\Delta u \to 0} M$$

Therefore

$$f(x) \le F'(x) \le f(x), \text{ implying } F'(x) = f(x)$$

This important theorem states that $F(x)$ is a primitive function of $f(x)$. As shown in Sec. B.6, any two primitive functions can differ only by a constant. Let $G(x)$ be a primitive function of $f(x)$, then $F(x) = G(x) + c$. Note that $F(a) = \int_a^a f(u)\, du = 0$. Then $F(a) = G(a) + c = 0$. Therefore, the indefinite integral

$$\int_a^x f(u)\, du \equiv F(x) = F(x) - 0 = F(x) - F(a) = G(x) + c - G(a) + c$$
$$= G(x) - G(a)$$

If we now consider the point x as fixed, the preceding result shows that to evaluate a definite integral $\int_a^b f(x)\, dx$ we need merely find a primitive function F such that $F' = f$; the value of the integral is $F(b) - F(a)$.

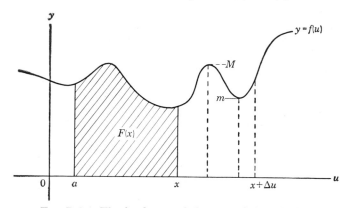

Fig. B.8.1. The fundamental theorem of the calculus.

It is because the indefinite integral of f is a primitive function of f that the customary notation $\int f(x)\, dx = F(x) + c$ is used. F is actually a primitive function, and c, the "constant of integration," expresses the fact that any two primitive functions can differ only by a constant.

B.9. Distribution Functions (Continuous Case). We define a cumulative distribution function F as any function F with the following properties:

F is defined over the range $-\infty < x < \infty$, that is, for all values of x.

F is monotonic nondecreasing, that is, if $x_1 < x_2$, then $F(x_1) \le F(x_2)$.

$\lim\limits_{x \to \infty} F(x) = 1.$

$\lim\limits_{x \to -\infty} F(x) = 0.$

If F is differentiable, its derivative f is a frequency function, or probability density function.   Note that if $F(a) = 0$, in which a is some value of x, then $f(x) = 0$ for all $x < a$; similarly, if $F(b) = 1$, then $f(x) = 0$ for all $x > b$.

Note also that since F is monotonic nondecreasing, $f(x) \geq 0$ for all values of x.

So far we have said nothing whatsoever about random variables or sampling theory.   The definitions of F and f are abstract mathematical definitions which show the properties which functions must have in order to qualify as distribution functions.   The reasons for choosing these properties become clear when we consider the informal meaning which we wish to give to $F(x)$, that is, the proportion of a population having values less than or equal to x. Obviously if $x_1 < x_2$ the proportion having at most the value x_1 cannot be greater than the proportion having at most the value x_2.   Therefore, we lay down the requirement that F is monotonic nondecreasing.   As the total proportion must be 1, we require that $\lim_{x \to \infty} F(x) = 1$; for an analogous reason we impose the requirement that $\lim_{x \to -\infty} F(x) = 0$.   It is not necessary to impose the additional requirement that $F(x) \geq 0$, because this is deducible from the other requirements.

The concept of a random variable X is introduced by the following definitions:

Probability $(X \leq x) = F(x)$.   [The probability that a random variable X will assume a value less than or equal to x is $F(x)$, where F has the properties previously described.]

Probability $(a \leq X \leq b) = F(b) - F(a)$.

The probability density of the random variable X is defined as $f(x)$, where f is the derivative of F.

B.10. Mathematical Expectation.   The mathematical expectation of any function of X, say $g(X)$, is defined as

$$E[g(X)] \equiv \int_R g(x)f(x)\, dx$$

Examples. 1. The expectation of X is $\int_R xf(x)\, dx$.

2. The expectation of X^2 is $\int_R x^2 f(x)\, dx$.

3. The expectation of $X - c$ is $\int_R (x - c)f(x)\, dx$.

Note that if g and h are two different functions,

$$E[g(X) + h(X)] \equiv \int_R [g(x) + h(x)]f(x)\, dx = \int_R g(x)f(x)\, dx + \int_R h(x)f(x)\, dx$$
$$= E[g(X)] + E[h(X)]$$

As the sum of two functions is itself a function, this implies that

$$E\left[\sum_{i=1}^{n} g_i(X) \right] = \sum_{i=1}^{n} E[g_i(X)]$$

for any functions $g_1, g_2, \ldots, g_n$. The student should satisfy himself that $E(aX + b) = aE(X) + b$, in which a and b are constants. These properties are summed up by the statement that E is a *linear operator*.

B.11. Power Series. An infinite series of the form

$$c_0 + c_1 x + c_2 x^2 + c_3 x^3 + \cdots + c_n x^n + \cdots$$

in which the c's are all constants is called a *power series*. There are many functions which can be written as power series, by a suitable choice of the constant coefficients. Let us assume that f is such a function, that is, that

$$f(x) = c_0 + c_1 x + c_2 x^2 + \cdots + c_n x^n + \cdots$$

Let us also assume that the nth derivative of f exists for all n, and that we can differentiate the terms of the infinite series just as we would a finite series. Then

$$f'(x) = c_1 + 2c_2 x + 3c_3 x^2 + \cdots + nc_n x^{n-1} + \cdots$$
$$f''(x) = 2c_2 + (3)(2)c_3 x + \cdots + (n)(n-1)c_n x^{n-2} + \cdots$$

$$\vdots \qquad\qquad \vdots$$

$$f^{(n)}(x) = n!c_n + (n+1)!c_{n+1}x + \cdots$$

Therefore,
$$f(0) = c_0$$
$$f'(0) = c_1$$
$$f''(0) = 2c_2 \qquad \text{or} \qquad c_2 = \frac{f''(0)}{2!}$$

$$\vdots$$

$$f^{(n)}(0) = n!c_n \qquad \text{or} \qquad c_n = \frac{f^{(n)}(0)}{n!}$$

Therefore,

$$f(x) = f(0) + f'(0)x + \frac{f''(0)}{2!}x^2 + \cdots + \frac{f^{(n)}(0)}{n!}x^n + \cdots$$

This series is called a *Taylor series*, after Brook Taylor (1685–1731), who discovered this method.

As an example consider the function given by $f(x) = e^x$. We have $f(0) = 1$; also

$$f'(x) = e^x \qquad \text{and} \qquad f'(0) = 1$$
$$f''(x) = e^x \qquad\qquad\qquad f''(0) = 1$$

$$\vdots \qquad\qquad\qquad\qquad \vdots$$

$$f^{(n)}(x) = e^x \qquad\qquad\qquad f^{(n)}(0) = 1$$

Therefore, $e^x = 1 + x + x^2/2! + x^3/3! + \cdots + x^n/n! + \cdots$

B.12. Moment-generating Functions.   Among the most important properties of a distribution are its moments.   The kth moment about the point c is
defined as $E[(X - c)^k]$.   The kth moment about the origin is thus $E(X^k)$.   It
is often convenient to find moments about the origin by means of the following
integral, called a *moment-generating function*.

$$E(e^{tX}) \equiv \int_R e^{tx} f(x) \, dx$$

To show that this integral provides a way of obtaining moments, we first
expand e^{tX} in a Taylor series:

$$E(e^{tX}) = E(1 + tX + t^2 X^2/2! + \cdots + t^k X^k/k! + \cdots)$$

Remembering that E is a linear operator and assuming that we can treat
this particular infinite series as though it were finite (this can be proved by
advanced methods), we obtain

$$E(e^{tX}) = 1 + tE(X) + \frac{t^2}{2!} E(X^2) + \cdots + \frac{t^k}{k!} E(X^k) + \cdots$$

Differentiating with respect to t, we obtain

$$E(X) + tE(X^2) + \frac{t^2}{2} E(X^3) + \cdots + \frac{t^{k-1}}{(k-1)!} E(X^k) + \cdots$$

For $t = 0$ the value of this series is $E(X)$.   Differentiating twice, we obtain

$$E(X^2) + tE(X^3) + \cdots + \frac{t^{k-2}}{(k-2)!} E(X^k) + \cdots$$

For $t = 0$ this becomes $E(X^2)$.   In general, by differentiating k times and
setting $t = 0$ we obtain $E(X^k)$.

As an example, the moment-generating function of $f(x) = e^{-x}$, $x \geq 0$, is

$$E(e^{tX}) \equiv \int_0^\infty e^{tx} e^{-x} \, dx = \int_0^\infty e^{x(t-1)} \, dx = \frac{e^{x(t-1)}}{t-1} \bigg|_0^\infty$$

As we are interested only in small values of t, we can consider t less than 1; the
evaluation of the definite integral is therefore

$$\frac{e^{-\infty}}{t-1} - \frac{e^0}{t-1} = 0 - \frac{1}{t-1} = (1-t)^{-1}$$

Then

$$\frac{d}{dt} (1-t)^{-1} = -1(1-t)^{-2}(-1) = (1-t)^{-2}$$

$$\frac{d^2}{dt^2} (1-t)^{-1} = 2(1-t)^{-3}$$

etc. Thus

$$E(X) = (1 - 0)^{-2} = 1$$
$$E(X^2) = 2(1 - 0)^{-3} = 2$$
$$\mu = 1$$
$$\sigma^2 = E(X^2) - [E(X)]^2 = 2 - 1 = 1$$

etc.

If two continuous distributions have the same moment-generating function, it is evident that they have the same moments. If they have the same moments, the two densities are the same. We shall prove this for the special case in which the difference of the densities can be expanded in a power series. Let the expansion of the difference be

$$f(x) - g(x) = c_0 + c_1 x + c_2 x^2 + \cdots + c_n x^n + \cdots$$

Then

$$\int_R [f(x) - g(x)]^2 \, dx = \int_R (c_0 + c_1 x + \cdots)[f(x) - g(x)] \, dx$$
$$= c_0 \int_R [f(x) - g(x)] \, dx + c_1 \int_R x[f(x) - g(x)] \, dx + \cdots$$
$$= c_0(1 - 1) + c_1 [E(X) - E(X)] + \cdots = 0$$

as all moments are assumed to be equal. But $[f(x) - g(x)]^2$ is necessarily either positive or zero, and since the integral is zero, it follows that $[f(x) - g(x)]^2$ is zero for every value of x and therefore that $f(x) = g(x)$ for all values. Thus if two distributions have the same moment-generating function the density functions are the same (though we have proved this only for a special case). It is this theorem which makes moment-generating functions so important in statistical theory, for often it is much easier to prove that two distributions have the same moment-generating function than to prove directly that their density functions are equal.

In theoretical work it is also useful to consider moment-generating functions of functions of X. Let g be any function; then the moment-generating function of g is defined as $E[e^{tg(X)}] \equiv \int_R e^{tg(x)} f(x) \, dx$.

B.13. Change of Variable. A device of great usefulness in many of the proofs that follow is that of change of variable. Suppose the distribution of the random variable X is given by $f(x)$. Now let Y be some monotonic increasing function of X, that is, $Y = g(X)$. What is the probability density of Y?

The probability that X will assume a value between x and $x + \Delta x$ is equal to the probability that Y will assume a value between y and $y + \Delta y$, where $y = g(x)$ and $y + \Delta y = g(x + \Delta x)$, that is,

$$\text{prob } (x \leq X \leq x + \Delta x) = \text{prob } (y \leq Y \leq y + \Delta y)$$

The probability density $f(y)$ is given by

$$f(y) \equiv \lim_{\Delta y \to 0} \frac{\text{prob } (y \leq Y \leq y + \Delta y)}{\Delta y} = \lim_{\Delta y \to 0} \frac{\text{prob } (x \leq X \leq x + \Delta x)}{\Delta y}$$

$$= \lim_{\Delta y \to 0} \frac{\text{prob } (x \leq X \leq x + \Delta x)}{\Delta x} \frac{\Delta x}{\Delta y}$$

Note that as $\Delta y \to 0$, $\Delta x \to 0$; thus the preceding expression is equal to[1]

$$\lim_{\Delta x \to 0} \frac{\text{prob } (x \leq X \leq x + \Delta x)}{\Delta x} \lim_{\Delta y \to 0} \frac{\Delta x}{\Delta y} \equiv f(x) \frac{dx}{dy}$$

We placed the restriction that Y be monotonic increasing in order that $\dfrac{dx}{dy}$ be positive, as obviously $f(y)$ must be positive or zero. This restriction can be removed by placing absolute value marks around $\dfrac{dx}{dy}$, that is, it can be proved that if Y is a monotonic function of X, $f(y) = f(x) \left| \dfrac{dx}{dy} \right|$.

B.14. Multiple Integration. Before discussing random sampling it is necessary to introduce multiple integration. Let z be a function of x and y, that is, $z = f(x,y)$. Suppose further that z is continuous for each point (a,b) in the xy plane, that is, $\lim_{\substack{x \to a \\ y \to b}} f(x,y) = f(a,b)$. Just as we defined the area under a curve as a definite integral, so we define the volume under a surface as a definite integral. Consider finding the volume between the xy plane and that part of the surface indicated in Fig. B.14.1. This will be the volume of the solid obtained by dropping perpendiculars from all points of the curve to the xy plane. We can make an approximation by dividing the solid into n slices parallel to the yz plane, each of length Δx, finding the approximate volume of each slice, and then adding the n volumes together. Consider the approximation to the volume of the ith slice, indicated in Fig. B.14.1. Divide this slice into m segments, each of length Δy. The volume of the ith slice will be approximated by the sum of the volumes of m prisms. The volume of the jth prism is $f(x_i,y_j) \, \Delta x \, \Delta y$, in which x_i is any value of x in the ith slice and y_j is any value of y in the jth segment. For the ith slice both Δx and x_i are constants, and the approximate volume is $\displaystyle\sum_{j=1}^{m} f(x_i,y_j) \, \Delta x \, \Delta y$. A better approximation is $\displaystyle\lim_{\substack{m \to \infty \\ \Delta y \to 0}} \sum_{j=1}^{m} f(x_i,y_j) \, \Delta x \, \Delta y$. Remembering that x_i and Δx are constants for the ith slice, this limit is a definite integral $\Delta x \displaystyle\int_{y_L}^{y_U} f(x_i,y) \, dy$, in which the

---

[1] This assumes that the limit of this product is the product of the respective limits. This can be proved by advanced methods.

limits of integration y_U and y_L are functions of x, that is, will depend upon the particular value x_i. The approximate sum of all slices is $\sum\limits_{i=1}^{n} \Delta x \int_{y_L}^{y_U} f(x_i,y)\, dy$.

As thinner and thinner slices are taken, that is, as $n \to \infty$ and $\Delta x \to 0$, the approximation becomes better, and we define the total volume as

$$\lim_{\substack{n \to \infty \\ \Delta x \to 0}} \sum_{i=1}^{n} \Delta x \int_{y_L}^{y_U} f(x_i,y)\, dy$$

abbreviated $\int_a^b dx \int_{y_L}^{y_U} f(x,y)\, dy$ or $\int_a^b \left[\int_{y_L}^{y_U} f(x,y)\, dy \right] dx$ or $\int_a^b \int_{y_L}^{y_U} f(x,y)\, dy\, dx$.
In performing the integration we integrate first with respect to y, treating x as

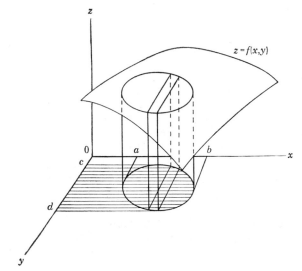

FIG. B.14.1. The volume under part of the surface $z = f(x,y)$.

a constant; then we integrate with respect to x. We could have begun by taking slices parallel to the xz plane, each of length Δy, in which case we would have ended with $\int_c^d \int_{x_L}^{x_U} f(x,y)\, dx\, dy$, with x_U and x_L being functions of y.

Example. Let $z = 2x + y$. What is the volume of the solid which is located between the xy plane and this surface and whose base is a circle given by the equation $x^2 + (y - b)^2 = r^2$? Solving for y, we obtain

$$y = b \pm \sqrt{r^2 - x^2}$$

For a given x, the limits of integration on y are therefore $b + \sqrt{r^2 - x^2}$ and $b - \sqrt{r^2 - x^2}$. The limits of integration on x are r and $-r$. The volume is

therefore

$$\int_{-r}^{r}\int_{b-\sqrt{r^2-x^2}}^{b+\sqrt{r^2-x^2}} (2x + y)\, dy\, dx = \int_{-r}^{r}\left[\left(2xy + \frac{y^2}{2}\right)\Big|_{b-\sqrt{r^2-x^2}}^{b+\sqrt{r^2-x^2}}\right] dx$$

$$= \int_{r}^{r}(4x\sqrt{r^2-x^2} + 2b\sqrt{r^2-x^2})\, dx = [-\tfrac{4}{3}(r^2 - x^2)^{3/2}$$

$$+ xb(r^2 - x^2)^{1/2} + br^2 \sin^{-1}(x/r)]\Big|_{-r}^{r}$$

in which the notation $\sin^{-1}(x/r)$ means the angle (in radians) whose sine is x/r. As there are 2π radians in a circle, $\sin^{-1}(1) = \pi/2$ and $\sin^{-1}(-1) = -\pi/2$. Thus the answer is $\pi b r^2$.*

In the special case $f(x,y) = f_1(x)f_2(y)$, that is, the case in which $f(x,y)$ is the product of two functions, each of only one variable, we have

$$\lim_{\substack{n\to\infty \\ \Delta x\to 0}} \sum_{i=1}^{n} \Delta x \int_{y_L}^{y_U} f(x_i,y)\, dy = \lim_{\substack{n\to\infty \\ \Delta x\to 0}} \sum_{i=1}^{n} \Delta x \int_{y_L}^{y_U} f_1(x_i)f_2(y)\, dy$$

$$= \lim_{\substack{n\to\infty \\ \Delta x\to 0}} \sum_{i=1}^{n} f_1(x_i)\, \Delta x \int_{y_L}^{y_U} f_2(y)\, dy = \int_{a}^{b} f_1(x)\, dx \int_{y_L}^{y_U} f_2(y)\, dy$$

In cases in which y_U and y_L are constants (that is, the same for all values of x, as when we find the volume between a surface and a rectangle in the xy plane), this latter product is the product of two ordinary single integrals.

As with the single integral, we can take the limit of the double integral as one or more of the limits approach zero; for example, $\int_{-\infty}^{\infty}\int_{-\infty}^{\infty} f(x,y)\, dy\, dx$ means

$$\lim_{\substack{b,y_U\to\infty \\ a,y_L\to-\infty}} \int_{a}^{b} \int_{y_L}^{y_U} f(x,y)\, dy\, dx.$$

Our definition can be extended to any number of variables. Let

$$z = f(x_1, x_2, \ldots, x_n)$$

in which each x_i is a variable. Further, let z be continuous at all points. Then $\lim_{\substack{\Delta x_1\to 0 \\ \Delta x_2\to 0}} \Sigma\Sigma \cdots \Sigma f(x_1, x_2, \ldots, x_n) \Delta x_1 \Delta x_2 \cdots \Delta x_n$ exists and is

$$\Delta x_n\to 0$$

abbreviated $\int_{R_{x_1}}\int_{R_{x_2}} \cdots \int_{R_{x_n}} f(x_1, x_2, \ldots, x_n)\, dx_1\, dx_2 \cdots dx_n$ in which R_{x_i} indicates the boundaries of x_i (the region of x_i) between which the integra-

* This answer, however, considers the volume *negative* for points such that $(2x + y) < 0$, i.e., all points of the solid below the xy plane. Actually, the volumes above and below the xy plane should be found seperately and then added, considering both positive.

tion is to be performed. As in the two-variable case, the integration is performed step by step and in any order desired. In performing each integration the fundamental theorem of the calculus is used, that is, that a definite integral is the difference between two values of a primitive function, remembering that in finding a primitive function each of the variables other than the variable of integration is treated as a constant.

It is a consequence of the definition that if g and f are any two continuous functions then the multiple integral of their sum is the sum of the two respective multiple integrals. Further, the integral of cf, c being any constant, is the product of c and the integral of f. That is,

$$\int\int \cdots \int (f + g)\Pi \, dx_i = \int\int \cdots \int f\Pi \, dx_i + \int\int \cdots \int g\Pi \, dx_i$$

and $\int\int \cdots \int cf\Pi \, dx_i = c\int\int \cdots \int f\Pi \, dx_i$, with $i = 1, 2, \ldots, n$. These two theorems are summed up in the statement that the multiple integral, like the single integral, is a *linear operator*.

Further, as in the two-variable case, if $f(x_1, x_2, \ldots, x_n) = \prod_{i=1}^{n} f_i(x_i)$, then

$$\int_{R_{x_1}}\int_{R_{x_2}} \cdots \int_{R_{x_n}} f(x_1, x_2, \ldots, x_n) \prod dx_i = \prod_{i=1}^{n} \int_{R_{x_i}} f_i(x_i) \, dx_i$$

and if the limits of integration are all constants, this is the product of n ordinary single integrals.

B.15. Joint Distributions of Random Variables. Let $f(x,y)$ be any function which is continuous for all values of x and y. Then f can be considered a joint density function if it satisfies the following conditions:

$f(x,y) \geq 0$ for all values of x and y

$$\int_{-\infty}^{\infty} \int_{-\infty}^{\infty} f(x,y) \, dx \, dy = 1$$

Now consider the two variables X and Y, whose values occur in pairs, that is, whenever X assumes a value x, Y assumes a value y. We call X and Y *random variables* when their joint probability density is given by a function of x and y that satisfies the two foregoing conditions, that is, probability density $(X = x; Y = y) = f(x,y)$.

Each of the variables X and Y will have its own probability density, which is obtained by integrating $f(x,y)$ on the other variable; that is, letting f_1 be the density function for X and f_2 the density function for Y, we have

$$f_1(x) = \int_{-\infty}^{\infty} f(x,y) \, dy$$

$$f_2(y) = \int_{-\infty}^{\infty} f(x,y) \, dx$$

Similarly, we can consider a joint density function for n random variables $X_1, X_2, \ldots, X_n$, satisfying the requirements

$$f(x_1, x_2, \ldots, x_n) \geq 0$$

$$\int_{-\infty}^{\infty} \int_{-\infty}^{\infty} \cdots \int_{-\infty}^{\infty} f(x_1, x_2, \ldots, x_n)\, dx_1\, dx_2 \cdots dx_n = 1$$

The density function f_i of the random variable X_i is obtained by integrating over all the other variables, that is,

$$f_i(x_i) = \int_{-\infty}^{\infty} \int_{-\infty}^{\infty} \cdots \int_{-\infty}^{\infty} f(x_1, x_2, \ldots, x_n)\, dx_1 \cdots dx_{i-1}\, dx_{i+1} \cdots dx_n$$

The $X_1, X_2, \ldots, X_n$ are *statistically independent* if and only if the joint density is the product of the individual densities, that is,

$$f(x_1, x_2, \ldots, x_n) = f_1(x_1)f_2(x_2) \cdots f_n(x_n)$$

Now we define a *random sample of size n* drawn from a population whose density function is f. Each member of the sample is considered a random variable X_i, $i = 1, 2, \ldots, n$. The sample is random if and only if the following two conditions hold:

1. The density function of each X_i is f. (This states in mathematical terminology the requirement that each member of the population has equal likelihood of being included in the sample.)

2. The joint density function g of the X_i is the product of their individual densities, that is, they are statistically independent, or

$$g(x_1, x_2, \ldots, x_n) = f(x_1)f(x_2) \cdots f(x_n)$$

(This second statement is equivalent to the requirement that the likelihood of inclusion of one member is unaffected by the inclusion of any other member, that is, that the members are drawn independently.)

As in the case of a single random variable, the mathematical expectation of a function of n random variables is defined as

$$E[g(X_1, X_2, \ldots, X_n)]$$
$$= \int_{R_1} \int_{R_2} \cdots \int_{R_n} g(x_1, x_2, \ldots, x_n)f(x_1, x_2, \ldots, x_n) \prod dx_i$$

in which R_i is the entire range $-\infty$ to ∞.

Note that if $g_1, g_2, \ldots, g_k$ are k functions of the n random variables, then

$$E\left(\sum_{i=1}^{k} g_i\right) = \sum_{i=1}^{k} E(g_i).$$ Further, if a and b are constants,

$$E[(ag(X_1, X_2, \ldots, X_n) + b] = aE[g(X_1, X_2, \ldots, X_n)] + b$$

The student should prove both these statements as exercises. As in the single variable case, E is a linear operator.

We can also define the moment-generating function of a function g of n random variables as $E[e^{g(X_1, X_2, \ldots, X_n)t}]$. A useful theorem is that the moment-generating function of the sum of n independent random variables is the product of their individual moment-generating functions, that is,

$$E[e^{(\Sigma X_i)t}] = \Pi E[e^{X_i t}]$$

Proof

$$E[e^{(\Sigma X_i)t}] \equiv \int\!\!\int \cdots \int e^{(\Sigma X_i)t} f(x_1, x_2, \ldots, x_n)\, dx_1\, dx_2 \cdots dx_n$$
$$= \int\!\!\int \cdots \int \Pi e^{X_i t} f_i(x_i)\, dx_i = \Pi \int e^{X_i t} f_i(x_i)\, dx_i = \Pi E[e^{X_i t}]$$

B.16. Expectation of Sample Moments About the Origin. Consider drawing a random sample $X_1, X_2, \ldots X_n$ from a population with density function f. Let g be any continuous function; then

$$E\left[\sum_{i=1}^{n} g(X_i) \right] = nE[g(X)]$$

Proof. This is merely a special case of the theorem stated in Sec. B.15, that

$$E\left[\sum_{i=1}^{k} g_i \right] = \sum_{i=1}^{k} [E(g_i)].$$

In this special case $k = n$ and

$$g_i(X_1, X_2, \ldots, X_n) = c_1 g(X_1) + c_2 g(X_2) + \cdots + c_j g(X_j) + \cdots + c_n g(X_n)$$

with $c_i = 1$ and $c_j = 0$ for all $j \neq i$. We therefore have

$$E\left[\sum_{i=1}^{n} g(X_i) \right] = \sum_{i=1}^{n} E[g(X_i)]$$

Remembering that in a random sample the density function of each X_i is f, the density function of a member X picked at random from the population, then $E[g(X_i)] = E[g(X)]$; therefore $\displaystyle\sum_{i=1}^{n} E[g(X_i)] = nE[g(X)]$.

Corollary

$$E\left[\frac{\Sigma (X_i)^k}{n} \right] = \frac{1}{n} nE(X^k) = E(X^k)$$

that is, the expected (mean) value of a sample moment about the origin is the corresponding population moment. This is what is meant by saying that the sample moments about the origin are unbiased estimates of the corresponding population moments. It does not follow that sample moments about the sample mean are unbiased estimates of moments about the population mean; in fact, the latter statement is not true.

B.17. Mean and Variance of the Sum of Independent Random Variables. Consider the sum of n independent random variables, $X_1, X_2, \ldots, X_n$, with X_i drawn from a population with mean μ_i and variance σ_i^2. The mean value (expectation) of the sum S is the sum of the population means and the variance of S is the sum of the population variances, that is,

$$\mu_S = \sum_{i=1}^{n} \mu_i$$

$$\sigma_S^2 = \sum_{i=1}^{n} \sigma_i^2$$

Proof. The first statement is a special case of the theorem

$$E\left[\sum_{i=1}^{k} g_i\right] = \sum_{i=1}^{k} E(g_i)$$

with $k = n$ and $g_i = \sum_{j=1}^{n} c_j X_j$ with $c_i = 1$ and $c_j = 0$ for all $j \neq i$. That is,

$E(\Sigma X_i) = \Sigma E(X_i) = \Sigma \mu_i$. To prove the second we expand as follows:

$$E[S - E(S)]^2 = E\{S^2 - 2SE(S) + [E(S)]^2\} = E(S^2) - [E(S)]^2$$

$$= E\left(\sum X_i\right)^2 - \left(\sum \mu_i\right)^2 = E\left(\sum X_i^2 + \sum_{i \neq j} X_i X_j\right)$$

$$-\left(\sum \mu_i^2 + \sum_{i \neq j} \mu_i \mu_j\right) = \sum E(X_i^2) + \sum_{i \neq j} E(X_i X_j) - \sum \mu_i^2 - \sum_{i \neq j} \mu_i \mu_j$$

As X_i and X_j (with $j \neq i$) are independent,

$$E(X_i X_j) = \int\int x_i x_j f(x_i, x_j) \, dx_i \, dx_j = \int x_i f_i(x_i) \, dx_i \int x_j f_j(x_j) \, dx_j$$
$$= E(X_i)E(X_j) = \mu_i \mu_j$$

We are left with $\Sigma E(X_i^2) - \Sigma \mu_i^2 = \Sigma[E(X_i^2) - \mu_i^2] = \Sigma \sigma_i^2$.

B.18. The Law of Large Numbers. Consider drawing a random sample $X_1, X_2, \ldots, X_n$ from a population with density function f and mean μ and variance σ^2. Then $\sigma_m^2 = \sigma^2/n$, that is, the variance of the sample mean m is the population variance divided by the size of the sample.

Proof

$$\sigma_m^2 \equiv E[m - E(m)]^2 = E(m - \mu)^2 = E\left(\frac{\Sigma x_i}{n} - \mu\right)^2$$

$$= E\left(\frac{\Sigma x_i - n\mu}{n}\right)^2 = \frac{1}{n^2} E\left[\sum (x_i - \mu)\right]^2$$

$$= \frac{1}{n^2} E\left[\sum (x_i - \mu)^2 + \sum_{i \neq j} (x_i - \mu)(x_j - \mu)\right]$$

$$= \frac{1}{n^2} \sum E(x_i - \mu)^2 + \frac{1}{n^2} \sum_{i \neq j} E[(x_i - \mu)(x_j - \mu)]$$

$$= \frac{1}{n^2} n\sigma^2 + \frac{1}{n^2} 2C_2^n E[(x_i - \mu)(x_j - \mu)]$$

But

$$\begin{aligned}
E[(x_i - \mu)(x_j - \mu)] &= \iint (x_i - \mu)(x_j - \mu)f(x_i)f(x_j) \, dx_i \, dx_j \\
&= \int (x_i - \mu)f(x_i) \, dx_i \int (x_, - \mu)f(x_j) \, dx_j \\
&= E(x_i - \mu)E(x_j - \mu) = 0
\end{aligned}$$

We are left with σ^2/n. As $n \to \infty$, $\sigma^2/n \to 0$; thus, as $E(m) = \mu$, m becomes an increasingly good estimate of μ as n increases; in fact, the probability that m will diverge from μ by more than a fixed amount approaches 0 as n approaches infinity. This is what is meant by saying that m converges *stochastically* to μ or that m is a *consistent* estimate of μ.

Actually, we could have proved our theorem by utilizing the previous theorem that the variance of the sum of n independent random variables is the sum of the variances and then observing that as $m = S/n$, $\sigma_m^2 = \sigma_s^2/n^2$; the details are left to the student.

B.19. Tchebysheff's Inequality. Consider drawing a random sample of size n from a population with density function f, mean μ, and variance σ^2. Then $P(|m - \mu| > b) < \sigma^2/nb^2$, that is, the probability that the sample mean m will diverge from the population mean μ by an amount greater than b is less than σ^2/nb^2.

Proof. Let the density function of the sample mean be g. Then

$$\sigma_m^2 \equiv \int_{-\infty}^{\infty} (m - \mu)^2 g(m) \, dm = \sigma^2/n$$

as proved previously. Let c be any positive number, and break up the integral into three parts:

$$\int_{-\infty}^{\mu - (c\sigma/\sqrt{n})} (m - \mu)^2 g(m) \, dm + \int_{\mu - (c\sigma/\sqrt{n})}^{\mu + (c\sigma/\sqrt{n})} (m - \mu)^2 g(m) \, dm$$
$$+ \int_{\mu + (c\sigma/\sqrt{n})}^{\infty} (m - \mu)^2 g(m) \, dm = \sigma^2/n$$

In the first integral we now replace $(m - \mu)^2$ by $c^2\sigma^2/n$. This substitution will reduce the value of this integral, because, in the range of integration, $m < \mu - (c\sigma/\sqrt{n})$ and thus $m - \mu < - (c\sigma/\sqrt{n})$; remembering that c, σ, and n are all positive and therefore both sides of this inequality are negative we have $|m - \mu| > c\sigma/\sqrt{n}$ and thus $(m - \mu)^2 > c^2\sigma^2/n$. Similarly, in the third integral we replace $(m - \mu)^2$ by $c^2\sigma^2/n$; by the same argument it can be shown that this substitution reduces the value of this integral. As $(m - \mu)^2$ and $g(m)$ are both positive, the value of the second integral must be positive. We have, therefore, $c^2\sigma^2/n \left[\int_{-\infty}^{\mu-(c\sigma/\sqrt{n})} g(m)\, dm + \int_{\mu+(c\sigma/\sqrt{n})}^{\infty} g(m)\, dm \right] < \sigma^2/n$.

But $\int_{-\infty}^{\mu-(c\sigma/\sqrt{n})} g(m)\, dm = \text{prob } (m < \mu - c\sigma/\sqrt{n}) = P(m - \mu < - c\sigma/\sqrt{n})$.

Similarly, $\int_{\mu+(c\sigma/\sqrt{n})}^{\infty} g(m)\, dm = P(m > \mu + c\sigma/\sqrt{n}) = P(m - \mu > c\sigma/\sqrt{n})$.

As we are dealing with mutually exclusive events, the sum of these two probabilities is $P(|m - \mu| > c\sigma/\sqrt{n})$. Thus $c^2 P(|m - \mu| > c\sigma/\sqrt{n}) < 1$, or $P(|m - \mu| > c\sigma/\sqrt{n}) < 1/c^2$. Let $b = c\sigma/\sqrt{n}$; then $1/c^2 = \sigma^2/nb^2$. Therefore $P(|m - \mu| > b) < \sigma^2/nb^2$.

B.20. Expectation of the Sample Variance. Consider drawing a random sample X_i, $i = 1, 2, \ldots, n$, from a population with density function f, mean μ, and variance σ^2. Let m and s^2 be the sample mean and variance respectively; then $E(s^2) = \sigma^2(n - 1)/n$.

Proof

$$E(s^2) = E\left[\frac{\Sigma(X_i - m)^2}{n}\right] = \frac{1}{n} E\left[\sum (X_i^2 - 2mX_i + m^2)\right]$$

$$= \frac{1}{n} E\left(\sum X_i^2 - 2m\sum X_i + nm^2\right) = \frac{1}{n} E\left(\sum X_i^2 - 2nm^2 + nm^2\right)$$

$$= \frac{1}{n} E\left(\sum X_i^2 - nm^2\right) = \frac{1}{n} nE(X^2) - E(m^2) = E(X^2) - E(m^2)$$

For any random variable Y, $E[Y - E(Y)]^2 = E(Y^2) - [E(Y)]^2$. In particular, $E(X^2) = \sigma^2 + \mu^2$ and $E(m^2) = \sigma_m^2 + \mu_m^2 = \sigma^2/n + \mu^2$. Therefore, $E(s^2) = \sigma^2 + \mu^2 - \sigma^2/n - \mu^2 = \sigma^2(1 - 1/n) = \sigma^2\left(\dfrac{n - 1}{n}\right)$.

Corollary. $E[s^2 n/(n - 1)] = \sigma^2$; that is, $s^2 n/(n - 1)$ is an unbiased estimate of σ^2.

B.21. Properties of Normal Distributions. The function

$$f(x) = \frac{1}{\sqrt{2\pi}\, k} e^{-(\frac{1}{2}k^2)(x-c)^2}$$

with k positive is suitable as a density function, that is, $f(x) \geq 0$ and

$$\int_{-\infty}^{\infty} f(x)\, dx = 1$$

Proof.   Clearly $f(x) \geq 0$, as $1/\sqrt{2\pi}\ k$ is positive and any power of e is positive.   To prove the second part let $y = (x - c)/k$, then

$$f(y) = f(x) \left| \frac{dx}{dy} \right| = f(x)k = \frac{1}{\sqrt{2\pi}} e^{-(y^2/2)}$$

We need only prove that $\int_{-\infty}^{\infty} e^{-(y^2/2)}\ dy = \sqrt{2\pi}$.   Unfortunately we can give only a partial proof.   Take

$$\left[\int_{-\infty}^{\infty} e^{-(y^2/2)}\ dy \right]^2 = \int_{-\infty}^{\infty} e^{-(y^2/2)}\ dy \int_{-\infty}^{\infty} e^{-(z^2/2)}\ dz$$

$$= \int_{-\infty}^{\infty} \int_{-\infty}^{\infty} e^{-(1/2)(y^2+z^2)}\ dy\ dz$$

The pair of values (y,z) can be considered as a point in the yz plane.   Then $y = r\cos\theta$, $z = r\sin\theta$, as shown in Fig. B.21.1 (this is called a transformation

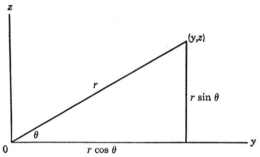

FIG. B.21.1. Transformation of rectangular coordinates (y,z) to polar coordinates (r,θ).

to *polar coordinates*).   Then $y^2 + z^2 = r^2(\cos^2\theta + \sin^2\theta) = r^2$.   We state without proof[1] that $dy\ dz = r\ dr\ d\theta$.   As y and z range from $-\infty$ to ∞, r ranges from 0 to ∞ and θ from 0 to 2π (radians).   Thus the double integral becomes

$$\int_0^{2\pi} \int_0^{\infty} re^{-(r^2/2)}\ dr\ d\theta = \int_0^{2\pi} \left[-e^{-(r^2/2)} \Big|_0^{\infty} \right] d\theta = \int_0^{2\pi} d\theta = 2\pi$$

Therefore $\quad \int_{-\infty}^{\infty} e^{-(y^2/2)}\ dy = \sqrt{2\pi} \quad$ and $\quad \int_{-\infty}^{\infty} \frac{1}{\sqrt{2\pi}} e^{-(y^2/2)}\ dy = 1$

---

[1] In making a joint transformation of two variables the Jacobian is used, that is,

$$dy\ dz = \begin{vmatrix} \dfrac{\partial y}{\partial r} & \dfrac{\partial y}{\partial \theta} \\[2mm] \dfrac{\partial z}{\partial r} & \dfrac{\partial z}{\partial \theta} \end{vmatrix} dr\ d\theta.$$ Good discussions of the Jacobian are given by Fry (7)

and Courant (1).

The moment-generating function of a distribution with density given by

$$f(x) = \frac{1}{\sqrt{2\pi}\, k}\, e^{-(1/2k^2)(x-c)^2} \text{ is } e^{ct+(k^2t^2/2)}.$$

Proof

$$E(e^{tx}) \equiv \int_{-\infty}^{\infty} \frac{1}{\sqrt{2\pi}\, k}\, e^{tx} e^{-(1/2k^2)(x-c)^2}\, dx$$

$$= \int_{-\infty}^{\infty} \frac{1}{\sqrt{2\pi}\, k}\, e^{-\frac{1}{2k^2}(x^2 - 2cx + c^2) + tx - \left(ct + \frac{k^2t^2}{2}\right) + \left(ct + \frac{k^2t^2}{2}\right)}\, dx$$

$$= e^{ct + \frac{k^2t^2}{2}} \int_{-\infty}^{\infty} \frac{1}{\sqrt{2\pi}\, k}\, e^{-\frac{1}{2k^2}(x^2 - 2cx + c^2 - 2k^2tx + 2k^2ct + k^4t^2)}\, dx$$

$$= e^{ct + \frac{k^2t^2}{2}} \int_{-\infty}^{\infty} \frac{1}{\sqrt{2\pi}\, k}\, e^{-\frac{1}{2k^2}[x - (c + k^2t)]^2}\, dx$$

As $c + k^2t$ is a constant, the function under the integral is in normal form; therefore the integral must have the value 1, and we are left with

$$E(e^{tx}) = e^{ct + \frac{k^2t^2}{2}}$$

Corollary. $\mu = c.$

Proof

$$\frac{dE(e^{tx})}{dt} = e^{ct + \frac{k^2t^2}{2}} (c + k^2t)$$

Letting $t = 0$ we obtain $1(c + 0) = c.$

Corollary. $\sigma^2 = k^2.$

Proof.   To find $E(X^2)$ we take

$$\frac{d^2E(e^{tx})}{dt^2} = e^{ct + \frac{k^2t^2}{2}} (k^2) + (c + k^2t) \frac{dE(e^{tx})}{dt}$$

Letting $t = 0$, we obtain $1(k^2) + (c)(c) = k^2 + c^2.$ Then

$$\sigma^2 = E(X^2) - [E(X)]^2 = k^2 + c^2 - c^2 = k^2$$

Thus we can write the normal density function as

$$f(x) = \frac{1}{\sqrt{2\pi}\, \sigma}\, e^{-\frac{1}{2\sigma^2}(x - \mu)^2}$$

Note that in the important special case $\mu = 0$, $\sigma = 1$, $E(e^{tx}) = e^{-t^2/2}.$

In any normal distribution the amount of probability in the interval μ to $\mu + b\sigma$ depends only upon b, that is,

$$\int_{\mu_1}^{\mu_1 + b\sigma_1} \phi(\mu_1, \sigma_1^2)\, dx = \int_{\mu_2}^{\mu_2 + b\sigma_2} \phi(\mu_2, \sigma_2^2)\, dx$$

for any μ_1, μ_2, σ_1, σ_2, in which ϕ means the normal function.

Proof.   Let $Y = \dfrac{X - \mu_1}{\sigma_1}$; then

$$f(y) = f(x)\left|\frac{dx}{dy}\right| = \frac{1}{\sqrt{2\pi}}\, e^{-y^2/2}$$

As x ranges from μ_1 to $\mu_1 + b\sigma_1$, y ranges from 0 to b; thus

$$\int_{\mu_1}^{\mu_1+b\sigma_1} \phi(\mu_1,\sigma_1^2)\, dx = \int_0^b \phi(0,1)\, dy$$

and the latter integral is obviously independent of the values of μ_1 and σ_1.

Any linear transformation leaves the functional form of a normal distribution unchanged, that is, if X is distributed with density $\phi(\mu, \sigma^2)$, and if $Y = aX + b$, then Y is distributed with density $\phi(a\mu + b, a^2\sigma^2)$.

Proof

$$\begin{aligned}
f(y) = f(x)\left|\frac{dx}{dy}\right| &= \frac{1}{\sqrt{2\pi}\,\sigma}\, e^{-\frac{1}{2\sigma^2}(x-\mu)^2}\, \frac{1}{|a|} \\
&= \frac{1}{\sqrt{2\pi}\,|a|\sigma}\, e^{-\frac{1}{2\sigma^2}\left(\frac{y-b}{a}-\mu\right)^2} \\
&= \frac{1}{\sqrt{2\pi}\,|a|\sigma}\, e^{-\frac{1}{2a^2\sigma^2}[y-(a\mu+b)]^2}
\end{aligned}$$

which is in normal form, with $c = a\mu + b$ and $k = |a|\sigma$.

The sum of n independent normally distributed random variates is itself normally distributed with mean equal to the sum of the means and variance equal to the sum of the variances, that is, if X_i is distributed according to $\phi(\mu_i, \sigma_i^2)\, i = 1, 2, \ldots, n$, and if all X_i are independent of each other, then ΣX_i is distributed according to $\phi(\Sigma\mu_i, \Sigma\sigma_i^2)$.

Proof.   We have proved in Sec. B.15 that the moment-generating function of the sum of n independent random variables is the product of their individual moment-generating functions, that is, $E[e^{(\Sigma X_i)t}] = \Pi E[e^{X_i t}]$. In this case $E[e^{X_i t}] = e^{\mu_i t + \sigma_i^2 t^2/2}$. Thus $E[e^{(\Sigma X_i)t}] = e^{(\Sigma\mu_i)t + (\Sigma\sigma_i^2)t^2/2}$, which is the moment-generating function for a normal distribution with mean $\Sigma\mu_i$ and variance $\Sigma\sigma_i^2$.

If X is normally distributed with mean μ_X and variance σ_X^2 and Y is normally distributed with mean μ_Y and variance σ_Y^2, and if X and Y are independent, then $X - Y$ is normally distributed with mean $\mu_X - \mu_Y$ and variance $\sigma_X^2 + \sigma_Y^2$.

Proof.   As X and Y are independent, X and Z are also independent, where $Z \equiv -Y$. Then

$$\begin{aligned}
E[e^{(X-Y)t}] = E[e^{(X+Z)t}] = E(e^{Xt})E(e^{Zt}) &= e^{\mu_x t + \sigma_x^2 t^2/2}e^{\mu_z t + \sigma_z^2 t^2/2} \\
&= e^{(\mu_x + \mu_z)t + (\sigma_x^2 + \sigma_z^2)t^2/2} = e^{(\mu_x - \mu_y)t + (\sigma_x^2 + \sigma_y^2)t^2/2}
\end{aligned}$$

which is the moment-generating function of a normal distribution with mean $\mu_x - \mu_y$ and variance $\sigma_x^2 + \sigma_y^2$.

B.22. Properties of Chi-square Distributions. In the text chi square with n degrees of freedom was defined as the sum of the squares of n independent random variates each distributed according to $\phi(0,1)$. It is more customary to define chi square as the random variate with the density given by

$$f(\chi_n^2) = \frac{1}{2^{(n/2)}\Gamma(n/2)} \, (\chi_n^2)^{(n/2)-1} e^{-\chi_n^2/2}$$

in which $\Gamma(n/2)$ is the gamma function, defined by $\Gamma(k) \equiv \int_0^\infty x^{k-1} e^{-x} \, dx$. We shall use this conventional definition and show that the moment-generating function is $(1 - 2t)^{-n/2}$. Let $z \equiv \chi_n^2$, then

$$E(e^{zt}) \equiv \int_0^\infty e^{zt} f(z) \, dz$$

$$= \frac{1}{2^{(n/2)}\Gamma(n/2)} \int_0^\infty e^{zt} z^{(n/2)-1} e^{-(z/2)} \, dz$$

$$= \frac{1}{2^{(n/2)}\Gamma(n/2)} \int_0^\infty e^{-(z/2)(1-2t)} z^{(n/2)-1} \, dz$$

Let $w \equiv (z/2)(1 - 2t)$; then $z = 2w/(1 - 2t)$ and $\dfrac{dz}{dw} = 2/(1 - 2t)$; thus

$$E(e^{zt}) = \frac{1}{2^{(n/2)}\Gamma(n/2)} \int_0^\infty e^{-w}(1 - 2t)^{1-(n/2)} 2^{(n/2)-1} w^{(n/2)-1}(1 - 2t)^{-1} 2 \, dw$$

$$= \frac{(1 - 2t)^{-(n/2)}}{\Gamma(n/2)} \int_0^\infty e^{-w} w^{(n/2)-1} \, dw = (1 - 2t)^{-n/2}$$

as the integral is by definition $\Gamma(n/2)$.

The moments of the χ_n^2 distribution are obtained from the moment-generating function as follows:

$$\frac{d(1 - 2t)^{-n/2}}{dt} = n(1 - 2t)^{-(n/2)-1}$$

Setting $t = 0$, we have $E(\chi_n^2) = n$. Differentiating again, we have

$$\frac{d^2(1 - 2t)^{-n/2}}{dt^2} = n(n + 2)(1 - 2t)^{-(n/2)-2}$$

Setting $t = 0$, we have $E[(\chi_n^2)^2] = n^2 + 2n$; then $\sigma^2 = n^2 + 2n - n^2 = 2n$.

The sum of squares of n independent random variates, each distributed according to $\phi(0,1)$, has the moment-generating function $(1 - 2t)^{-n/2}$ and therefore has the χ_n^2 distribution.

Proof. Let $Y \equiv \Sigma X_i^2$, each X_i being distributed according to $\phi(0,1)$, and each being independent of the others. Then

$$E(e^{Yt}) = \Pi E(e^{X_i^2 t}) = [E(e^{X^2 t})]^n$$

But
$$E(e^{X^2 t}) \equiv \int_{-\infty}^{\infty} e^{x^2 t} \phi(0,1) \, dx = \int_{-\infty}^{\infty} e^{x^2 t} \frac{1}{\sqrt{2\pi}} e^{-(x^2/2)} \, dx$$

$$= \frac{1}{\sqrt{2\pi}} \int_{-\infty}^{\infty} e^{-(x^2/2)(1-2t)} \, dx$$

Let $w \equiv x(1 - 2t)^{\frac{1}{2}}$, then
$$\frac{dx}{dw} = (1 - 2t)^{-\frac{1}{2}}$$
and
$$E(e^{X^2 t}) = \frac{(1 - 2t)^{-\frac{1}{2}}}{\sqrt{2\pi}} \int_{-\infty}^{\infty} e^{-(w^2/2)} \, dw = (1 - 2t)^{-\frac{1}{2}}$$

as the integral has the value $\sqrt{2\pi}$ [or, we could put the denominator under the integral and observe that under the integral we would have the function $\phi(0,1)$, thus making the integral 1]. Thus $E(e^{Yt}) = (1 - 2t)^{-n/2}$, and therefore Y is distributed as χ_n^2.

If χ_m^2 and χ_n^2 are distributed independently, then $\chi_m^2 + \chi_n^2$ is distributed as χ_{m+n}^2.

Proof

$$E[e^{(\chi_m^2 + \chi_n^2)t}] = E(e^{\chi_m^2 t}) E(e^{\chi_n^2 t}) = (1 - 2t)^{-m/2}(1 - 2t)^{-n/2} = (1 - 2t)^{-(m+n)/2}$$

which is the moment-generating function for χ_{m+n}^2.

B.23. Distribution of t_n. If X is normally distributed with zero mean and unit variance and Y is independently distributed as χ_n^2, then the distribution of $t_n \equiv \dfrac{X}{\sqrt{Y/n}}$ is given by

$$f(t_n) = \frac{1}{\sqrt{n\pi} \, \Gamma(n/2)} \Gamma\left(\frac{n+1}{2}\right) \left(\frac{t^2}{n} + 1\right)^{-(n+1)/2}$$

Proof

$$f(x,y) = f(x)f(y) = \frac{1}{\sqrt{2\pi}} e^{-(x^2/2)} \frac{1}{2^{n/2}\Gamma(n/2)} y^{(n/2)-1} e^{-y/2}$$

$$= \frac{1}{\sqrt{2\pi} \, 2^{n/2}\Gamma(n/2)} y^{(n/2)-1} e^{-(x^2+y)/2}$$

Let $t \equiv \dfrac{x}{\sqrt{y/n}}$ be a change of variable, holding y fixed; also let

$$c \equiv \frac{1}{\sqrt{2\pi} \, 2^{n/2}\Gamma(n/2)}$$

Then
$$f(t,y) = f(x,y) \left| \frac{dx}{dt} \right| = cy^{(n-1)/2} e^{-(t^2 y + ny)/2n} n^{-\frac{1}{2}}$$

Then
$$f(:) = \int_{R_y} f(t,y) \, dy = cn^{-\frac{1}{2}} \int_0^{\infty} y^{(n-1)/2} e^{-(t^2 y + ny)/2n} \, dy$$

Now let $w \equiv (t^2 y + ny)/2n$, holding t fixed; then

$$f(t) = \int_0^\infty f(t,w)\, dw$$

$$= c2^{(n+1)/2}n^{-\frac{1}{2}} \left(\frac{t^2}{n} + 1\right)^{-(n+1)/2} \int_0^\infty w^{(n+1)/2-1}e^{-w}\, dw$$

$$= c2^{(n+1)/2}n^{-\frac{1}{2}} \left(\frac{t^2}{n} + 1\right)^{-(n+1)/2}\Gamma\left(\frac{n+1}{2}\right)$$

$$= \frac{1}{\sqrt{n\pi}\,\Gamma(n/2)}\,\Gamma\left(\frac{n+1}{2}\right)\left(\frac{t^2}{n} + 1\right)^{-(n+1)/2}$$

B.24. Distribution of $F_{m,n}$. If X and Y are independently distributed as χ_m^2 and χ_n^2 respectively, then the distribution of $F_{m,n} \equiv \dfrac{X/m}{Y/n}$ is given by

$$f(F_{m,n}) = \frac{\Gamma\left(\dfrac{m+n}{2}\right)}{\Gamma\left(\dfrac{m}{2}\right)\Gamma\left(\dfrac{n}{2}\right)}\left(\frac{m}{n}\right)^{m/2}F^{\frac{m}{2}-1}\left(1 + \frac{m}{n}F\right)^{-(m+n)/2}$$

Proof

$$f(x,y) = f(x)f(y) = \frac{1}{2^{m/2}\Gamma(m/2)2^{n/2}\Gamma(n/2)}\,x^{\frac{m}{2}-1}y^{\frac{n}{2}-1}e^{-(x+y)/2}$$

Let

$$c \equiv \frac{1}{2^{m/2}\Gamma(m/2)2^{n/2}\Gamma(n/2)} \qquad \text{and} \qquad w \equiv x/y$$

with y fixed. Then $f(w,y) = f(x,y)\left|\dfrac{dx}{dw}\right|$

and

$$f(w) = \int_0^\infty f(w,y)\, dy = cw^{\frac{m}{2}-1}\int_0^\infty y^{\frac{m+n}{2}-1}e^{-(y/2)(w+1)}\, dy$$

Letting $z \equiv (y/2)(w+1)$, with w fixed, then

$$f(w) = cw^{\frac{m}{2}-1}(w+1)^{-(m+n)/2}2^{(m+n)/2}\int_0^\infty z^{\frac{m+n}{2}-1}e^{-z}\, dz$$

$$= c2^{(m+n)/2}\Gamma\left(\frac{m+n}{2}\right)w^{\frac{m}{2}-1}(w+1)^{-(m+n)/2}$$

Let

$$F_{m,n} \equiv \frac{x/m}{y/n} = \frac{n}{m}\,w$$

Then

$$f(F_{m,n}) = f(w)\frac{m}{n} = \frac{\Gamma\left(\dfrac{m+n}{2}\right)}{\Gamma\left(\dfrac{m}{2}\right)\Gamma\left(\dfrac{n}{2}\right)}\left(\frac{m}{n}\right)^{m/2}F^{\frac{m}{2}-1}\left(1 + \frac{m}{n}F\right)^{-(m+n)/2}$$

B.25. The Linear Mean Regression Line. Let X and Y be jointly distributed random variates; then to determine a linear function $Y_p = aX + b$ such that $E(Y - Y_p)^2$ is a minimum we set $a = \rho_{xy} \dfrac{\sigma_y}{\sigma_x}$ and

$$b = \mu_y - \rho_{xy} \frac{\sigma_y}{\sigma_x} \mu_x$$

Proof

$$
\begin{aligned}
E(Y - Y_p)^2 &= E(Y^2 - 2YY_p + Y_p^2) = E(Y^2) - 2E(YY_p) + E(Y_p^2) \\
&= E(Y^2) - 2E(aXY + bY) + E(a^2X^2 + 2abX + b^2) \\
&= E(Y^2) - 2aE(XY) - 2bE(Y) + a2E(X^2) + 2abE(X) + b^2
\end{aligned}
$$

Differentiating with respect to a, holding b fixed, we obtain

$$\frac{dE(Y - Y_p)^2}{da} = -2E(XY) + 2aE(X)^2 + 2bE(X)$$

Differentiating with respect to b, holding a fixed, we obtain

$$\frac{dE(Y - Y_p)^2}{db} = -2E(Y) + 2aE(X) + 2b$$

Setting both derivatives equal to 0 and solving simultaneously, we obtain

$$a = \frac{E(XY) - E(X)E(Y)}{E(X^2) - [E(X)]^2} = \rho_{xy} \frac{\sigma_y}{\sigma_x}$$

and

$$b = E(Y) - aE(X) = \mu_y - \rho_{xy} \frac{\sigma_y}{\sigma_x} \mu_x$$

As both second derivatives are positive, we conclude that a and b minimize $E(Y - Y_p)^2$. An exactly equivalent proof holds for a sample, that is, with all parameters replaced by statistics.

B.26. Bivariate Normal Distributions. We write bivariate normal distributions in the following form:

$$f(x,y) = \frac{1}{2\pi\sigma_x\sigma_y \sqrt{1 - \rho^2}} e^{-\frac{1}{2(1-\rho^2)}\left[\left(\frac{x-\mu_x}{\sigma_x}\right)^2 - 2\rho\left(\frac{x-\mu_x}{\sigma_x}\right)\left(\frac{y-\mu_y}{\sigma_y}\right) + \left(\frac{y-\mu_y}{\sigma_y}\right)^2\right]}$$

Then

$$f(x) = \int_{-\infty}^{\infty} f(x,y) \, dy$$

Let

$$w \equiv \frac{x - \mu_x}{\sigma_x} \quad \text{and} \quad z \equiv \frac{y - \mu_y}{\sigma_y}$$

Then

$$\frac{dy}{dz} = \sigma_y$$

and

$$\int_{-\infty}^{\infty} f(x,y) \, dy = \frac{1}{\sqrt{2\pi}\,\sigma_x} \int_{-\infty}^{\infty} \frac{1}{\sqrt{2\pi}\sqrt{1 - \rho^2}} e^{-\frac{1}{2(1-\rho^2)}(w^2 - 2\rho wz + z^2)} \, dz$$

Note that

$$w^2 - 2\rho wz + z^2 = z^2 - 2\rho wz + \rho^2 w^2 + w^2 - \rho^2 w^2$$
$$= (z - \rho w)^2 + w^2(1 - \rho^2)$$

Thus the integral becomes

$$\int_{-\infty}^{\infty} \frac{1}{\sqrt{2\pi}\sqrt{1-\rho^2}} e^{-\frac{1}{2(1-\rho^2)}(z-\rho w)^2 - \frac{w^2}{2}} dz$$

$$= e^{-\frac{w^2}{2}} \int_{-\infty}^{\infty} \frac{1}{\sqrt{2\pi}\sqrt{1-\rho^2}} e^{-\frac{1}{2(1-\rho^2)}(z-\rho w)^2} dz$$

As w is treated as a constant, the value of the latter integral is 1, as it is the integral of a normal density function with variance $(1 - \rho^2)$ and mean ρw. Thus

$$f(x) = \frac{1}{\sqrt{2\pi}\,\sigma_x} e^{-\frac{w^2}{2}} = \frac{1}{\sqrt{2\pi}\,\sigma_x} e^{-\frac{1}{2\sigma_x^2}(x-\mu_x)^2}$$

which is a normal density function. By symmetry,

$$f(y) = \frac{1}{\sqrt{2\pi}\,\sigma_y} e^{-\frac{1}{2\sigma_y^2}(y-\mu_y)^2}$$

Note that

$$f(x|y) = f(x,y)/f(y) = \frac{1}{\sqrt{2\pi}\,\sigma_x\sqrt{1-\rho^2}} e^{-\frac{1}{2(1-\rho^2)}(w^2 - 2\rho wz + z^2) + \frac{1}{2}z^2}$$

$$= \frac{1}{\sqrt{2\pi}\,\sigma_x\sqrt{1-\rho^2}} e^{-\frac{1}{2(1-\rho^2)}[w^2 - 2\rho wz + z^2 - (1-\rho^2)z^2]}$$

$$= \frac{1}{\sqrt{2\pi}\,\sigma_x\sqrt{1-\rho^2}} e^{-\frac{1}{2(1-\rho^2)}(w - \rho z)^2}$$

$$= \frac{1}{\sqrt{2\pi}\,\sigma_x\sqrt{1-\rho^2}} e^{-\frac{1}{2(1-\rho^2)\sigma_x^2}\left[x - \mu_x - \rho\frac{\sigma_x}{\sigma_y}(y-\mu_y)\right]^2}$$

$$= \frac{1}{\sqrt{2\pi}\,\sigma_x\sqrt{1-\rho^2}} e^{-\frac{1}{2(1-\rho^2)\sigma_x^2}\left\{x - \left[\mu_x + \rho\frac{\sigma_x}{\sigma_y}(y-\mu_y)\right]\right\}^2}$$

which is the normal density with variance $\sigma_x^2(1 - \rho^2)$ and mean

$$\mu_x + \rho\frac{\sigma_x}{\sigma_y}(y - \mu_y)$$

This shows that all conditional distributions are normal and further that the mean is a linear function of y, that is, that the mean regression of X on Y is the straight line

$$m_{x|y} = \rho\frac{\sigma_x}{\sigma_y}(y - \mu_y) + \mu_x$$

The variance of each conditional distribution is $\sigma_x^2(1 - \rho^2)$ and thus does not depend upon the value of Y. Therefore, the conditional distributions of bivariate normal distributions are homoscedastic.

Let $f(x,y)$ be any constant K; then

$$K = \frac{1}{2\pi\sigma_x\sigma_y \sqrt{1-\rho^2}} e^{-\frac{1}{2(1-\rho^2)}(w^2 - 2\rho wz + z^2)}$$

Therefore, $w^2 - 2\rho wz + z^2 = C$, in which C is some positive constant. Then

$$\frac{1}{\sigma_x^2}(x - \mu_x)^2 - \frac{2\rho}{\sigma_x\sigma_y}(x - \mu_x)(y - \mu_y) + \frac{1}{\sigma_y^2}(y - \mu_y)^2 = C$$

Considering this a quadratic in $(x - \mu_x)$ and $(y - \mu_y)$ and applying the discriminant, we have

$$b^2 - 4ac = \frac{4\rho^2}{\sigma_x^2\sigma_y^2} - \frac{4}{\sigma_x^2\sigma_y^2} = \frac{4(\rho^2 - 1)}{\sigma_x^2\sigma_y^2} \leq 0$$

Therefore, unless $\rho^2 = 1$, the curves of equal probability are ellipses in the $(x - \mu_x)(y - \mu_y)$ plane, and therefore in the xy plane.

Appendix C

MISCELLANEOUS TABLES

TABLE C.1. SQUARES AND SQUARE ROOTS OF NUMBERS FROM
1 TO 1,000*

Number	Square	Square root	Number	Square	Square root
1	1	1.0000	41	16 81	6.4031
2	4	1.4142	42	17 64	6.4807
3	9	1.7321	43	18 49	6.5574
4	16	2.0000	44	19 36	6.6332
5	25	2.2361	45	20 25	6.7082
6	36	2.4495	46	21 16	6.7823
7	49	2.6458	47	22 09	6.8557
8	64	2.8284	48	23 04	6.9282
9	81	3.0000	49	24 01	7.0000
10	1 00	3.1623	50	25 00	7.0711
11	1 21	3.3166	51	26 01	7.1414
12	1 44	3.4641	52	27 04	7.2111
13	1 69	3.6056	53	28 09	7.2801
14	1 96	3.7417	54	29 16	7.3485
15	2 25	3.8730	55	30 25	7.4162
16	2 56	4.0000	56	31 36	7.4833
17	2 89	4.1231	57	32 49	7.5498
18	3 24	4.2426	58	33 64	7.6158
19	3 61	4.3589	59	34 81	7.6811
20	4 00	4.4721	60	36 00	7.7460
21	4 41	4.5826	61	37 21	7.8102
22	4 84	4.6904	62	38 44	7.8740
23	5 29	4.7958	63	39 69	7.9373
24	5 76	4.8990	64	40 96	8.0000
25	6 25	5.0000	65	42 25	8.0623
26	6 76	5.0990	66	43 56	8.1240
27	7 29	5.1962	67	44 89	8.1854
28	7 84	5.2915	68	46 24	8.2462
29	8 41	5.3852	69	47 61	8.3066
30	9 00	5.4772	70	49 00	8.3666
31	9 61	5.5678	71	50 41	8.4261
32	10 24	5.6569	72	51 84	8.4853
33	10 89	5.7446	73	53 29	8.5440
34	11 56	5.8310	74	54 76	8.6023
35	12 25	5.9161	75	56 25	8.6603
36	12 96	6.0000	76	57 76	8.7178
37	13 69	6.0828	77	59 29	8.7750
38	14 44	6.1644	78	60 84	8.8318
39	15 21	6.2450	79	62 41	8.8882
40	16 00	6.3246	80	64 00	8.9443

* By permission from *Statistics for students of psychology and education*, by H. Sorenson. Copyright 1936, McGraw-Hill Book Company, Inc.

TABLE C.1. SQUARES AND SQUARE ROOTS OF NUMBERS FROM
1 TO 1,000* (*Continued*)

Number	Square	Square root	Number	Square	Square root
81	65 61	9.0000	121	1 46 41	11.0000
82	67 24	9.0554	122	1 48 84	11.0454
83	68 89	9.1104	123	1 51 29	11.0905
84	70 56	9.1652	124	1 53 76	11.1355
85	72 25	9.2195	125	1 56 25	11.1803
86	73 96	9.2736	126	1 58 76	11.2250
87	75 69	9.3274	127	1 61 29	11.2694
88	77 44	9.3808	128	1 63 84	11.3137
89	79 21	9.4340	129	1 66 41	11.3578
90	81 00	9.4868	130	1 69 00	11.4018
91	82 81	9.5394	131	1 71 61	11.4455
92	84 64	9.5917	132	1 74 24	11.4891
93	86 49	9.6437	133	1 76 89	11.5326
94	88 36	9.6954	134	1 79 56	11.5758
95	90 25	9.7468	135	1 82 25	11.6190
96	92 16	9.7980	136	1 84 96	11.6619
97	94 09	9.8489	137	1 87 69	11.7047
98	96 04	9.8995	138	1 90 44	11.7473
99	98 01	9.9499	139	1 93 21	11.7898
100	1 00 00	10.0000	140	1 96 00	11.8322
101	1 02 01	10.0499	141	1 98 81	11.8743
102	1 04 04	10.0995	142	2 01 64	11.9164
103	1 06 09	10.1489	143	2 04 49	11.9583
104	1 08 16	10.1980	144	2 07 36	12.0000
105	1 10 25	10.2470	145	2 10 25	12.0416
106	1 12 36	10.2956	146	2 13 16	12.0830
107	1 14 49	10.3441	147	2 16 09	12.1244
108	1 16 64	10.3923	148	2 19 04	12.1655
109	1 18 81	10.4403	149	2 22 01	12.2066
110	1 21 00	10.4881	150	2 25 00	12.2474
111	1 23 21	10.5357	151	2 28 01	12.2882
112	1 25 44	10.5830	152	2 31 04	12.3288
113	1 27 69	10.6301	153	2 34 09	12.3693
114	1 29 96	10.6771	154	2 37 16	12.4097
115	1 32 25	10.7238	155	2 40 25	12.4499
116	1 34 56	10.7703	156	2 43 36	12.4900
117	1 36 89	10.8167	157	2 46 49	12.5300
118	1 39 24	10.8628	158	2 49 64	12.5698
119	1 41 61	10.9087	159	2 52 81	12.6095
120	1 44 00	10.9545	160	2 56 00	12.6491

TABLE C.1. SQUARES AND SQUARE ROOTS OF NUMBERS FROM
1 TO 1,000* (*Continued*)

Number	Square	Square root	Number	Square	Square root
161	2 59 21	12.6886	201	4 04 01	14.1774
162	2 62 44	12.7279	202	4 08 04	14.2127
163	2 65 69	12.7671	203	4 12 09	14.2478
164	2 68 96	12.8062	204	4 16 16	14.2829
165	2 72 25	12.8452	205	4 20 25	14.3178
166	2 75 56	12.8841	206	4 24 36	14.3527
167	2 78 89	12.9228	207	4 28 49	14.3875
168	2 82 24	12.9615	208	4 32 64	14.4222
169	2 85 61	13.0000	209	4 36 81	14.4568
170	2 89 00	13.0384	210	4 41 00	14.4914
171	2 92 41	13.0767	211	4 45 21	14.5258
172	2 95 84	13.1149	212	4 49 44	14.5602
173	2 99 29	13.1529	213	4 53 69	14.5945
174	3 02 76	13.1909	214	4 57 96	14.6287
175	3 06 25	13.2288	215	4 62 25	14.6629
176	3 09 76	13.2665	216	4 66 56	14.6969
177	3 13 29	13.3041	217	4 70 89	14.7309
178	3 16 84	13.3417	218	4 75 24	14.7648
179	3 20 41	13.3791	219	4 79 61	14.7986
180	3 24 00	13.4164	220	4 84 00	14.8324
181	3 27 61	13.4536	221	4 88 41	14.8661
182	3 31 24	13.4907	222	4 92 84	14.8997
183	3 34 89	13.5277	223	4 97 29	14.9332
184	3 38 56	13.5647	224	5 01 76	14.9666
185	3 42 25	13.6015	225	5 06 25	15.0000
186	3 45 96	13.6382	226	5 10 76	15.0333
187	3 49 69	13.6748	227	5 15 29	15.0665
188	3 53 44	13.7113	228	5 19 84	15.0997
189	3 57 21	13.7477	229	5 24 41	15.1327
190	3 61 00	13.7840	230	5 29 00	15.1658
191	3 64 81	13.8203	231	5 33 61	15.1987
192	3 68 64	13.8564	232	5 38 24	15.2315
193	3 72 49	13.8924	233	5 42 89	15.2643
194	3 76 36	13.9284	234	5 47 56	15.2971
195	3 80 25	13.9642	235	5 52 25	15.3297
196	3 84 16	14.0000	236	5 56 96	15.3623
197	3 88 09	14.0357	237	5 61 69	15.3948
198	3 92 04	14.0712	238	5 66 44	15.4272
199	3 96 01	14.1067	239	5 71 21	15.4596
200	4 00 00	14.1421	240	5 76 00	15.4919

* By permission from *Statistics for students of psychology and education,* by H.
Sorenson. Copyright 1936, McGraw-Hill Book Company, Inc.

TABLE C.1. SQUARES AND SQUARE ROOTS OF NUMBERS FROM 1 TO 1,000* (*Continued*)

Number	Square	Square root	Number	Square	Square root
241	5 80 81	15.5242	281	7 89 61	16.7631
242	5 85 64	15.5563	282	7 95 24	16.7929
243	5 90 49	15.5885	283	8 00 89	16.8226
244	5 95 36	15.6205	284	8 06 56	16.8523
245	6 00 25	15.6525	285	8 12 25	16.8819
246	6 05 16	15.6844	286	8 17 96	16.9115
247	6 10 09	15.7162	287	8 23 69	16.9411
248	6 15 04	15.7480	288	8 29 44	16.9706
249	6 20 01	15.7797	289	8 35 21	17.0000
250	6 25 00	15.8114	290	8 41 00	17.0294
251	6 30 01	15.8430	291	8 46 81	17.0587
252	6 35 04	15.8745	292	8 52 64	17.0880
253	6 40 09	15.9060	293	8 58 49	17.1172
254	6 45 16	15.9374	294	8 64 36	17.1464
255	6 50 25	15.9687	295	8 70 25	17.1756
256	6 55 36	16.0000	296	8 76 16	17.2047
257	6 60 49	16.0312	297	8 82 09	17.2337
258	6 65 64	16.0624	298	8 88 04	17.2627
259	6 70 81	16.0935	299	8 94 01	17.2916
260	6 76 00	16.1245	300	9 00 00	17.3205
261	6 81 21	16.1555	301	9 06 01	17.3494
262	6 86 44	16.1864	302	9 12 04	17.3781
263	6 91 69	16.2173	303	9 18 09	17.4069
264	6 96 96	16.2481	304	9 24 16	17.4356
265	7 02 25	16.2788	305	9 30 25	17.4642
266	7 07 56	16.3095	306	9 36 36	17.4929
267	7 12 89	16.3401	307	9 42 49	17.5214
268	7 18 24	16.3707	308	9 48 64	17.5499
269	7 23 61	16.4012	309	9 54 81	17.5784
270	7 29 00	16.4317	310	9 61 00	17.6068
271	7 34 41	16.4621	311	9 67 21	17.6352
272	7 39 84	16.4924	312	9 73 44	17.6635
273	7 45 29	16.5227	313	9 79 69	17.6918
274	7 50 76	16.5529	314	9 85 96	17.7200
275	7 56 25	16.5831	315	9 92 25	17.7482
276	7 61 76	16.6132	316	9 98 56	17.7764
277	7 67 29	16.6433	317	10 04 89	17.8045
278	7 72 84	16.6733	318	10 11 24	17.8326
279	7 78 41	16.7033	319	10 17 61	17.8606
280	7 84 00	16.7332	320	10 24 00	17.8885

* By permission from *Statistics for students of psychology and education*, by H. Sorenson. Copyright 1930, McGraw-Hill Book Company, Inc.

TABLE C.1. SQUARES AND SQUARE ROOTS OF NUMBERS FROM 1 TO 1,000* (*Continued*)

Number	Square	Square root	Number	Square	Square root
321	10 30 41	17.9165	361	13 03 21	19.0000
322	10 36 84	17.9444	362	13 10 44	19.0263
323	10 43 29	17.9722	363	13 17 69	19.0526
324	10 49 76	18.0000	364	13 24 96	19.0788
325	10 56 25	18.0278	365	13 32 25	19.1050
326	10 62 76	18.0555	366	13 39 56	19.1311
327	10 69 29	18.0831	367	13 46 89	19.1572
328	10 75 84	18.1108	368	13 54 24	19.1833
329	10 82 41	18.1384	369	13 61 61	19.2094
330	10 89 00	18.1659	370	13 69 00	19.2354
331	10 95 61	18.1934	371	13 76 41	19.2614
332	11 02 24	18.2209	372	13 83 84	19.2873
333	11 08 89	18.2483	373	13 91 29	19.3132
334	11 15 56	18.2757	374	13 98 76	19.3391
335	11 22 25	18.3030	375	14 06 25	19.3649
336	11 28 96	18.3303	376	14 13 76	19.3907
337	11 35 69	18.3576	377	14 21 29	19.4165
338	11 42 44	18.3848	378	14 28 84	19.4422
339	11 49 21	18.4120	379	14 36 41	19.4679
340	11 56 00	18.4391	380	14 44 00	19.4936
341	11 62 81	18.4662	381	14 51 61	19.5192
342	11 69 64	18.4932	382	14 59 24	19.5448
343	11 76 49	18.5203	383	14 66 89	19.5704
344	11 83 36	18.5472	384	14 74 56	19.5959
345	11 90 25	18.5742	385	14 82 25	19.6214
346	11 97 16	18.6011	386	14 89 96	19.6469
347	12 04 09	18.6279	387	14 97 69	19.6723
348	12 11 04	18.6548	388	15 05 44	19.6977
349	12 18 01	18.6815	389	15 13 21	19.7231
350	12 25 00	18.7083	390	15 21 00	19.7484
351	12 32 01	18.7350	391	15 28 81	19.7737
352	12 39 04	18.7617	392	15 36 64	19.7990
353	12 46 09	18.7883	393	15 44 49	19.8242
354	12 53 16	18.8149	394	15 52 36	19.8494
355	12 60 25	18.8414	395	15 60 25	19.8746
356	12 67 36	18.8680	396	15 68 16	19.8997
357	12 74 49	18.8944	397	15 76 09	19.9249
358	12 81 64	18.9209	398	15 84 04	19.9499
359	12 88 81	18.9473	399	15 92 01	19.9750
360	12 96 00	18.9737	400	16 00 00	20.0000

* By permission from *Statistics for students of psychology and education*, by H. Sorenson.   Copyright 1936, McGraw-Hill Book Company, Inc.

Table C.1. Squares and Square Roots of Numbers from
1 to 1,000* (*Continued*)

Number	Square	Square root	Number	Square	Square root
401	16 08 01	20.0250	441	19 44 81	21.0000
402	16 16 04	20.0499	442	19 53 64	21.0238
403	16 24 09	20.0749	443	19 62 49	21.0476
404	16 32 16	20.0998	444	19 71 36	21.0713
405	16 40 25	20.1246	445	19 80 25	21.0950
406	16 48 36	20.1494	446	19 89 16	21.1187
407	16 56 49	20.1742	447	19 98 09	21.1424
408	16 64 64	20.1990	448	20 07 04	21.1660
409	16 72 81	20.2237	449	20 16 01	21.1896
410	16 81 00	20.2485	450	20 25 00	21.2132
411	16 89 21	20.2731	451	20 34 01	21.2368
412	16 97 44	20.2978	452	20 43 04	21.2603
413	17 05 69	20.3224	453	20 52 09	21.2838
414	17 13 96	20.3470	454	20 61 16	21.3073
415	17 22 25	20.3715	455	20 70 25	21.3307
416	17 30 56	20.3961	456	20 79 36	21.3542
417	17 38 89	20.4206	457	20 88 49	21.3776
418	17 47 24	20.4450	458	20 97 64	21.4009
419	17 55 61	20.4695	459	21 06 81	21.4243
420	17 64 00	20.4939	460	21 16 00	21.4476
421	17 72 41	20.5183	461	21 25 21	21.4709
422	17 80 84	20.5426	462	21 34 44	21.4942
423	17 89 29	20.5670	463	21 43 69	21.5174
424	17 97 76	20.5913	464	21 52 96	21.5407
425	18 06 25	20.6155	465	21 62 25	21.5639
426	18 14 76	20.6398	466	21 71 56	21.5870
427	18 23 29	20.6640	467	21 80 89	21.6102
428	18 31 84	20.6882	468	21 90 24	21.6333
429	18 40 41	20.7123	469	21 99 61	21.6564
430	18 49 00	20.7364	470	22 09 00	21.6795
431	18 57 61	20.7605	471	22 18 41	21.7025
432	18 66 24	20.7846	472	22 27 84	21.7256
433	18 74 89	20.8087	473	22 37 29	21.7486
434	18 83 56	20.8327	474	22 46 76	21.7715
435	18 92 25	20.8567	475	22 56 25	21.7945
436	19 00 96	20.8806	476	22 65 76	21.8174
437	19 09 69	20.9045	477	22 75 29	21.8403
438	19 18 44	20.9284	478	22 84 84	21.8632
439	19 27 21	20.9523	479	22 94 41	21.8861
440	19 36 00	20.9762	480	23 04 00	21.9089

* By permission from *Statistics for students of psychology and education*, by H. Sorenson. Copyright 1936, McGraw-Hill Book Company, Inc.

TABLE C.1. SQUARES AND SQUARE ROOTS OF NUMBERS FROM
1 TO 1,000* (*Continued*)

Number	Square	Square root	Number	Square	Square root
481	23 13 61	21.9317	521	27 14 41	22.8254
482	23 23 24	21.9545	522	27 24 84	22.8473
483	23 32 89	21.9773	523	27 35 29	22.8692
484	23 42 56	22.0000	524	27 45 76	22.8910
485	23 52 25	22.0227	525	27 56 25	22.9129
486	23 61 96	22.0454	526	27 66 76	22.9347
487	23 71 69	22.0681	527	27 77 29	22.9565
488	23 81 44	22.0907	528	27 87 84	22.9783
489	23 91 21	22.1133	529	27 98 41	23.0000
490	24 01 00	22.1359	530	28 09 00	23.0217
491	24 10 81	22.1585	531	28 19 61	23.0434
492	24 20 64	22.1811	532	28 30 24	23.0651
493	24 30 49	22.2036	533	28 40 89	23.0868
494	24 40 36	22.2261	534	28 51 56	23.1084
495	24 50 25	22.2486	535	28 62 25	23.1301
496	24 60 16	22.2711	536	28 72 96	23.1517
497	24 70 09	22.2935	537	28 83 69	23.1733
498	24 80 04	22.3159	538	28 94 44	23.1948
499	24 90 01	22.3383	539	29 05 21	23.2164
500	25 00 00	22.3607	540	29 16 00	23.2379
501	25 10 01	22.3830	541	29 26 81	23.2594
502	25 20 04	22.4054	542	29 37 64	23.2809
503	25 30 09	22.4277	543	29 48 49	23.3024
504	25 40 16	22.4499	544	29 59 36	23.3238
505	25 50 25	22.4722	545	29 70 25	23.3452
506	25 60 36	22.4944	546	29 81 16	23.3666
507	25 70 49	22.5167	547	29 92 09	23.3880
508	25 80 64	22.5389	548	30 03 04	23.4094
509	25 90 81	22.5610	549	30 14 01	23.4307
510	26 01 00	22.5832	550	30 25 00	23.4521
511	26 11 21	22.6053	551	30 36 01	23.4734
512	26 21 44	22.6274	552	30 47 04	23.4947
513	26 31 69	22.6495	553	30 58 09	23.5160
514	26 41 96	22.6716	554	30 69 16	23.5372
515	26 52 25	22.6936	555	30 80 25	23.5584
516	26 62 56	22.7156	556	30 91 36	23.5797
517	26 72 89	22.7376	557	31 02 49	23.6008
518	26 83 24	22.7596	558	31 13 64	23.6220
519	26 93 61	22.7816	559	31 24 81	23.6432
520	27 04 00	22.8035	560	31 36 00	23.6643

* By permission from *Statistics for students of psychology and education*, by H. Sorenson. Copyright 1936, McGraw-Hill Book Company, Inc.

TABLE C.1. SQUARES AND SQUARE ROOTS OF NUMBERS FROM
1 TO 1,000* (*Continued*)

Number	Square	Square root	Number	Square	Square root
561	31 47 21	23.6854	601	36 12 01	24.5153
562	31 58 44	23.7065	602	36 24 04	24.5357
563	31 69 69	23.7276	603	36 36 09	24.5561
564	31 80 96	23.7487	604	36 48 16	24.5764
565	31 92 25	23.7697	605	36 60 25	24.5967
566	32 03 56	23.7908	606	36 72 36	24.6171
567	32 14 89	23.8118	607	36 84 49	24.6374
568	32 26 24	23.8328	608	36 96 64	24.6577
569	32 37 61	23.8537	609	37 08 81	24.6779
570	32 49 00	23.8747	610	37 21 00	24.6982
571	32 60 41	23.8956	611	37 33 21	24.7184
572	32 71 84	23.9165	612	37 45 44	24.7385
573	32 83 29	23.9374	613	37 57 69	24.7588
574	32 94 76	23.9583	614	37 69 96	24.7790
575	33 06 25	23.9792	615	37 82 25	24.7992
576	33 17 76	24.0000	616	37 94 56	24.8193
577	33 29 29	24.0208	617	38 06 89	24.8395
578	33 40 84	24.0416	618	38 19 24	24.8596
579	33 52 41	24.0624	619	38 31 61	24.8797
580	33 64 00	24.0832	620	38 44 00	24.8998
581	33 75 61	24.1039	621	38 56 41	24.9199
582	33 87 24	24.1247	622	38 68 84	24.9399
583	33 98 89	24.1454	623	38 81 29	24.9600
584	34 10 56	24.1661	624	38 93 76	24.9800
585	34 22 25	24.1868	625	39 06 25	25.0000
586	34 33 96	24.2074	626	39 18 76	25.0200
587	34 45 69	24.2281	627	39 31 29	25.0400
588	34 57 44	24.2487	628	39 43 84	25.0599
589	34 69 21	24.2693	629	39 56 41	25.0799
590	34 81 00	24.2899	630	39 69 00	25.0998
591	34 92 81	24.3105	631	39 81 61	25.1197
592	35 04 64	24.3311	632	39 94 24	25.1396
593	35 16 49	24.3516	633	40 06 89	25.1595
594	35 28 36	24.3721	634	40 19 56	25.1794
595	35 40 25	24.3926	635	40 32 25	25.1992
596	35 52 16	24.4131	636	40 44 96	25.2190
597	35 64 09	24.4336	637	40 57 69	25.2389
598	35 76 04	24.4540	638	40 70 44	25.2587
599	35 88 01	24.4745	639	40 83 21	25.2784
600	36 00 00	24.4949	640	40 96 00	25.2982

* By permission from *Statistics for students of psychology and education*, by H.
Sorenson. Copyright 1936, McGraw-Hill Book Company, Inc.

TABLE C.1. SQUARES AND SQUARE ROOTS OF NUMBERS FROM 1 TO 1,000* (Continued)

Number	Square	Square root	Number	Square	Square root
641	41 08 81	25.3180	681	46 37 61	26.0960
642	41 21 64	25.3377	682	46 51 24	26.1151
643	41 34 49	25.3574	683	46 64 89	26.1343
644	41 47 36	25.3772	684	46 78 56	26.1534
645	41 60 25	25.3969	685	46 92 25	26.1725
646	41 73 16	25.4165	686	47 05 96	26.1916
647	41 86 09	25.4362	687	47 19 69	26.2107
648	41 99 04	25.4558	688	47 33 44	26.2298
649	42 12 01	25.4755	689	47 47 21	26.2488
650	42 25 00	25.4951	690	47 61 00	26.2679
651	42 38 01	25.5147	691	47 74 81	26.2869
652	42 51 04	25.5343	692	47 88 64	26.3059
653	42 64 09	25.5539	693	48 02 49	26.3249
654	42 77 16	25.5734	694	48 16 36	26.3439
655	42 90 25	25.5930	695	48 30 25	26.3629
656	43 03 36	25.6125	696	48 44 16	26.3818
657	43 16 49	25.6320	697	48 58 09	26.4008
658	43 29 64	25.6515	698	48 72 04	26.4197
659	43 42 81	25.6710	699	48 86 01	26.4386
660	43 56 00	25.6905	700	49 00 00	26.4575
661	43 69 21	25.7099	701	49 14 01	26.4764
662	43 82 44	25.7294	702	49 28 04	26.4953
663	43 95 69	25.7488	703	49 42 09	26.5141
664	44 08 96	25.7682	704	49 56 16	26.5330
665	44 22 25	25.7876	705	49 70 25	26.5518
666	44 35 56	25.8070	706	49 84 36	26.5707
667	44 48 89	25.8263	707	49 98 49	26.5895
668	44 62 24	25.8457	708	50 12 64	26.6083
669	44 75 61	25.8650	709	50 26 81	26.6271
670	44 89 00	25.8844	710	50 41 00	26.6458
671	45 02 41	25.9037	711	50 55 21	26.6646
672	45 15 84	25.9230	712	50 69 44	26.6833
673	45 29 29	25.9422	713	50 83 69	26.7021
674	45 42 76	25.9615	714	50 97 96	26.7208
675	45 56 25	25.9808	715	51 12 25	26.7395
676	45 69 76	26.0000	716	51 26 56	26.7582
677	45 83 29	26.0192	717	51 40 89	26.7769
678	45 96 84	26.0384	718	51 55 24	26.7955
679	46 10 41	26.0576	719	51 69 61	26.8142
680	46 24 00	26.0768	720	51 84 00	26.8328

* By permission from *Statistics for students of psychology and education*, by H. Sorenson. Copyright 1936, McGraw-Hill Book Company, Inc.

TABLE C.1. SQUARES AND SQUARE ROOTS OF NUMBERS FROM
1 TO 1,000* (*Continued*)

Number	Square	Square root	Number	Square	Square root
721	51 98 41	26.8514	761	57 91 21	27.5862
722	52 12 84	26.8701	762	58 06 44	27.6043
723	52 27 29	26.8887	763	58 21 69	27.6225
724	52 41 76	26.9072	764	58 36 96	27.6405
725	52 56 25	26.9258	765	58 52 25	27.6586
726	52 70 76	26.9444	766	58 67 56	27.6767
727	52 85 29	26.9629	767	58 82 89	27.6948
728	52 99 84	26.9815	768	58 98 24	27.7128
729	53 14 41	27.0000	769	59 13 61	27.7308
730	53 29 00	27.0185	770	59 29 00	27.7489
731	53 43 61	27.0370	771	59 44 41	27.7669
732	53 58 24	27.0555	772	59 59 84	27.7849
733	53 72 89	27.0740	773	59 75 29	27.8029
734	53 87 56	27.0924	774	59 90 76	27.8209
735	54 02 25	27.1109	775	60 06 25	27.8388
736	54 16 96	27.1293	776	60 21 76	27.8568
737	54 31 69	27.1477	777	60 37 29	27.8747
738	54 46 44	27.1662	778	60 52 84	27.8927
739	54 61 27	27.1846	779	60 68 41	27.9106
740	54 76 00	27.2029	780	60 84 00	27.9285
741	54 90 81	27.2213	781	60 99 61	27.9464
742	55 05 64	27.2397	782	61 15 24	27.9643
743	55 20 49	27.2580	783	61 30 89	27.9821
744	55 35 36	27.2764	784	61 46 56	28.0000
745	55 50 25	27.2947	785	61 62 25	28.0179
746	55 65 16	27.3130	786	61 77 96	28.0357
747	55 80 09	27.3313	787	61 93 69	28.0535
748	55 95 04	27.3496	788	62 09 44	28.0713
749	56 10 01	27.3679	789	62 25 21	28.0891
750	56 25 00	27.3861	790	62 41 00	28.1069
751	56 40 01	27.4044	791	62 56 81	28.1247
752	56 55 04	27.4226	792	62 72 64	28.1425
753	56 70 09	27.4408	793	62 88 49	28.1603
754	56 85 16	27.4591	794	63 04 36	28.1780
755	57 00 25	27.4773	795	63 20 25	28.1957
756	57 15 36	27.4955	796	63 36 16	28.2135
757	57 30 49	27.5136	797	63 52 09	28.2312
758	57 45 64	27.5318	798	63 68 04	28.2489
759	57 60 81	27.5500	799	63 84 01	28.2666
760	57 76 00	27.5681	800	64 00 00	28.2843

TABLE C.1. SQUARES AND SQUARE ROOTS OF NUMBERS FROM
1 TO 1,000* (*Continued*)

Number	Square	Square root	Number	Square	Square root
801	64 16 01	28.3019	841	70 72 81	29.0000
802	64 32 04	28.3196	842	70 89 64	29.0172
803	64 48 09	28.3373	843	71 06 49	29.0345
804	64 64 16	28.3049	844	71 23 36	29.0517
805	64 80 25	28.3725	845	71 40 25	29.0689
806	64 96 36	28.3901	846	71 57 16	29.0861
807	65 12 49	28.4077	847	71 74 09	29.1033
808	65 28 64	28.4253	848	71 91 04	29.1204
809	65 44 81	28.4429	849	72 08 01	29.1376
810	65 61 00	28.4605	850	72 25 00	29.1548
811	65 77 21	28.4781	851	72 42 01	29.1719
812	65 93 44	28.4956	852	72 59 04	29.1890
813	66 09 69	28.5132	853	72 76 09	29.2062
814	66 25 96	28.5307	854	72 93 16	29.2233
815	66 42 25	28.5482	855	73 10 25	29.2404
816	66 58 56	28.5657	856	73 27 36	29.2575
817	66 74 89	28.5832	857	73 44 49	29.2746
818	66 91 24	28.6007	858	73 61 64	29.2916
819	67 07 61	28.6082	859	73 78 81	29.3087
820	67 24 00	28.6356	860	73 96 00	29.3258
821	67 40 41	28.6531	861	74 13 21	29.3428
822	67 56 84	28.6705	862	74 30 44	29.3598
823	67 73 29	28.6880	863	74 47 69	29.3769
824	67 89 76	28.7054	864	74 64 96	29.3939
825	68 06 25	28.7228	865	74 82 25	29.4109
826	68 22 76	28.7402	866	74 99 56	29.4279
827	68 39 29	28.7576	867	75 16 89	29.4449
828	68 55 84	28.7750	868	75 34 24	29.4618
829	68 72 41	28.7924	869	75 51 61	29.4788
830	68 89 00	28.8097	870	75 69 00	29.4958
831	69 05 61	28.8271	871	75 86 41	29.5127
832	69 22 24	28.8444	872	76 03 84	29.5296
833	69 38 89	28.8617	873	76 21 29	29.5466
834	69 55 56	28.8791	874	76 38 76	29.5635
835	69 72 25	28.8964	875	76 56 25	29.5804
836	69 88 96	28.9137	876	76 73 76	29.5973
837	70 05 69	28.9310	877	76 91 29	29.6142
838	70 22 44	28.9482	878	77 08 84	29.6311
839	70 39 21	28.9655	879	77 26 41	29.6479
840	70 56 00	28.9828	880	77 44 00	29.6648

* By permission from *Statistics for students of psychology and education*, by H. Sorenson. Copyright 1936, McGraw-Hill Book Company, Inc.

TABLE C.1. SQUARES AND SQUARE ROOTS OF NUMBERS FROM
1 TO 1,000* (*Continued*)

Number	Square	Square root	Number	Square	Square root
881	77 61 61	29.6816	921	84 82 41	30.3480
882	77 79 24	29.6985	922	85 00 84	30.3645
883	77 96 89	29.7153	923	85 19 29	30.3809
884	78 14 56	29.7321	924	85 37 76	30.3974
885	78 32 25	29.7489	925	85 56 25	30.4138
886	78 49 96	29.7658	926	85 74 76	30.4302
887	78 67 69	29.7825	927	85 93 29	30.4467
888	78 85 44	29.7993	928	86 11 84	30.4631
889	79 03 21	29.8161	929	86 30 41	30.4795
890	79 21 00	29.8329	930	86 49 00	30.4959
891	79 38 81	29.8496	931	86 67 61	30.5123
892	79 56 64	29.8664	932	86 86 24	30.5287
893	79 74 49	29.8831	933	87 04 89	30.5450
894	79 92 36	29.8998	934	87 23 56	30.5614
895	80 10 25	29.9166	935	87 42 25	30.5778
896	80 28 16	29.9333	936	87 60 96	30.5941
897	80 46 09	29.9500	937	87 79 69	30.6105
898	80 64 04	29.9666	938	87 98 44	30.6268
899	80 82 01	29.9833	939	88 17 21	30.6431
900	81 00 00	30.0000	940	88 36 00	30.6594
901	81 18 01	30.0167	941	88 54 81	30.6757
902	81 36 04	30.0333	942	88 73 64	30.6920
903	81 54 09	30.0500	943	88 92 49	30.7083
904	81 72 16	30.0666	944	89 11 36	30.7246
905	81 90 25	30.0832	945	89 30 25	30.7409
906	82 08 36	30.0998	946	89 49 16	30.7571
907	82 26 49	30.1164	947	89 68 09	30.7734
908	82 44 64	30.1330	948	89 87 04	30.7896
909	82 62 81	30.1496	949	90 06 01	30.8058
910	82 81 00	30.1662	950	90 25 00	30.8221
911	82 99 21	30.1828	951	90 44 01	30.8383
912	83 17 44	30.1993	952	90 63 04	30.8545
913	83 35 69	30.2159	953	90 82 09	30.8707
914	83 53 96	30.2324	954	91 01 16	30.8869
915	83 72 25	30.2490	955	91 20 25	30.9031
916	83 90 56	30.2655	956	91 39 36	30.9192
917	84 08 89	30.2820	957	91 58 49	30.9354
918	84 27 24	30.2985	958	91 77 64	30.9516
919	84 45 61	30.3150	959	91 96 81	30.9677
920	84 64 00	30.3315	960	92 16 00	30.9839

TABLE C.1. SQUARES AND SQUARE ROOTS OF NUMBERS FROM
1 TO 1,000* (*Continued*)

Number	Square	Square root	Number	Square	Square root
961	92 35 21	31.0000	981	96 23 61	31.3209
962	92 54 44	31.0161	982	96 43 24	31.3369
963	92 73 69	31.0322	983	96 62 89	31.3528
964	92 92 96	31.0483	984	96 82 56	31.3688
965	93 12 25	31.0644	985	97 02 25	31.3847
966	93 31 56	31.0805	986	97 21 96	31.4006
967	93 50 89	31.0966	987	97 41 69	31.4166
968	93 70 24	31.1127	988	97 61 44	31.4325
969	93 89 61	31.1288	989	97 81 21	31.4484
970	94 09 00	31.1448	990	98 01 00	31.4643
971	94 28 41	31.1609	991	98 20 81	31.4802
972	94 47 84	31.1769	992	98 40 64	31.4960
973	94 67 29	31.1929	993	98 60 49	31.5119
974	94 86 76	31.2090	994	98 80 36	31.5278
975	95 06 25	31.2250	995	99 00 25	31.5436
976	95 25 76	31.2410	996	99 20 16	31.5595
977	95 45 29	31.2570	997	99 40 09	31.5753
978	95 64 84	31.2730	998	99 60 04	31.5911
979	95 84 41	31.2890	999	99 80 01	31.6070
980	96 04 00	31.3050	1000	100 00 00	31.6228

* By permission from *Statistics for students of psychology and education,* by H. Sorenson. Copyright 1936, McGraw-Hill Book Company, Inc.

TABLE C.2. FOUR-PLACE COMMON LOGARITHMS OF NUMBERS
(BASE 10)*

N.	0	1	2	3	4	5	6	7	8	9
0	—	0000	3010	4771	6021	6990	7782	8451	9031	9542
1	0000	0414	0792	1139	1461	1761	2041	2304	2553	2788
2	3010	3222	3424	3617	3802	3979	4150	4314	4472	4624
3	4771	4914	5051	5185	5315	5441	5563	5682	5798	5911
4	6021	6128	6232	6335	6435	6532	6628	6721	6812	6902
5	6990	7076	7160	7243	7324	7404	7482	7559	7634	7709
6	7782	7853	7924	7993	8062	8129	8195	8261	8325	8388
7	8451	8513	8573	8633	8692	8751	8808	8865	8921	8976
8	9031	9085	9138	9191	9243	9294	9345	9395	9445	9494
9	9542	9590	9638	9685	9731	9777	9823	9868	9912	9956
10	0000	0043	0086	0128	0170	0212	0253	0294	0334	0374
11	0414	0453	0492	0531	0569	0607	0645	0682	0719	0755
12	0792	0828	0864	0899	0934	0969	1004	1038	1072	1106
13	1139	1173	1206	1239	1271	1303	1335	1367	1399	1430
14	1461	1492	1523	1553	1584	1614	1644	1673	1703	1732
15	1761	1790	1818	1847	1875	1903	1931	1959	1987	2014
16	2041	2068	2095	2122	2148	2175	2201	2227	2253	2279
17	2304	2330	2355	2380	2405	2430	2455	2480	2504	2529
18	2553	2577	2601	2625	2648	2672	2695	2718	2742	2765
19	2788	2810	2833	2856	2878	2900	2934	2945	2967	2989
20	3010	3032	3054	3075	3096	3118	3139	3160	3181	3201
21	3222	3243	3263	3284	3304	3324	3345	3365	3385	3404
22	3424	3444	3464	3483	3502	3522	3541	3560	3579	3598
23	3617	3636	3655	3674	3692	3711	3729	3747	3766	3784
24	3802	3820	3838	3856	3874	3892	3909	3927	3945	3962
25	3979	3997	4014	4031	4048	4065	4082	4099	4116	4133
26	4150	4166	4183	4200	4216	4232	4249	4265	4281	4298
27	4314	4330	4346	4362	4378	4393	4409	4425	4440	4456
28	4472	4487	4502	4518	4533	4548	4564	4579	4594	4609
29	4624	4639	4654	4669	4683	4698	4713	4728	4742	4757
30	4771	4786	4800	4814	4829	4843	4857	4871	4886	4900
31	4914	4928	4942	4955	4969	4983	4997	5011	5024	5038
32	5051	5065	5079	5092	5105	5119	5132	5145	5159	5172
33	5185	5198	5211	5224	5237	5250	5263	5276	5289	5302
34	5315	5328	5340	5353	5366	5378	5391	5403	5416	5428
35	5441	5453	5465	5478	5490	5502	5514	5527	5539	5551
36	5563	5575	5587	5599	5611	5623	5635	5647	5658	5670
37	5682	5694	5705	5717	5729	5740	5752	5763	5775	5786
38	5798	5809	5821	5832	5843	5855	5866	5877	5888	5899
39	5911	5922	5933	5944	5955	5966	5977	5988	5999	6010
40	6021	6031	6042	6053	6064	6075	6085	6096	6107	6117
41	6128	6138	6149	6160	6170	6180	6191	6201	6212	6222
42	6232	6243	6253	6263	6274	6284	6294	6304	6314	6325
43	6335	6345	6355	6365	6375	6385	6395	6405	6415	6425
44	6435	6444	6454	6464	6474	6484	6493	6503	6513	6522
45	6532	6542	6551	6561	6571	6580	6590	6599	6609	6618
46	6628	6637	6646	6656	6665	6675	6684	6693	6702	6712
47	6721	6730	6739	6749	6758	6767	6776	6785	6794	6803
48	6812	6821	6830	6839	6848	6857	6866	6875	6884	6893
49	6902	6911	6920	6928	6937	6946	6955	6964	6972	6981
50	6990	6998	7007	7016	7024	7033	7042	7050	7059	7067
N.	0	1	2	3	4	5	6	7	8	9

Prop. Parts

	22	21		20	19		18	17		16	15		14	13		12	11		9	8
1	2.2	2.1	1	2.0	1.9	1	1.8	1.7	1	1.6	1.5	1	1.4	1.3	1	1.2	1.1	1	0.9	0.8
2	4.4	4.2	2	4.0	3.8	2	3.6	3.4	2	3.2	3.0	2	2.8	2.6	2	2.4	2.2	2	1.8	1.6
3	6.6	6.3	3	6.0	5.7	3	5.4	5.1	3	4.8	4.5	3	4.2	3.9	3	3.6	3.3	3	2.7	2.4
4	8.8	8.4	4	8.0	7.6	4	7.2	6.8	4	6.4	6.0	4	5.6	5.2	4	4.8	4.4	4	3.6	3.2
5	11.0	10.5	5	10.0	9.5	5	9.0	8.5	5	8.0	7.5	5	7.0	6.5	5	6.0	5.5	5	4.5	4.0
6	13.2	12.6	6	12.0	11.4	6	10.8	10.2	6	9.6	9.0	6	8.4	7.8	6	7.2	6.6	6	5.4	4.8
7	15.4	14.7	7	14.0	13.3	7	12.6	11.9	7	11.2	10.5	7	9.8	9.1	7	8.4	7.7	7	6.3	5.6
8	17.6	16.8	8	16.0	15.2	8	14.4	13.6	8	12.8	12.0	8	11.2	10.4	8	9.6	8.8	8	7.2	6.4
9	19.8	18.9	9	18.0	17.1	9	16.2	15.3	9	14.4	13.5	9	12.6	11.7	9	10.8	9.9	9	8.1	7.2

TABLE C.2. FOUR-PLACE COMMON LOGARITHMS OF NUMBERS (BASE 10)* (Continued)

N.	0	1	2	3	4	5	6	7	8	9
50	6990	6998	7007	7016	7024	7033	7042	7050	7059	7067
51	7076	7084	7093	7101	7110	7118	7126	7135	7143	7152
52	7160	7168	7177	7185	7193	7202	7210	7218	7226	7235
53	7243	7251	7259	7267	7275	7284	7292	7300	7308	7316
54	7324	7332	7340	7348	7356	7364	7372	7380	7388	7396
55	7404	7412	7419	7427	7435	7443	7451	7459	7466	7474
56	7482	7490	7497	7505	7513	7520	7528	7536	7543	7551
57	7559	7566	7574	7582	7589	7597	7604	7612	7619	7627
58	7634	7642	7649	7657	7664	7672	7679	7686	7694	7701
59	7709	7716	7723	7731	7738	7745	7752	7760	7767	7774
60	7782	7789	7796	7803	7810	7818	7825	7832	7839	7846
61	7853	7860	7868	7875	7882	7889	7896	7903	7910	7917
62	7924	7931	7938	7945	7952	7959	7966	7973	7980	7987
63	7993	8000	8007	8014	8021	8028	8035	8041	8048	8055
64	8062	8069	8075	8082	8089	8096	8102	8109	8116	8122
65	8129	8136	8142	8149	8156	8162	8169	8176	8182	8189
66	8195	8202	8209	8215	8222	8228	8235	8241	8248	8254
67	8261	8267	8274	8280	8287	8293	8299	8306	8312	8319
68	8325	8331	8338	8344	8351	8357	8363	8370	8376	8382
69	8388	8395	8401	8407	8414	8420	8426	8432	8439	8445
70	8451	8457	8463	8470	8476	8482	8488	8494	8500	8506
71	8513	8519	8525	8531	8537	8543	8549	8555	8561	8567
72	8573	8579	8585	8591	8597	8603	8609	8615	8621	8627
73	8633	8639	8645	8651	8657	8663	8669	8675	8681	8686
74	8692	8698	8704	8710	8716	8722	8727	8733	8739	8745
75	8751	8756	8762	8768	8774	8779	8785	8791	8797	8802
76	8808	8814	8820	8825	8831	8837	8842	8848	8854	8859
77	8865	8871	8876	8882	8887	8893	8899	8904	8910	8915
78	8921	8927	8932	8938	8943	8949	8954	8960	8965	8971
79	8976	8982	8987	8993	8998	9004	9009	9015	9020	9025
80	9031	9036	9042	9047	9053	9058	9063	9069	9074	9079
81	9085	9090	9096	9101	9106	9112	9117	9122	9128	9133
82	9138	9143	9149	9154	9159	9165	9170	9175	9180	9186
83	9191	9196	9201	9206	9212	9217	9222	9227	9232	9238
84	9243	9248	9253	9258	9263	9269	9274	9279	9284	9289
85	9294	9299	9304	9309	9315	9320	9325	9330	9335	9340
86	9345	9350	9355	9360	9365	9370	9375	9380	9385	9390
87	9395	9400	9405	9410	9415	9420	9425	9430	9435	9440
88	9445	9450	9455	9460	9465	9469	9474	9479	9484	9489
89	9494	9499	9504	9509	9513	9518	9523	9528	9533	9538
90	9542	9547	9552	9557	9562	9566	9571	9576	9581	9586
91	9590	9595	9600	9605	9609	9614	9619	9624	9628	9633
92	9638	9643	9647	9652	9657	9661	9666	9671	9675	9680
93	9685	9689	9694	9699	9703	9708	9713	9717	9722	9727
94	9731	9736	9741	9745	9750	9754	9759	9763	9768	9773
95	9777	9782	9786	9791	9795	9800	9805	9809	9814	9818
96	9823	9827	9832	9836	9841	9845	9850	9854	9859	9863
97	9868	9872	9877	9881	9886	9890	9894	9899	9903	9908
98	9912	9917	9921	9926	9930	9934	9939	9943	9948	9952
99	9956	9961	9965	9969	9974	9978	9983	9987	9991	9996
100	0000	0004	0009	0013	0017	0022	0026	0030	0035	0039
N.	0	1	2	3	4	5	6	7	8	9

Prop. Parts

	9		8		7		6		5		4
1	0.9	1	0.8	1	0.7	1	0.6	1	0.5	1	0.4
2	1.8	2	1.6	2	1.4	2	1.2	2	1.0	2	0.8
3	2.7	3	2.4	3	2.1	3	1.8	3	1.5	3	1.2
4	3.6	4	3.2	4	2.8	4	2.4	4	2.0	4	1.6
5	4.5	5	4.0	5	3.5	5	3.0	5	2.5	5	2.0
6	5.4	6	4.8	6	4.2	6	3.6	6	3.0	6	2.4
7	6.3	7	5.6	7	4.9	7	4.2	7	3.5	7	2.8
8	7.2	8	6.4	8	5.6	8	4.8	8	4.0	8	3.2
9	8.1	9	7.2	9	6.3	9	5.4	9	4.5	9	3.6

* By permission from *College algebra*, by L. Smail. Copyright 1931, McGraw-Hill Book Company, Inc.

TABLE C.3. NATURAL LOGARITHMS (BASE e)*

.10–.99

N	.00	.01	.02	.03	.04	.05	.06	.07	.08	.09
.1	−2.303	−2.207	−2.120	−2.040	−1.966	−1.897	−1.833	−1.772	−1.715	−1.661
.2	−1.609	−1.561	−1.514	−1.470	−1.427	−1.386	−1.347	−1.309	−1.273	−1.238
.3	−1.204	−1.171	−1.139	−1.109	−1.079	−1.050	−1.022	− .994	− .968	− .942
.4	− .916	− .892	− .868	− .844	− .821	− .799	− .777	− .755	− .734	− .713
.5	− .693	− .673	− .654	− .635	− .616	− .598	− .580	− .562	− .545	− .528
.6	− .511	− .494	− .478	− .462	− .446	− .431	− .416	− .400	− .386	− .371
.7	− .357	− .342	− .329	− .315	− .301	− .288	− .274	− .261	− .248	− .236
.8	− .223	− .211	− .198	− .186	− .174	− .163	− .151	− .139	− .128	− .117
.9	− .105	− .094	− .083	− .073	− .062	− .051	− .041	− .030	− .020	− .010

1.0–9.9

N	.0	.1	.2	.3	.4	.5	.6	.7	.8	.9
1.0	.000	.095	.182	.262	.336	.405	.470	.531	.588	.642
2.0	.693	.742	.788	.833	.875	.916	.956	.993	1.030	1.065
3.0	1.099	1.131	1.163	1.194	1.224	1.253	1.281	1.308	1.335	1.361
4.0	1.386	1.411	1.435	1.459	1.482	1.504	1.526	1.548	1.569	1.589
5.0	1.609	1.629	1.649	1.668	1.686	1.705	1.723	1.740	1.758	1.775
6.0	1.792	1.808	1.825	1.841	1.856	1.872	1.887	1.902	1.917	1.932
7.0	1.946	1.960	1.974	1.988	2.001	2.015	2.028	2.041	2.054	2.067
8.0	2.079	2.092	2.104	2.116	2.128	2.140	2.152	2.163	2.175	2.186
9.0	2.197	2.208	2.219	2.230	2.241	2.251	2.262	2.272	2.282	2.293

To obtain the natural logarithm of numbers above 10:
    divide the number by 10 and add 2.303 to the ln obtained,
    or divide the number by 100 and add 4.605 to the ln obtained,
    or divide the number by 1,000 and add 6.908 to the ln obtained, etc.

To obtain the natural logarithm of numbers less than .1:
    multiply the number by 10 and subtract 2.303 from the ln obtained,
    or multiply by 100 and subtract 4.605 from the ln obtained,
    or multiply by 1,000 and subtract 6.908 from the ln obtained, etc.

SPECIAL VALUES

α	β	$\ln \dfrac{1 - \beta}{\alpha}$	$\ln \dfrac{\beta}{1 - \alpha}$
.01	.01	4.595	−4.595
.01	.05	4.554	−2.986
.05	.01	2.986	−4.554
.05	.05	2.944	−2.944

*By permission from *Introduction to statistical analysis*, by W. J. Dixon and F. J. Massey. Copyright 1951, McGraw-Hill Book Company, Inc.

TABLE C.4. TRIGONOMETRIC FUNCTIONS*

ANGLE	SIN	COS	TAN	ANGLE	SIN	COS	TAN
0°	.000	1.000	.000	45°	.707	.707	1.000
1°	.018	.999	.018	46°	.719	.695	1.036
2°	.035	.999	.035	47°	.731	.682	1.072
3°	.052	.998	.052	48°	.743	.669	1.111
4°	.070	.997	.070	49°	.755	.656	1.150
5°	.087	.996	.087	50°	.766	.643	1.192
6°	.105	.994	.105	51°	.777	.629	1.235
7°	.122	.992	.123	52°	.788	.616	1.280
8°	.139	.990	.141	53°	.799	.602	1.327
9°	.156	.988	.158	54°	.809	.588	1.376
10°	.174	.985	.176	55°	.819	.574	1.428
11°	.191	.982	.194	56°	.829	.559	1.483
12°	.208	.978	.213	57°	.839	.545	1.540
13°	.225	.974	.231	58°	.848	.530	1.600
14°	.242	.970	.249	59°	.857	.515	1.664
15°	.259	.966	.268	60°	.866	.500	1.732
16°	.276	.961	.287	61°	.875	.485	1.804
17°	.292	.956	.306	62°	.883	.469	1.881
18°	.309	.951	.325	63°	.891	.454	1.963
19°	.326	.946	.344	64°	.899	.438	2.050
20°	.342	.940	.364	65°	.906	.423	2.144
21°	.358	.934	.384	66°	.914	.407	2.246
22°	.375	.927	.404	67°	.921	.391	2.356
23°	.391	.921	.424	68°	.927	.375	2.475
24°	.407	.914	.445	69°	.934	.358	2.605
25°	.423	.906	.466	70°	.940	.342	2.747
26°	.438	.899	.488	71°	.946	.326	2.904
27°	.454	.891	.510	72°	.951	.309	3.078
28°	.469	.883	.532	73°	.956	.292	3.271
29°	.485	.875	.554	74°	.961	.276	3.487
30°	.500	.866	.577	75°	.966	.259	3.732
31°	.515	.857	.601	76°	.970	.242	4.011
32°	.530	.848	.625	77°	.974	.225	4.331
33°	.545	.839	.649	78°	.978	.208	4.705
34°	.559	.829	.675	79°	.982	.191	5.145
35°	.574	.819	.700	80°	.985	.174	5.671
36°	.588	.809	.727	81°	.988	.156	6.314
37°	.602	.799	.754	82°	.990	.139	7.115
38°	.616	.788	.781	83°	.992	.122	8.144
39°	.629	.777	.810	84°	.994	.105	9.514
40°	.643	.766	.839	85°	.996	.087	11.430
41°	.656	.755	.869	86°	.997	.070	14.300
42°	.669	.743	.900	87°	.998	.052	19.081
43°	.682	731	.933	88°	.999	.035	28.636
44°	.695	.719	.966	89°	.999	.018	57.290

* By permission from *College algebra*, by L. Smail. Copyright 1931, McGraw-Hill Book Company, Inc.

TABLE C.5. TRANSFORMATION OF r TO z (AND ρ TO ξ)*

$$z \equiv \frac{1}{2} \log_e \frac{1+r}{1-r}$$

r	z	r	z	r	z	r	z	r	z	r	z
.25†	.26	.40	.42	.55	.62	.70	.87	.85	1.26	.950	1.83
.26	.27	.41	.44	.56	.63	.71	.89	.86	1.29	.955	1.89
.27	.28	.42	.45	.57	.65	.72	.91	.87	1.33	.960	1.95
.28	.29	.43	.46	.58	.66	.73	.93	.88	1.38	.965	2.01
.29	.30	.44	.47	.59	.68	.74	.95	.89	1.42	.970	2.09
.30	.31	.45	.48	.60	.69	.75	.97	.90	1.47	.975	2.18
.31	.32	.46	.50	.61	.71	.76	1.00	.905	1.50	.980	2.30
.32	.33	.47	.51	.62	.73	.77	1.02	.910	1.53	.985	2.44
.33	.34	.48	.52	.63	.74	.78	1.05	.915	1.56	.990	2.65
.34	.35	.49	.54	.64	.76	.79	1.07	.920	1.59	.995	2.99
.35	.37	.50	.55	.65	.78	.80	1.10	.925	1.62		
.36	.38	.51	.56	.66	.79	.81	1.13	.930	1.66		
.37	.39	.52	.58	.67	.81	.82	1.16	.935	1.70		
.38	.40	.53	.59	.68	.83	.83	1.19	.940	1.74		
.39	.41	.54	.60	.69	.85	.84	1.22	.945	1.78		

* By permission from *Fundamental statistics in psychology and education*, by J. P. Guilford. Copyright 1950, McGraw-Hill Book Company, Inc. The values in Table C.5 were derived by interpolation from Table VB of R. A. Fisher, *Statistical methods for Research workers*, published by Oliver & Boyd, Ltd., Edinburgh, by permission of the author and publishers.

† For all values of r below .25, $r = z$.

TABLE C.6. DERIVATIVES

$$\frac{d}{dx}[f(x) + g(x)] = f'(x) + g'(x)$$

$$\frac{d}{dx}[f(x)g(x)] = f(x)g'(x) + g(x)f'(x)$$

$$\frac{d}{dx}[f(x)]^c = c[f(x)]^{c-1}f'(x)$$

$$\frac{d}{dx}\left[\frac{f(x)}{g(x)}\right] = \frac{g(x)f'(x) - f(x)g'(x)}{[g(x)]^2}$$

$$\frac{d}{dx}c^{f(x)} = \log_e c\, f'(x)e^{f(x)\log_e c}$$

$$\frac{d}{dx}c = 0$$

$$\frac{d}{dx}x = 1$$

$$\frac{d}{dx}cf(x) = cf'(x)$$

$$\frac{d}{dx}cx = c$$

$$\frac{d}{dx}x^c = cx^{c-1}$$

$$\frac{d}{dx}e^{f(x)} = e^{f(x)}f'(x)$$

$$\frac{d}{dx}e^x = e^x$$

$$\frac{d}{dx}\log_c f(x) = \frac{1}{\log_e c}\frac{f'(x)}{f(x)}$$

$$\frac{d}{dx}\log_e f(x) = \frac{f'(x)}{f(x)}$$

$$\frac{d}{dx}\log_e x = \frac{1}{x}$$

$$\frac{d}{dx}\sin x = \cos x$$

$$\frac{d}{dx}\cos x = -\sin x$$

$$\frac{d}{dx}\tan x = \sec^2 x$$

TABLE C.7. PRIMITIVE FUNCTIONS (INDEFINITE INTEGRALS)

$$\int [f(x) + g(x)]\, dx = \int f(x)\, dx + \int g(x)\, dx$$

$$\int af(x)\, dx = a \int f(x)\, dx$$

$$\int a\, dx = ax + c$$

$$\int ax^b\, dx = \frac{ax^{b+1}}{b+1} + c \qquad b \neq -1$$

$$\int \frac{1}{x}\, dx = \log_e x + c$$

$$\int \log_e x\, dx = x \log_e x - x + c$$

$$\int a^x\, dx = \frac{a^x}{\log_e a} + c \qquad a \text{ positive}$$

$$\int e^x\, dx = e^x + c$$

$$\int e^{ax}\, dx = \frac{1}{a} e^{ax} + c$$

$$\int \frac{1}{x} \log_e x\, dx = \frac{1}{2} (\log_e x)^2 + c$$

$$\int \frac{a}{x+b}\, dx = a \log_e (x+b) + c$$

$$\int xe^{ax^2}\, dx = \frac{e^{ax^2}}{2a} + c$$

$$\int \sin x\, dx = -\cos x + c$$

$$\int \cos x\, dx = \sin x + c$$

$$\int x^n \cos x\, dx = x^n \sin x - n \int x^{n-1} \sin x\, dx \qquad n \text{ positive}$$

$$(x \text{ in radians; } 2\pi \text{ radians} = 360°)$$

$$\int x^n \sin x\, dx = -x^n \cos x + n \int x^{n-1} \cos x\, dx \qquad (x \text{ in radians}) \qquad n \text{ positive}$$

$$\int x^n e^x\, dx = x^n e^x - n \int x^{n-1} e^x\, dx \qquad n \text{ positive}$$

Appendix D

TABLES OF SAMPLING DISTRIBUTIONS

Notes on the Use of Tables

Table D.1. Ordinates of the normal density function with zero mean and unit variance. For negative values, use the relation $f(-x) = f(x)$. Linear interpolation is reasonably accurate.

Table D.2. Cumulative normal distributions. For negative values, use the relation $F(-x) = 1 - F(x)$. Linear interpolation is reasonably accurate.

Table D.3. Cumulative chi-square distributions. For values of n larger than 30, use the fact that $\sqrt{2\chi_n^2} - \sqrt{2n-1}$ is approximately normally distributed with zero mean and unit variance.

Table D.4. Cumulative t distributions. For negative values, use the relation $F(-t) = 1 - F(t)$. Interpolate on the reciprocals of the numbers of degrees of freedom. For example, to find the .99 value for 60 degrees of freedom we take the values for 40 and 120 degrees, which are 2.423 and 2.358; the interpolated value is

$$2.358 + \frac{\frac{1}{40} - \frac{1}{60}}{\frac{1}{40} - \frac{1}{120}} (2.423 - 2.358) = 2.3905$$

which is very close to the value in the table of 2.390. Linear interpolation gives the value 2.374.

Table D.5. Cumulative F distributions. For the values .10, .05, .025, .01, and .005 use the relation

$$\text{prob} \left(F_{m,n} < F_1 \right) = \text{prob} \left(F_{n,m} > \frac{1}{F_1} \right) = 1 - \text{prob} \left(F_{n,m} < \frac{1}{F_1} \right)$$

For example, to find the value F_1 such that prob $(F_{4,7} < F_1) = .025$, we take

$$\text{prob} (F_{4,7} < F_1) = 1 - \text{prob} (F_{7,4} < 1/F_1) = .025$$
$$\text{prob} (F_{7,4} < 1/F_1) = .975$$

From the table, $1/F_1 = 9.07$; therefore, $F_1 = .110$. Interpolation should be made on the reciprocals of m and n, as with the t table. For example, to find the .99 value for $F_{17,25}$ we take

$$F_{17,25} = F_{15,20} - \frac{(\frac{1}{20} - \frac{1}{25})}{(\frac{1}{20} - \frac{1}{30})} (F_{15,20} - F_{15,30})$$

$$- \frac{(\frac{1}{15} - \frac{1}{17})}{(\frac{1}{15} - \frac{1}{20})} (F_{15,20} - F_{20,20}) = 2.79$$

TABLE D.1. ORDINATES OF NORMAL DENSITY FUNCTION WITH ZERO MEAN AND UNIT VARIANCE

$$f(x) = \phi(0,1) \equiv \frac{1}{\sqrt{2\pi}} e^{-x^2/2}$$

x	.00	.01	.02	.03	.04	.05	.06	.07	.08	.09
.0	.3989	.3989	.3989	.3988	.3986	.3984	.3982	.3980	.3977	.3973
.1	.3970	.3965	.3961	.3956	.3951	.3945	.3939	.3932	.3925	.3918
.2	.3910	.3902	.3894	.3885	.3876	.3867	.3857	.3847	.3836	.3825
.3	.3814	.3802	.3790	.3778	.3765	.3752	.3739	.3725	.3712	.3697
.4	.3683	.3668	.3653	.3637	.3621	.3605	.3589	.3572	.3555	.3538
.5	.3521	.3503	.3485	.3467	.3448	.3429	.3410	.3391	.3372	.3352
.6	.3332	.3312	.3292	.3271	.3251	.3230	.3209	.3187	.3166	.3144
.7	.3123	.3101	.3079	.3056	.3034	.3011	.2989	.2966	.2943	.2920
.8	.2897	.2874	.2850	.2827	.2803	.2780	.2756	.2732	.2709	.2685
.9	.2661	.2637	.2613	.2589	.2565	.2541	.2516	.2492	.2468	.2444
1.0	.2420	.2396	.2371	.2347	.2323	.2299	.2275	.2251	.2227	.2203
1.1	.2179	.2155	.2131	.2107	.2083	.2059	.2036	.2012	.1989	.1965
1.2	.1942	.1919	.1895	.1872	.1849	.1826	.1804	.1781	.1758	.1736
1.3	.1714	.1691	.1669	.1647	.1626	.1604	.1582	.1561	.1539	.1518
1.4	.1497	.1476	.1456	.1435	.1415	.1394	.1374	.1354	.1334	.1315
1.5	.1295	.1276	.1257	.1238	.1219	.1200	.1182	.1163	.1145	.1127
1.6	.1109	.1092	.1074	.1057	.1040	.1023	.1006	.0989	.0973	.0957
1.7	.0940	.0925	.0909	.0893	.0878	.0863	.0848	.0833	.0818	.0804
1.8	.0790	.0775	.0761	.0748	.0734	.0721	.0707	.0694	.0681	.0669
1.9	.0656	.0644	.0632	.0620	.0608	.0596	.0584	.0573	.0562	.0551
2.0	.0540	.0529	.0519	.0508	.0498	.0488	.0478	.0468	.0459	.0449
2.1	.0440	.0431	.0422	.0413	.0404	.0396	.0387	.0379	.0371	.0363
2.2	.0355	.0347	.0339	.0332	.0325	.0317	.0310	.0303	.0297	.0290
2.3	.0283	.0277	.0270	.0264	.0258	.0252	.0246	.0241	.0235	.0229
2.4	.0224	.0219	.0213	.0208	.0203	.0198	.0194	.0189	.0184	.0180
2.5	.0175	.0171	.0167	.0163	.0158	.0154	.0151	.0147	.0143	.0139
2.6	.0136	.0132	.0129	.0126	.0122	.0119	.0116	.0113	.0110	.0107
2.7	.0104	.0101	.0099	.0096	.0093	.0091	.0088	.0086	.0084	.0081
2.8	.0079	.0077	.0075	.0073	.0071	.0069	.0067	.0065	.0063	.0061
2.9	.0060	.0058	.0056	.0055	.0053	.0051	.0050	.0048	.0047	.0046
3.0	.0044	.0043	.0042	.0040	.0039	.0038	.0037	.0036	.0035	.0034
3.1	.0033	.0032	.0031	.0030	.0029	.0028	.0027	.0026	.0025	.0025
3.2	.0024	.0023	.0022	.0022	.0021	.0020	.0020	.0019	.0018	.0018
3.3	.0017	.0017	.0016	.0016	.0015	.0015	.0014	.0014	.0013	.0013
3.4	.0012	.0012	.0012	.0011	.0011	.0010	.0010	.0010	.0009	.0009
3.5	.0009	.0008	.0008	.0008	.0008	.0007	.0007	.0007	.0007	.0006
3.6	.0006	.0006	.0006	.0005	.0005	.0005	.0005	.0005	.0005	.0004
3.7	.0004	.0004	.0004	.0004	.0004	.0004	.0003	.0003	.0003	.0003
3.8	.0003	.0003	.0003	.0003	.0003	.0002	.0002	.0002	.0002	.0002
3.9	.0002	.0002	.0002	.0002	.0002	.0002	.0002	.0002	.0001	.0001

TABLE D.2. CUMULATIVE NORMAL DISTRIBUTIONS

$$F(x) = \int_{-\infty}^{x} \phi(0,1)\, dt \equiv \int_{-\infty}^{x} \frac{1}{\sqrt{2\pi}}\, e^{-t^2/2}\, dt$$

$$= \int_{-\infty}^{\mu+x\sigma} \frac{1}{\sqrt{2\pi}\,\sigma}\, e^{-(1/2\sigma^2)(t-\mu)^2}\, dt \equiv \int_{-\infty}^{\mu+x\sigma} \phi(\mu,\sigma^2)\, dt$$

x	.00	.01	.02	.03	.04	.05	.06	.07	.08	.09
.0	.5000	.5040	.5080	.5120	.5160	.5199	.5239	.5279	.5319	.5359
.1	.5398	.5438	.5478	.5517	.5557	.5596	.5636	.5675	.5714	.5753
.2	.5793	.5832	.5871	.5910	.5948	.5987	.6026	.6064	.6103	.6141
.3	.6179	.6217	.6255	.6293	.6331	.6368	.6406	.6443	.6480	.6517
.4	.6554	.6591	.6628	.6664	.6700	.6736	.6772	.6808	.6844	.6879
.5	.6915	.6950	.6985	.7019	.7054	.7088	.7123	.7157	.7190	.7224
.6	.7257	.7291	.7324	.7357	.7389	.7422	.7454	.7486	.7517	.7549
.7	.7580	.7611	.7642	.7673	.7704	.7734	.7764	.7794	.7823	.7852
.8	.7881	.7910	.7939	.7967	.7995	.8023	.8051	.8078	.8106	.8133
.9	.8159	.8186	.8212	.8238	.8264	.8289	.8315	.8340	.8365	.8389
1.0	.8413	.8438	.8461	.8485	.8508	.8531	.8554	.8577	.8599	.8621
1.1	.8643	.8665	.8686	.8708	.8729	.8749	.8770	.8790	.8810	.8830
1.2	.8849	.8869	.8888	.8907	.8925	.8944	.8962	.8980	.8997	.9015
1.3	.9032	.9049	.9066	.9082	.9099	.9115	.9131	.9147	.9162	.9177
1.4	.9192	.9207	.9222	.9236	.9251	.9265	.9279	.9292	.9306	.9319
1.5	.9332	.9345	.9357	.9370	.9382	.9394	.9406	.9418	.9429	.9441
1.6	.9452	.9463	.9474	.9484	.9495	.9505	.9515	.9525	.9535	.9545
1.7	.9554	.9564	.9573	.9582	.9591	.9599	.9608	.9616	.9625	.9633
1.8	.9641	.9649	.9656	.9664	.9671	.9678	.9686	.9693	.9699	.9706
1.9	.9713	.9719	.9726	.9732	.9738	.9744	.9750	.9756	.9761	.9767
2.0	.9772	.9778	.9783	.9788	.9793	.9798	.9803	.9808	.9812	.9817
2.1	.9821	.9826	.9830	.9834	.9838	.9842	.9846	.9850	.9854	.9857
2.2	.9861	.9864	.9868	.9871	.9875	.9878	.9881	.9884	.9887	.9890
2.3	.9893	.9896	.9898	.9901	.9904	.9906	.9909	.9911	.9913	.9916
2.4	.9918	.9920	.9922	.9925	.9927	.9929	.9931	.9932	.9934	.9936
2.5	.9938	.9940	.9941	.9943	.9945	.9946	.9948	.9949	.9951	.9952
2.6	.9953	.9955	.9956	.9957	.9959	.9960	.9961	.9962	.9963	.9964
2.7	.9965	.9966	.9967	.9968	.9969	.9970	.9971	.9972	.9973	.9974
2.8	.9974	.9975	.9976	.9977	.9977	.9978	.9979	.9979	.9980	.9981
2.9	.9981	.9982	.9982	.9983	.9984	.9984	.9985	.9985	.9986	.9986
3.0	.9987	.9987	.9987	.9988	.9988	.9989	.9989	.9989	.9990	.9990
3.1	.9990	.9991	.9991	.9991	.9992	.9992	.9992	.9992	.9993	.9993
3.2	.9993	.9993	.9994	.9994	.9994	.9994	.9994	.9995	.9995	.9995
3.3	.9995	.9995	.9995	.9996	.9996	.9996	.9996	.9996	.9996	.9997
3.4	.9997	.9997	.9997	.9997	.9997	.9997	.9997	.9997	.9997	.9998

x	1.282	1.645	1.960	2.326	2.576	3.090	3.291	3.891	4.417
$F(x)$	.90	.95	.975	.99	.995	.999	.9995	.99995	.999995
$2[1 - F(x)]$	.20	.10	.05	.02	.01	.002	.001	.0001	.00001

TABLE D.3. CUMULATIVE CHI-SQUARE DISTRIBUTIONS*

$$F(\chi_n^2) = \int_0^{\chi_n^2} \frac{1}{2^{n/2}\Gamma(n/2)} x^{(n/2)-1} e^{-x/2}\, dx$$

n	.995	.990	.975	.950	.900	.750	.500	.250	.100	.050	.025	.010	.005
1	7.88	6.63	5.02	3.84	2.71	1.32	.455	.102	.0158	$.0^3393$	$.0^3982$	$.0^3157$	$.0^4393$
2	10.6	9.21	7.38	5.99	4.61	2.77	1.39	.575	.211	.103	.0506	.0201	.0100
3	12.8	11.3	9.35	7.81	6.25	4.11	2.37	1.21	.584	.352	.216	.115	.0717
4	14.9	13.3	11.1	9.49	7.78	5.39	3.36	1.92	1.06	.711	.484	.297	.207
5	16.7	15.1	12.8	11.1	9.24	6.63	4.35	2.67	1.61	1.15	.831	.554	.412
6	18.5	16.8	14.4	12.6	10.6	7.84	5.35	3.45	2.20	1.64	1.24	.872	.676
7	20.3	18.5	16.0	14.1	12.0	9.04	6.35	4.25	2.83	2.17	1.69	1.24	.989
8	22.0	20.1	17.5	15.5	13.4	10.2	7.34	5.07	3.49	2.73	2.18	1.65	1.34
9	23.6	21.7	19.0	16.9	14.7	11.4	8.34	5.90	4.17	3.33	2.70	2.09	1.73
10	25.2	23.2	20.5	18.3	16.0	12.5	9.34	6.74	4.87	3.94	3.25	2.56	2.16
11	26.8	24.7	21.9	19.7	17.3	13.7	10.3	7.58	5.58	4.57	3.82	3.05	2.60
12	28.3	26.2	23.3	21.0	18.5	14.8	11.3	8.44	6.30	5.23	4.40	3.57	3.07
13	29.8	27.7	24.7	22.4	19.8	16.0	12.3	9.30	7.04	5.89	5.01	4.11	3.57
14	31.3	29.1	26.1	23.7	21.1	17.1	13.3	10.2	7.79	6.57	5.63	4.66	4.07
15	32.8	30.6	27.5	25.0	22.3	18.2	14.3	11.0	8.55	7.26	6.26	5.23	4.60
16	34.3	32.0	28.8	26.3	23.5	19.4	15.3	11.9	9.31	7.96	6.91	5.81	5.14
17	35.7	33.4	30.2	27.6	24.8	20.5	16.3	12.8	10.1	8.67	7.56	6.41	5.70
18	37.2	34.8	31.5	28.9	26.0	21.6	17.3	13.7	10.9	9.39	8.23	7.01	6.26
19	38.6	36.2	32.9	30.1	27.2	22.7	18.3	14.6	11.7	10.1	8.91	7.63	6.84
20	40.0	37.6	34.2	31.4	28.4	23.8	19.3	15.5	12.4	10.9	9.59	8.26	7.43
21	41.4	38.9	35.5	32.7	29.6	24.9	20.3	16.3	13.2	11.6	10.3	8.90	8.03
22	42.8	40.3	36.8	33.9	30.8	26.0	21.3	17.2	14.0	12.3	11.0	9.54	8.64
23	44.2	41.6	38.1	35.2	32.0	27.1	22.3	18.1	14.8	13.1	11.7	10.2	9.26
24	45.6	43.0	39.4	36.4	33.2	28.2	23.3	19.0	15.7	13.8	12.4	10.9	9.89
25	46.9	44.3	40.6	37.7	34.4	29.3	24.3	19.9	16.5	14.6	13.1	11.5	10.5
26	48.3	45.6	41.9	38.9	35.6	30.4	25.3	20.8	17.3	15.4	13.8	12.2	11.2
27	49.6	47.0	43.2	40.1	36.7	31.5	26.3	21.7	18.1	16.2	14.6	12.9	11.8
28	51.0	48.3	44.5	41.3	37.9	32.6	27.3	22.7	18.9	16.9	15.3	13.6	12.5
29	52.3	49.6	45.7	42.6	39.1	33.7	28.3	23.6	19.8	17.7	16.0	14.3	13.1
30	53.7	50.9	47.0	43.8	40.3	34.8	29.3	24.5	20.6	18.5	16.8	15.0	13.8

* By permission from *Introduction to the theory of statistics*, by A. M. Mood. Copyright 1950, McGraw-Hill Book Company, Inc. This table is abridged from Catherine M. Thompson, Tables of percentage points of the incomplete beta function and of the chi-square distribution, *Biometrika*, vol. 32, 1941, published with permission of the author and of the editor of *Biometrika*.

TABLE D.4. CUMULATIVE t DISTRIBUTIONS*

$$F(t_n) = \int_{-\infty}^{t_n} \frac{1}{\sqrt{n\pi}\ \Gamma(n/2)}\ \Gamma\left(\frac{n+1}{2}\right)\left(\frac{x^2}{n}+1\right)^{-(n+1)/2} dx$$

F n	.75	.90	.95	.975	.99	.995	.9995
1	1.000	3.078	6.314	12.706	31.821	63.657	636.619
2	.816	1.886	2.920	4.303	6.965	9.925	31.598
3	.765	1.638	2.353	3.182	4.541	5.841	12.941
4	.741	1.533	2.132	2.776	3.747	4.604	8.610
5	.727	1.476	2 015	2.571	3.365	4.032	6.859
6	.718	1.440	1.943	2.447	3.143	3.707	5.959
7	.711	1.415	1.895	2.365	2.998	3.499	5.405
8	.706	1.397	1.860	2.306	2.896	3.355	5.041
9	.703	1.383	1.833	2.262	2.821	3.250	4.781
10	.700	1.372	1.812	2.228	2.764	3.169	4.587
11	.697	1.363	1.796	2.201	2.718	3.106	4.437
12	.695	1.356	1.782	2.179	2.681	3.055	4.318
13	.694	1.350	1.771	2.160	2.650	3.012	4.221
14	.692	1.345	1.761	2.145	2.624	2.977	4.140
15	.691	1.341	1.753	2.131	2.602	2.947	4.073
16	.690	1.337	1.746	2.120	2.583	2.921	4.015
17	.689	1.333	1.740	2.110	2.567	2.898	3.965
18	.688	1.330	1.734	2.101	2.552	2.878	3.922
19	.688	1.328	1.729	2.093	2.539	2.861	3.883
20	.687	1.325	1.725	2.086	2.528	2.845	3.850
21	.686	1.323	1.721	2.080	2.518	2.831	3.819
22	.686	1.321	1.717	2.074	2.508	2.819	3.792
23	.685	1.319	1.714	2.069	2.500	2.807	3.767
24	.685	1.318	1.711	2.064	2.492	2.797	3.745
25	.684	1.316	1.708	2.060	2.485	2.787	3.725
26	.684	1.315	1.706	2.056	2.479	2.779	3.707
27	.684	1.314	1.703	2.052	2.473	2.771	3.690
28	.683	1.313	1.701	2.048	2.467	2.763	3.674
29	.683	1.311	1.699	2.045	2.462	2.756	3.659
30	.683	1.310	1.697	2.042	2.457	2.750	3.646
40	.681	1.303	1.684	2.021	2.423	2.704	3.551
60	.679	1.296	1.671	2.000	2.390	2.660	3.460
120	.677	1.289	1.658	1.980	2.358	2.617	3.373
∞	.674	1.282	1.645	1.960	2.326	2.576	3.291

* By permission from *Introduction to the theory of statistics*, by A. M. Mood. Copyright 1950, McGraw-Hill Book Company, Inc.   This table is abridged from Table IV of R. A. Fisher and F. Yates, *Statistical tables for biological, agricultural, and medical research*, published by Oliver & Boyd, Ltd., Edinburgh, by permission of the authors and publishers.

TABLE D.5. CUMULATIVE F DISTRIBUTIONS*

(m degrees of freedom in numerator; n in denominator)

$$F(F_{m,n}) = \int_0^{F_{m,n}} \frac{\Gamma\left(\dfrac{m+n}{2}\right)}{\Gamma\left(\dfrac{m}{2}\right)\Gamma\left(\dfrac{n}{2}\right)} \left(\frac{m}{n}\right)^{m/2} x^{(m/2)-1}\left(1+\frac{mx}{n}\right)^{-(m+n)/2} dx$$

n	F	1	2	3	4	5	6	7	8	9	10	12	15	20	30	60	120	∞
1	.90	39.9	49.5	53.6	55.8	57.2	58.2	58.9	59.4	59.9	60.2	60.7	61.2	61.7	62.3	62.8	63.1	63.3
	.95	161	200	216	225	230	234	237	239	241	242	244	246	248	250	252	253	254
	.975	648	800	864	900	922	937	948	957	963	969	977	985	993	1000	1010	1010	1020
	.99	4,050	5,000	5,400	5,620	5,760	5,860	5,930	5,980	6,020	6,060	6,110	6,160	6,210	6,260	6,310	6,340	6,370
	.995	16,200	20,000	21,600	22,500	23,100	23,400	23,700	23,900	24,100	24,200	24,400	24,600	24,800	25,000	25,200	25,400	25,500
2	.90	8.53	9.00	9.16	9.24	9.29	9.33	9.35	9.37	9.38	9.39	9.41	9.42	9.44	9.46	9.47	9.48	9.49
	.95	18.5	19.0	19.2	19.2	19.3	19.3	19.4	19.4	19.4	19.4	19.4	19.4	19.5	19.5	19.5	19.5	19.5
	.975	38.5	39.0	39.2	39.2	39.3	39.3	39.4	39.4	39.4	39.4	39.4	39.4	39.4	39.5	39.5	39.5	39.5
	.99	98.5	99.0	99.2	99.2	99.3	99.3	99.4	99.4	99.4	99.4	99.4	99.4	99.4	99.5	99.5	99.5	99.5
	.995	199	199	199	199	199	199	199	199	199	199	199	199	199	199	199	199	199
3	.90	5.54	5.46	5.39	5.34	5.31	5.28	5.27	5.25	5.24	5.23	5.22	5.20	5.18	5.17	5.15	5.14	5.13
	.95	10.1	9.55	9.28	9.12	9.01	8.94	8.89	8.85	8.81	8.79	8.74	8.70	8.66	8.62	8.57	8.55	8.53
	.975	17.4	16.0	15.4	15.1	14.9	14.7	14.6	14.5	14.5	14.4	14.3	14.3	14.2	14.1	14.0	13.9	13.9
	.99	34.1	30.8	29.5	28.7	28.2	27.9	27.7	27.5	27.3	27.2	27.1	26.9	26.7	26.5	26.3	26.2	26.1
	.995	55.5	49.8	47.5	46.2	45.4	44.8	44.4	44.1	43.9	43.7	43.4	43.1	42.8	42.5	42.1	42.0	41.8
4	.90	4.54	4.32	4.19	4.11	4.05	4.01	3.98	3.95	3.94	3.92	3.90	3.87	3.84	3.82	3.79	3.78	3.76
	.95	7.71	6.94	6.59	6.39	6.26	6.16	6.09	6.04	6.00	5.96	5.91	5.86	5.80	5.75	5.69	5.66	5.63
	.975	12.2	10.6	9.98	9.60	9.36	9.20	9.07	8.98	8.90	8.84	8.75	8.66	8.56	8.46	8.36	8.31	8.26
	.99	21.2	18.0	16.7	16.0	15.5	15.2	15.0	14.8	14.7	14.5	14.4	14.2	14.0	13.8	13.7	13.6	13.5
	.995	31.3	26.3	24.3	23.2	22.5	22.0	21.6	21.4	21.1	21.0	20.7	20.4	20.2	19.9	19.6	19.5	19.3
5	.90	4.06	3.78	3.62	3.52	3.45	3.40	3.37	3.34	3.32	3.30	3.27	3.24	3.21	3.17	3.14	3.12	3.11
	.95	6.61	5.79	5.41	5.19	5.05	4.95	4.88	4.82	4.77	4.74	4.68	4.62	4.56	4.50	4.43	4.40	4.37
	.975	10.0	8.43	7.76	7.39	7.15	6.98	6.85	6.76	6.68	6.62	6.52	6.43	6.33	6.23	6.12	6.07	6.02
	.99	16.3	13.3	12.1	11.4	11.0	10.7	10.5	10.3	10.2	10.1	9.89	9.72	9.55	9.38	9.20	9.11	9.02
	.995	22.8	18.3	16.5	15.6	14.9	14.5	14.2	14.0	13.8	13.6	13.4	13.1	12.9	12.7	12.4	12.3	12.1
6	.90	3.78	3.46	3.29	3.18	3.11	3.05	3.01	2.98	2.96	2.94	2.90	2.87	2.84	2.80	2.76	2.74	2.72
	.95	5.99	5.14	4.76	4.53	4.39	4.28	4.21	4.15	4.10	4.06	4.00	3.94	3.87	3.81	3.74	3.70	3.67
	.975	8.81	7.26	6.60	6.23	5.99	5.82	5.70	5.60	5.52	5.46	5.37	5.27	5.17	5.07	4.96	4.90	4.85
	.99	13.7	10.9	9.78	9.15	8.75	8.47	8.26	8.10	7.98	7.87	7.72	7.56	7.40	7.23	7.06	6.97	6.88
	.995	18.6	14.5	12.9	12.0	11.5	11.1	10.8	10.6	10.4	10.2	10.0	9.81	9.59	9.36	9.12	9.00	8.88
7	.90	3.59	3.26	3.07	2.96	2.88	2.83	2.78	2.75	2.72	2.70	2.67	2.63	2.59	2.56	2.51	2.49	2.47
	.95	5.59	4.74	4.35	4.12	3.97	3.87	3.79	3.73	3.68	3.64	3.57	3.51	3.44	3.38	3.30	3.27	3.23
	.975	8.07	6.54	5.89	5.52	5.29	5.12	4.99	4.90	4.82	4.76	4.67	4.57	4.47	4.36	4.25	4.20	4.14
	.99	12.2	9.55	8.45	7.85	7.46	7.19	6.99	6.84	6.72	6.62	6.47	6.31	6.16	5.99	5.82	5.74	5.65
	.995	16.2	12.4	10.9	10.1	9.52	9.16	8.89	8.68	8.51	8.38	8.18	7.97	7.75	7.53	7.31	7.19	7.08
8	.90	3.46	3.11	2.92	2.81	2.73	2.67	2.62	2.59	2.56	2.54	2.50	2.46	2.42	2.38	2.34	2.32	2.29
	.95	5.32	4.46	4.07	3.84	3.69	3.58	3.50	3.44	3.39	3.35	3.28	3.22	3.15	3.08	3.01	2.97	2.93
	.975	7.57	6.06	5.42	5.05	4.82	4.65	4.53	4.43	4.36	4.30	4.20	4.10	4.00	3.89	3.78	3.73	3.67
	.99	11.3	8.65	7.59	7.01	6.63	6.37	6.18	6.03	5.91	5.81	5.67	5.52	5.36	5.20	5.03	4.95	4.86
	.995	14.7	11.0	9.60	8.81	8.30	7.95	7.69	7.50	7.34	7.21	7.01	6.81	6.61	6.40	6.18	6.06	5.95

F-distribution (inverted beta distribution) percentage points. Numerator degrees of freedom across the top; denominator degrees of freedom at left.

n_2	P	1	2	3	4	5	6	7	8	9	10	12	15	20	30	60	120	∞
9	.90	3.36	3.01	2.81	2.69	2.61	2.55	2.51	2.47	2.44	2.42	2.38	2.34	2.30	2.25	2.21	2.18	2.16
	.95	5.12	4.26	3.86	3.63	3.48	3.37	3.29	3.23	3.18	3.14	3.07	3.01	2.94	2.86	2.79	2.75	2.71
	.975	7.21	5.71	5.08	4.72	4.48	4.32	4.20	4.10	4.03	3.96	3.87	3.77	3.67	3.56	3.45	3.39	3.33
	.99	10.6	8.02	6.99	6.42	6.06	5.80	5.61	5.47	5.35	5.26	5.11	4.96	4.81	4.65	4.48	4.40	4.31
	.995	13.6	10.1	8.72	7.96	7.47	7.13	6.88	6.69	6.54	6.42	6.23	6.03	5.83	5.62	5.41	5.30	5.19
10	.90	3.29	2.92	2.73	2.61	2.52	2.46	2.41	2.38	2.35	2.32	2.28	2.24	2.20	2.15	2.11	2.08	2.06
	.95	4.96	4.10	3.71	3.48	3.33	3.22	3.14	3.07	3.02	2.98	2.91	2.84	2.77	2.70	2.62	2.58	2.54
	.975	6.94	5.46	4.83	4.47	4.24	4.07	3.95	3.85	3.78	3.72	3.62	3.52	3.42	3.31	3.20	3.14	3.08
	.99	10.0	7.56	6.55	5.99	5.64	5.39	5.20	5.06	4.94	4.85	4.71	4.56	4.41	4.25	4.08	4.00	3.91
	.995	12.8	9.43	8.08	7.34	6.87	6.54	6.30	6.12	5.97	5.85	5.66	5.47	5.27	5.07	4.86	4.75	4.64
12	.90	3.18	2.81	2.61	2.48	2.39	2.33	2.28	2.24	2.21	2.19	2.15	2.10	2.06	2.01	1.96	1.93	1.90
	.95	4.75	3.89	3.49	3.26	3.11	3.00	2.91	2.85	2.80	2.75	2.69	2.62	2.54	2.47	2.38	2.34	2.30
	.975	6.55	5.10	4.47	4.12	3.89	3.73	3.61	3.51	3.44	3.37	3.28	3.18	3.07	2.96	2.85	2.79	2.72
	.99	9.33	6.93	5.95	5.41	5.06	4.82	4.64	4.50	4.39	4.30	4.16	4.01	3.86	3.70	3.54	3.45	3.36
	.995	11.8	8.51	7.23	6.52	6.07	5.76	5.52	5.35	5.20	5.09	4.91	4.72	4.53	4.33	4.12	4.01	3.90
15	.90	3.07	2.70	2.49	2.36	2.27	2.21	2.16	2.12	2.09	2.06	2.02	1.97	1.92	1.87	1.82	1.79	1.76
	.95	4.54	3.68	3.29	3.06	2.90	2.79	2.71	2.64	2.59	2.54	2.48	2.40	2.33	2.25	2.16	2.11	2.07
	.975	6.20	4.77	4.15	3.80	3.58	3.41	3.29	3.20	3.12	3.06	2.96	2.86	2.76	2.64	2.52	2.46	2.40
	.99	8.68	6.36	5.42	4.89	4.56	4.32	4.14	4.00	3.89	3.80	3.67	3.52	3.37	3.21	3.05	2.96	2.87
	.995	10.8	7.70	6.48	5.80	5.37	5.07	4.85	4.67	4.54	4.42	4.25	4.07	3.88	3.69	3.48	3.37	3.26
20	.90	2.97	2.59	2.38	2.25	2.16	2.09	2.04	2.00	1.96	1.94	1.89	1.84	1.79	1.74	1.68	1.64	1.61
	.95	4.35	3.49	3.10	2.87	2.71	2.60	2.51	2.45	2.39	2.35	2.28	2.20	2.12	2.04	1.95	1.90	1.84
	.975	5.87	4.46	3.86	3.51	3.29	3.13	3.01	2.91	2.84	2.77	2.68	2.57	2.46	2.35	2.22	2.16	2.09
	.99	8.10	5.85	4.94	4.43	4.10	3.87	3.70	3.56	3.46	3.37	3.23	3.09	2.94	2.78	2.61	2.52	2.42
	.995	9.94	6.99	5.82	5.17	4.76	4.47	4.26	4.09	3.96	3.85	3.68	3.50	3.32	3.12	2.92	2.81	2.69
30	.90	2.88	2.49	2.28	2.14	2.05	1.98	1.93	1.88	1.85	1.82	1.77	1.72	1.67	1.61	1.54	1.50	1.46
	.95	4.17	3.32	2.92	2.69	2.53	2.42	2.33	2.27	2.21	2.16	2.09	2.01	1.93	1.84	1.74	1.68	1.62
	.975	5.57	4.18	3.59	3.25	3.03	2.87	2.75	2.65	2.57	2.51	2.41	2.31	2.20	2.07	1.94	1.87	1.79
	.99	7.56	5.39	4.51	4.02	3.70	3.47	3.30	3.17	3.07	2.98	2.84	2.70	2.55	2.39	2.21	2.11	2.01
	.995	9.18	6.35	5.24	4.62	4.23	3.95	3.74	3.58	3.45	3.34	3.18	3.01	2.82	2.63	2.42	2.30	2.18
60	.90	2.79	2.39	2.18	2.04	1.95	1.87	1.82	1.77	1.74	1.71	1.66	1.60	1.54	1.48	1.40	1.35	1.29
	.95	4.00	3.15	2.76	2.53	2.37	2.25	2.17	2.10	2.04	1.99	1.92	1.84	1.75	1.65	1.53	1.47	1.39
	.975	5.29	3.93	3.34	3.01	2.79	2.63	2.51	2.41	2.33	2.27	2.17	2.06	1.94	1.82	1.67	1.58	1.48
	.99	7.08	4.98	4.13	3.65	3.34	3.12	2.95	2.82	2.72	2.63	2.50	2.35	2.20	2.03	1.84	1.73	1.60
	.995	8.49	5.80	4.73	4.14	3.76	3.49	3.29	3.13	3.01	2.90	2.74	2.57	2.39	2.19	1.96	1.83	1.69
120	.90	2.75	2.35	2.13	1.99	1.90	1.82	1.77	1.72	1.68	1.65	1.60	1.55	1.48	1.41	1.32	1.26	1.19
	.95	3.92	3.07	2.68	2.45	2.29	2.18	2.09	2.02	1.96	1.91	1.83	1.75	1.66	1.55	1.43	1.35	1.25
	.975	5.15	3.80	3.23	2.89	2.67	2.52	2.39	2.30	2.22	2.16	2.05	1.94	1.82	1.69	1.53	1.43	1.31
	.99	6.85	4.79	3.95	3.48	3.17	2.96	2.79	2.66	2.56	2.47	2.34	2.19	2.03	1.86	1.66	1.53	1.38
	.995	8.18	5.54	4.50	3.92	3.55	3.28	3.09	2.93	2.81	2.71	2.54	2.37	2.19	1.98	1.75	1.61	1.43
∞	.90	2.71	2.30	2.08	1.94	1.85	1.77	1.72	1.67	1.63	1.60	1.55	1.49	1.42	1.34	1.24	1.17	1.00
	.95	3.84	3.00	2.60	2.37	2.21	2.10	2.01	1.94	1.88	1.83	1.75	1.67	1.57	1.46	1.32	1.22	1.00
	.975	5.02	3.69	3.12	2.79	2.57	2.41	2.29	2.19	2.11	2.05	1.94	1.83	1.71	1.57	1.39	1.27	1.00
	.99	6.63	4.61	3.78	3.32	3.02	2.80	2.64	2.51	2.41	2.32	2.18	2.04	1.88	1.70	1.47	1.32	1.00
	.995	7.88	5.30	4.28	3.72	3.35	3.09	2.90	2.74	2.62	2.52	2.36	2.19	2.00	1.79	1.53	1.36	1.00

* By permission from *Introduction to the theory of statistics*, by A. M. Mood. Copyright 1950, McGraw-Hill Book Company, Inc. This table is abridged from Tables of percentage points of the inverted beta distribution, *Biometrika*, vol. 33, 1943, published with the permission of the authors Maxine Merrington and Catherine M. Thompson, and of the editor of *Biometrika*.

TABLE D.6. CRITICAL VALUES OF r FOR SIGN TEST*
(Two-tailed percentage points for the binomial for $p = .5$)

N	1%	5%	10%	25%	N	1%	5%	10%	25%
1					46	13	15	16	18
2					47	14	16	17	19
3				0	48	14	16	17	19
4				0	49	15	17	18	19
5			0	0	50	15	17	18	20
6		0	0	1	51	15	18	19	20
7		0	0	1	52	16	18	19	21
8	0	0	1	1	53	16	18	20	21
9	0	1	1	2	54	17	19	20	22
10	0	1	1	2	55	17	19	20	22
11	0	1	2	3	56	17	20	21	23
12	1	2	2	3	57	18	20	21	23
13	1	2	3	3	58	18	21	22	24
14	1	2	3	4	59	19	21	22	24
15	2	3	3	4	60	19	21	23	25
16	2	3	4	5	61	20	22	23	25
17	2	4	4	5	62	20	22	24	25
18	3	4	5	6	63	20	23	24	26
19	3	4	5	6	64	21	23	24	26
20	3	5	5	6	65	21	24	25	27
21	4	5	6	7	66	22	24	25	27
22	4	5	6	7	67	22	25	26	28
23	4	6	7	8	68	22	25	26	28
24	5	6	7	8	69	23	25	27	29
25	5	7	7	9	70	23	26	27	29
26	6	7	8	9	71	24	26	28	30
27	6	7	8	10	72	24	27	28	30
28	6	8	9	10	73	25	27	28	31
29	7	8	9	10	74	25	28	29	31
30	7	9	10	11	75	25	28	29	32
31	7	9	10	11	76	26	28	30	32
32	8	9	10	12	77	26	29	30	32
33	8	10	11	12	78	27	29	31	33
34	9	10	11	13	79	27	30	31	33
35	9	11	12	13	80	28	30	32	34
36	9	11	12	14	81	28	31	32	34
37	10	12	13	14	82	28	31	33	35
38	10	12	13	14	83	29	32	33	35
39	11	12	13	15	84	29	32	33	36
40	11	13	14	15	85	30	32	34	36
41	11	13	14	16	86	30	33	34	37
42	12	14	15	16	87	31	33	35	37
43	12	14	15	17	88	31	34	35	38
44	13	15	16	17	89	31	34	36	38
45	13	15	16	18	90	32	35	36	39

* By permission from *Introduction to statistical analysis*, by W. J. Dixon and F. J. Massey. Copyright 1951, McGraw-Hill Book Company, Inc. This table originally appeared in The statistical sign test, by W. J. Dixon and A. M. Mood, *Journal of the American Statistical Association*, vol. 41, pp. 557–566, 1946, and is reprinted by permission of the authors and publisher.

TABLE D.7. CRITICAL VALUES FOR NUMBER OF RUNS (r) IN SAMPLES OF n_1 a'S AND n_2 b'S, $u_{.025}$ BEING LARGEST INTEGER SUCH THAT $P(r \leq u_{.025}) \leq .025$ AND $u_{.975}$ BEING SMALLEST INTEGER SUCH THAT $P(r \geq u_{.975}) \leq .025$*

$u_{.025}$

n_2 \ n_1	2	3	4	5	6	7	8	9	10	11	12	13	14	15	16	17	18	19	20
2																			
3																			
4																			
5			2	2															
6		2	2	3	3														
7		2	2	3	3	3													
8		2	3	3	3	4	4												
9		2	3	3	4	4	5	5											
10		2	3	3	4	5	5	5	6										
11		2	3	4	4	5	5	6	6	7									
12	2	2	3	4	4	5	6	6	7	7	7								
13	2	2	3	4	5	5	6	6	7	7	8	8							
14	2	2	3	4	5	5	6	7	7	8	8	9	9						
15	2	3	3	4	5	6	6	7	7	8	8	9	9	10					
16	2	3	4	4	5	6	6	7	8	8	9	9	10	10	11				
17	2	3	4	4	5	6	7	7	8	9	9	10	10	11	11	11			
18	2	3	4	5	5	6	7	8	8	9	9	10	10	11	11	12	12		
19	2	3	4	5	6	6	7	8	8	9	10	10	11	11	12	12	13	13	
20	2	3	4	5	6	6	7	8	9	9	10	10	11	12	12	13	13	13	14

* Adapted by permission from *Introduction to statistical analysis*, by W. J. Dixon and F. J. Massey. Copyright 1951, McGraw-Hill Book Company, Inc. This table is an abridgment, with permission, from Frieda S. Swed and C. Eisenhart, Tables for testing randomness of grouping in a sequence of alternatives, *Annals of Mathematical Statistics*, vol. 14, p. 66, 1943.

TABLE D.7. CRITICAL VALUES FOR NUMBER OF RUNS (r) IN SAMPLES OF n_1 a'S AND n_2 b'S, $u_{.025}$ BEING LARGEST INTEGER SUCH THAT $P(r \leq u_{.025}) \leq .025$ AND $u_{.975}$ BEING SMALLEST INTEGER SUCH THAT $P(r \geq u_{.975}) \leq .025$* $(Continued)$

$u_{.975}$

n_2 \ n_1	2	3	4	5	6	7	8	9	10	11	12	13	14	15	16	17	18	19	20
1																			
2																			
3																			
4	6																		
5	6	8	9	10															
6	6	8	9	10	11														
7	6	8	10	11	12	13													
8	6	8	10	11	12	13	14												
9	6	8	10	12	13	14	14	15											
10	6	8	10	12	13	14	15	16	16										
11	6	8	10	12	13	14	15	16	17	17									
12	6	8	10	12	13	14	16	16	17	18	19								
13	6	8	10	12	14	15	16	17	18	19	19	20							
14	6	8	10	12	14	15	16	17	18	19	20	20	21						
15	6	8	10	12	14	15	16	18	18	19	20	21	22	22					
16	6	8	10	12	14	16	17	18	19	20	21	21	22	23	23				
17	6	8	10	12	14	16	17	18	19	20	21	22	23	23	24	25			
18	6	8	10	12	14	16	17	18	19	20	21	22	23	24	25	25	26		
19	6	8	10	12	14	16	17	18	20	21	22	23	23	24	25	26	26	27	
20	6	8	10	12	14	16	17	18	20	21	22	23	24	25	25	26	27	27	28

* Adapted by permission from *Introduction to statistical analysis*, by W. J. Dixon and F. J. Massey. Copyright 1951, McGraw-Hill Book Company, Inc. This table is an abridgment, with permission, from Frieda S. Swed and C. Eisenhart, Tables for testing randomness of grouping in a sequence of alternatives, *Annals of Mathematical Statistics*, vol. 14, p. 66, 1943.

TABLE D.7. CRITICAL VALUES FOR NUMBER OF RUNS (r) IN SAMPLES OF n_1 a'S AND n_2 b'S, $u_{.025}$ BEING LARGEST INTEGER SUCH THAT $P(r \leq u_{.025}) \leq .025$ AND $u_{.975}$ BEING SMALLEST INTEGER SUCH THAT $P(r \geq u_{.975}) \leq .025$* *(Continued)*

$n_1 = n_2$	$u_{.025}$	$u_{.975}$	$n_1 = n_2$	$u_{.025}$	$u_{.975}$
20	14	28	40	31	51
21	15	29	42	33	53
22	16	30	44	35	55
23	16	32	46	37	57
24	17	33	48	38	60
25	18	34	50	40	62
26	19	35	55	45	67
27	20	36	60	49	73
28	21	37	65	54	78
29	22	38	70	58	84
30	22	40	75	63	89
32	24	42	80	68	94
34	26	44	85	72	100
36	28	46	90	77	105
38	30	48	95	82	110
			100	86	116

The values listed permit one to make a two-tailed test at the .05 level or a one-tailed test at the .025 level.

For values of n_1 and n_2 larger than 20, a normal approximation can be used. The mean is $\dfrac{2n_1n_2}{n_1 + n_2} + 1$, and the variance is $\dfrac{2n_1n_2(2n_1n_2 - n_1 - n_2)}{(n_1 + n_2)^2(n_1 + n_2 - 1)}$.

* Adapted by permission from *Introduction to statistical analysis*, by W. J. Dixon and F. J. Massey. Copyright 1951, McGraw-Hill Book Company, Inc. This table is an abridgment, with permission, from Frieda S. Swed and C. Eisenhart, Tables for testing randomness of grouping in a sequence of alternatives, *Annals of Mathematical Statistics*, vol. 14, p. 66, 1943.

TABLE D.8. PROBABILITY (*p*) THAT SMALLER SUM OF RANKS IN
WILCOXON'S MATCHED-PAIRS SIGNED-RANKS TEST WILL BE
EQUAL TO OR LESS THAN *T*, IF DIFFERENCES IN
POPULATION ARE SYMMETRICALLY DISTRIBUTED
ABOUT ZERO*

(*T* is given in the body of the table, to the nearest integer. *N* is the
number of differences)

N	$p = .05$	$p = .02$	$p = .01$
6	0		
7	2	0	
8	4	2	0
9	6	3	2
10	8	5	3
11	11	7	5
12	14	10	7
13	17	13	10
14	21	16	13
15	25	20	16
16	30	24	20
17	35	28	23
18	40	33	28
19	46	38	32
20	52	43	38
21	59	49	43
22	66	56	49
23	73	62	55
24	81	69	61
25	89	77	68

* Table D.8. is reproduced from Frank Wilcoxon, *Some rapid approximate statistical procedures*, published by American Cyanamid Co., New York, 1949. It is here published with the kind permission of the author and his publishers. The author states that the table was obtained by rounding off values given by John W. Tukey in Memorandum Report 17, *The simplest signed rank tests*, Statistical Research Group, Princeton University, 1949.

GLOSSARY

$\equiv$		is equal by definition to
Cov_{xy}	$\equiv$	covariance, that is, $E\{[X - E(X)][Y - E(Y)]\}$
E	$\equiv$	expectation or mean value. $E[g(x)] \equiv \displaystyle\sum_{\text{all } x} g(x)f(x)$ in the discrete

case and $\displaystyle\int_{R_x} g(x)f(x)\,dx$ in the continuous case.

$E(X)$	$\equiv$	the arithmetic mean
m	$\equiv$	the arithmetic mean of a sample
mom_c^k	$\equiv$	the kth moment about the point c, that is, $E[(X - c)^k]$
μ	$\equiv$	mu, the arithmetic mean of a population
$N(\mu,\sigma^2)$	$\equiv$	a normal distribution with mean μ and variance σ^2 *or* a normal population with mean μ and variance σ^2, depending upon the context
p-mcc	$\equiv$	Pearson product-moment coefficient of correlation, that is,

$$\mathrm{Cov}_{xy}/\sqrt{\mathrm{Var}_x\,\mathrm{Var}_y}$$

$\phi(\mu,\sigma^2)$	$\equiv$	a normal frequency function with mean μ and variance σ^2
r	$\equiv$	the sample p-mcc
ρ	$\equiv$	rho, the population p-mcc
s	$\equiv$	the sample standard deviation
s^2	$\equiv$	the sample variance
σ	$\equiv$	sigma, the population standard deviation
σ^2	$\equiv$	the population variance
Var_x	$\equiv$	variance, that is, $E[X - E(X)]^2$

ANSWERS TO ODD-NUMBERED EXERCISES

CHAPTER 1

1.3.1. b, f. **1.3.3.** (a) Each screw is a member; its diameter is its value. (b) Each performance is a member; its value is satisfactory or unsatisfactory. (c) Each blood cell is a member; its value is red or white. (d) Each conversation is a member; its value is its duration. (e) Each tube is a member; its value is defective or nondefective. **1.7.1.** $(\frac{1}{4},0)$, $(\frac{1}{2},1)$, $(\frac{1}{4},2)$. **1.7.3.** $(\frac{2}{3},0)$, $(\frac{1}{3},1)$. **1.7.5.** $(\frac{21}{55},0)$, $(\frac{28}{55},1)$, $(\frac{6}{55},2)$; $(\frac{21}{55},0)$, $(\frac{49}{55},1)$, $(1,2)$. **1.7.7.** (a) $(\frac{3}{5},x_1)$, $(\frac{1}{5},x_2)$, $(\frac{1}{5},x_3)$. (b) $(\frac{1}{6},-1)$, $(\frac{1}{6},0)$, $(\frac{2}{3},1)$; $(\frac{1}{6},-1)$, $(\frac{1}{3},0)$, $(1,1)$. (c) $(\frac{3}{4}$, absence$)$, $(\frac{1}{4}$, presence$)$. (d) $(\frac{1}{2}$, for$)$, $(\frac{1}{2}$, against$)$. **1.8.1.** $(.24,1)$, $(.76,2)$; $(.24,1)$, $(1,2)$. **1.8.3.** $(\frac{6}{495},1)$, $(\frac{219}{495},2)$, $(\frac{270}{495},3)$; $(\frac{6}{495},1)$, $(\frac{15}{33},2)$, $(1,3)$. **1.8.5.** $(\frac{2}{15},0)$, $(\frac{8}{15},1)$, $(\frac{1}{3},2)$; $(\frac{7}{15}$, same$)$, $(\frac{8}{15}$, different$)$. **1.8.7.** $P^n_{n_1,n_2,\ldots,n_k} = n!/n_1!n_2! \cdots n_k!$ **1.8.9.** $(\frac{1}{216},3)$, $(\frac{3}{216},4)$, $(\frac{6}{216},5)$, $(\frac{10}{216},6)$, $(\frac{15}{216},7)$, $(\frac{21}{216},8)$, $(\frac{25}{216},9)$, $(\frac{27}{216},10)$, $(\frac{27}{216},11)$, $(\frac{25}{216},12)$, $(\frac{21}{216},13)$, etc. **1.8.11.** $(\frac{35}{165},0)$, $(\frac{84}{165},1)$, $(\frac{42}{165},2)$, $(\frac{4}{165},3)$. **1.8.13.** $f(x) = C^{30}_x 2^{30-x}/3^{30}$.

CHAPTER 2

2.2.1. (a) Random. (b) Violates second condition (independence). (c) Random. (d) Random. (e) Violates first condition; for example, a name on page 2100 has a greater probability of being drawn than a name on page 1386, if each of the two pages contains the same number of names. (f) Violates both conditions. (g) Violates first condition. (h) Violates both conditions. **2.2.3.** Both conditions. A person in a small community has greater probability of being included in the sample than a person in a large community. The second condition is obviously violated. **2.2.5.** (a) $(1,0)$. (b) $(\frac{1}{3},-.5)$ $(\frac{1}{3},0)$ $(\frac{1}{3},.5)$. (c) $(.3,0)$ $(.6,.5)$ $(.1,1)$. (d) $(.1,0)$ $(.4,.5)$ $(.3,1)$ $(.2,1.5)$. **2.2.7.** (a) $(1,0)$. (b) $(1,0)$. (c) $(.4,.25)$, $(.6,.5)$. (d) $(.2,.5)$, $(.4,.75)$, $(.4,1)$. **2.2.9.** (a) $(1,0)$. (b) $(.25,0)$, $(.75,1)$. (c) $(.1,0)$, $(.9,1)$. (d)

$(.4,1)$, $(.6,2)$. **2.2.11.** $f(x) = C_x^{70}C_{5-x}^{30}/C_5^{100}$. **2.3.1.** $\frac{1}{120}$. **2.3.3.** (a) $C_3^{30}C_4^{60}/$
C_7^{90}. (b) $(C_7^{60} + C_1^{30}C_6^{60} + C_2^{30}C_5^{60})/C_7^{90}$. (c) $(C_4^{30}C_3^{60} + C_5^{30}C_2^{60} + C_6^{30}C_1^{60} +$
$C_7^{30})/C_7^{90}$. (d) C_7^{60}/C_7^{90}. **2.3.5.** (a) $\frac{13}{204}$. (b) $\frac{13}{102}$. (c) $\frac{25}{204}$. (d) $\frac{19}{102}$.
2.3.7. (a) $\frac{79}{256}$. (b) $\frac{8}{256}$. (c) $\frac{255}{256}$. (d) $\frac{57}{64}$. **2.3.9.** (a) $\frac{2}{7}$. (b) $\frac{1}{7}$.
(c) $\frac{37}{42}$. (d) $\frac{9}{14}$. (e) $\frac{23}{42}$. (f) $\frac{31}{84}$. **2.3.11.** (a) $\frac{7}{12}$. (b) $\frac{5}{12}$. (c) $\frac{2}{3}$.
(d) $\frac{1}{3}$. (e) $\frac{1}{4}$. (f) $\frac{1}{12}$. (g) $\frac{1}{2}$. (h) $\frac{1}{6}$. (i) $\frac{1}{3}$. (j) $\frac{5}{6}$. (k) $\frac{5}{6}$. **2.3.13.**
(a) $.31466$ . . . . (b) $.68533$ . . . . (c) $.48$. (d) $.17866$ . . . . (e) $.048$.
(f) $.7066$ . . . . (g) $.65866$ . . . . **2.4.1.** (a) $\frac{1}{6}$. (b) $\frac{2}{3}$. (c) $\frac{1}{2}$. **2.4.3.**
(a) $\frac{1}{12}$. (b) $\frac{1}{6}$. (c) $\frac{2}{3}$. (d) $\frac{1}{42}$. (e) $\frac{7}{24}$. (f) $\frac{7}{48}$. (g) $\frac{23}{192}$. (h) $\frac{5}{12}$.
2.4.5. $(\frac{9}{10})^5$. **2.4.7.** $.21$. **2.4.9.** (a) $\frac{1}{90}$. (b) $\frac{2}{15}$.

CHAPTER 3

3.1.1.

	0	1	2
H_0	1	0	0
H_1	$\frac{1}{2}$	$\frac{1}{2}$	0
H_2	$\frac{1}{6}$	$\frac{2}{3}$	$\frac{1}{6}$
H_3	0	$\frac{1}{2}$	$\frac{1}{2}$
H_4	0	0	1

3.1.3. (a) $f(x) = C_x^4 C_{4-x}^{28}/C_4^{32}$. (b) $f(x) = C_x^{16}C_{4-x}^{16}/C_4^{32}$. (c) $f(x) = C_x^{24}C_{4-x}^{8}/$
C_4^{32}. Unless the ratings are independent, the second condition for random
sampling will be violated even though the candidates themselves are chosen at
random.

3.1.5.

	0	1	2	3
H_0	1	0	0	0
H_1	$\frac{2}{3}$	$\frac{1}{3}$	0	0
H_2	$\frac{5}{12}$	$\frac{1}{2}$	$\frac{1}{12}$	0
H_3	$\frac{5}{21}$	$\frac{15}{28}$	$\frac{3}{14}$	$\frac{1}{84}$
H_4	$\frac{5}{42}$	$\frac{5}{14}$	$\frac{5}{14}$	$\frac{1}{21}$
H_5	$\frac{1}{21}$	$\frac{5}{14}$	$\frac{5}{14}$	$\frac{5}{42}$

etc

3.1.7. (*a*) $f(x) = C_x^{100} C_{8-x}^{80} / C_8^{180}$.   (*b*) $f(x) = C_x^{190} C_{15-x}^{175} / C_{15}^{365}$.   (*c*) $f(x) =$ $C_x^{1,000} C_{25-x}^{1,000} / C_{25}^{2,000}$.   (*d*) $f(x) = C_x^{N_1} C_{n-x}^{N-N_1} / C_n^N$.   **3.2.1.** (*a*) Reject at .01 level of confidence.   (*b*) Reject at .02 level of confidence.   (*c*) Do not reject ($p =$ .20).   (*d*) Do not reject ($p = 1$); do not accept, either.   **3.2.3.** (*a*) Reject at .0004 level of confidence.   (*b*) Reject at .0009 level of confidence.   (*c*) Reject at .01 level.   (*d*) Reject at .04 level.   **3.2.5.** Reject at .015625 level. **3.3.1.** 2.   **3.4.1.** See Table 3.5.3.   **3.7.1.** .024.   **3.7.3.** Reject at .022 level. **3.7.5.** Borderline; the p value is .054.   **3.7.7.** Reject at .05 level.   **3.7.9.** Reject at .02 level.

CHAPTER 4

4.3.1. (*a*) 1.   (*b*) 2.   (*c*) $^{55}\!/_{21}$.   (*d*) 1.95.   (*e*) 1.40.   **4.3.3.** (*a*) for.   (*b*) for.   **4.3.5.** (*a*) 1; .5.   (*b*) 1.5; .75.   (*c*) $\frac{1}{3}$; $\frac{2}{9}$.   (*d*) .6; $^{28}\!/_{75}$.   (*e*) $^{8}\!/_{11}$; $^{252}\!/_{605}$. **4.3.7.** (*a*) .4; .09.   (*b*) .8; .21.   **4.3.9.** H_0: 0; 0. H_1: .5; .25. H_2: 1; .4286. H_3: 1.5; .5356. H_4: 2; .5720. H_5: 2.5; .5356. H_6: 3; .4286. H_7: 3.5; .25. H_8: 4; 0.   The mean of the number of orange chips in a sample is in each case four times the mean number of orange chips hypothesized.   If we take as a statistic not the number of orange chips but the mean number, all the above means are divided by four; that is, the mean of the mean number of orange chips in a sample is in each case the mean number of orange chips hypothesized. **4.3.11.** H_0: 0; 0. H_1: 2.5; 1.87. H_2: 5; 2.50. H_3: 7.5; 1.88. H_4: 10; 0.   If we take as statistic the mean number of orange chips in a sequence of 10 draws, each of the means is divided by 10, and is equal in each case to the mean num-ber hypothesized.   **4.4.1.** (*a*) $\sum_{i=1}^{k} x_i^2 f(x_i)$.   (*b*) $\sum_{i=1}^{m} (x - i)^2 f(i)$.   (*c*) $\sum_{j=6}^{i} y_j$.

(*d*) $\sum_{i=2}^{b} (i - c)^i$.   (*e*) $\sum_{i=1}^{15} (i + a)^{i+2}$.   (*f*) $\prod_{x=5}^{40} x$.   **4.4.3.** (*a*) $\sum_{i=15}^{25} C_i^{70} C_{30-i}^{30} / C_{30}^{100}$.

(*b*) $\sum_{i=15}^{30} C_i^{70} C_{30-i}^{30} / C_{30}^{100}$.   (*c*) $\sum_{i=0}^{20} C_i^{70} C_{30-i}^{30} / C_{30}^{100}$.   **4.4.5.** (*a*) $\sum_{i=20}^{30} C_i^{30} (\frac{1}{2})^{30}$.   (*b*)

$\sum_{i=10}^{20} C_i^{30} (\frac{1}{2})^{30}$.   (*c*) $\sum_{i=0}^{25} C_i^{30} (\frac{1}{2})^{30}$.   **4.7.1.** (*a*) .15.   (*b*) No median.   (*c*) .1619. (*d*) .001415.   (*e*) .038.   **4.7.3.** $E(X^3) - 3E(X)E(X^2) + 2[E(X)]^2$.

CHAPTER 5

5.4.1. (*a*) Hypergeometric; $\mu = \sum_{x=0}^{20} x f(x)$; $\sigma^2 = \sum_{x=0}^{20} (x - \mu)^2 f(x)$ with

$f(x) = C_x^{N_1} C_{20-x}^{600-N_1} / C_{20}^{600}$.   (*b*) Binomial; $\mu = \sum_{x=0}^{50} x f(x)$; $\sigma^2 = \sum_{x=0}^{50} (x - \mu)^2 f(x)$

with $f(x) = C_x^{50}(\frac{1}{6})^x(\frac{5}{6})^{50-x}$. (c) Binomial; $\mu = \sum\limits_{x=0}^{50} xf(x)$; $\sigma^2 = \sum\limits_{x=0}^{50} (x - \mu)^2 f(x)$

with $f(x) = C_x^{50}(\frac{1}{3})^x(\frac{2}{3})^{50-x}$. (d) Binomial; $\mu = \sum\limits_{x=0}^{50} xf(x)$; $\sigma^2 = \sum\limits_{x=0}^{50} (x - $

$\mu)^2 f(x)$ with $f(x) = C_x^{50}(\frac{5}{36})^x(\frac{31}{36})^{50-x}$. (e) Binomial; $\mu = \sum\limits_{x=0}^{100} xf(x)$; $\sigma^2 = $

$\sum\limits_{x=0}^{100} (x - \mu)^2 f(x)$ with $f(x) = C_x^{100}(\frac{1}{2})^{100}$. (f) Hypergeometric; $\mu = \sum\limits_{x=0}^{10} xf(x)$;

$\sigma^2 = \sum\limits_{x=0}^{10} (x - \mu)^2 f(x)$ with $f(x) = C_x^{13} C_{10-x}^{39}/C_{10}^{52}$. (g) Binomial; $\mu = \sum\limits_{x=0}^{50} xf(x)$;

$\sigma^2 = \sum\limits_{x=0}^{50} (x - \mu)^2 f(x)$ with $f(x) = C_x^{50}(\frac{1}{32})^x(\frac{31}{32})^{50-x}$. (h) Binomial; $\mu = $

$\sum\limits_{x=0}^{1} xf(x)$; $\sigma^2 = \sum\limits_{x=0}^{1} (x - \mu)^2 f(x)$ with $f(x) = C_x^1(\frac{272}{637})^x(\frac{365}{637})^{1-x}$. (i)

Binomial; $\mu = \sum\limits_{x=0}^{1} xf(x)$; $\sigma^2 = \sum\limits_{x=0}^{1} (x - \mu)^2 f(x)$ with $f(x) = C_x^1(\frac{38}{91})^x(\frac{53}{91})^{1-x}$.
(j) Neither. **5.4.3.** $\mu = p$; $\sigma^2 = pq$. **5.4.5.** The variance of the number of
A's is npq. As the proportion of A's is the number divided by the sample
size, the variance of the proportion is $npq/n^2 = pq/n$. **5.5.1.** (a) $f(x) = $

$C_x^{50}(\frac{1}{3})^x(\frac{2}{3})^{50-x}$. (b) $f(x) = C_x^n(N_1/N)^x[(N - N_1)/N]^{n-x}$. **5.5.3.** $\sum\limits_{x=0}^{9}$

$C_x^{25}p^x(1 - p)^{25-x}$.

5.6.1.

x	Observed	Binomial
6	.005	.000
5	.005	.000
4	.010	.006
3	.035	.043
2	.155	.180
1	.405	.400
0	.385	.371

CHAPTER 6

6.1.1. (a) $f(x) = e^{-1}/x!$. (b) $f(x) = (np)^x e^{-np}/x!$. **6.5.1.** $\sum\limits_{x=0}^{2} 10^x e^{-10}/x!$.

6.5.3. .82.

CHAPTER 8

8.3.1. (a) $5/808$.   (b) $5/808$.   (c) 0.   (d) $20/808$.   (e) $75/808$.   (f) $733/808$.
8.3.3. (a) $f(x) = 1 - x/2$.   (b) $f(1) = \frac{1}{2}$.   (c) $F(x) = x - x^2/4$.   (d) $3/16$.
(e) .4225.   **8.3.5.** (a) $f(x) = x^2/2 - \frac{1}{6}$.   (b) $F(x) = x^3/6 - x/6$.   (c) $11/16$.
8.3.7. (a) $1/x$.   (b) .12.   **8.3.9.** (a) $-3x^2/14 + x$.   (b) $-x^3/14 + x^2/2 - 6/14$.   **8.5.1.** (a) 2.   (b) .61.   **8.5.3.** (a) $2 \log x - 3$.   (b) $e^{1.5}$.   (c) .30.
8.5.5. a, c, d, e, f, g, j, k.   **8.7.1.** Exercise 8.3.1: .421; .232.   Exercise 8.3.2: $\frac{1}{3}$; $1/12$.   Exercise 8.3.3: $2/3$; $2/9$.   Exercise 8.3.4: 2; $\frac{1}{2}$.   Exercise 8.3.5: $13/8$; $203/2880$.   Exercise 8.3.6: $19/12$; $11/144$.   Exercise 8.3.7: 1.718; .24.   Exercise 8.3.8: .386; .04.   Exercise 8.3.9: $257/168$; $11467/141120$.   **8.7.3.** (a) -1.   (b) 1.

CHAPTER 9

9.2.1. (a) Cannot.   (b) 0; $1/\sqrt{\pi}$.   (c) 3; $1/3\sqrt{2\pi}$.   (d) -3; $1/3\sqrt{2\pi}$.
(e) 0, $1/\sqrt{2}$.   (f) 3, $1/\sqrt{2\pi}$.   **9.2.3.** $\int_{79.5}^{120.5} (1/2\sqrt{15\pi})e^{-(1/60)(x-105)^2}\,dx$.
9.2.5. $\int^{150.5} (1/6\sqrt{5\pi})e^{-(1/180)(x-100)^2}\,dx$.   **9.4.1.** (a) $1/3\sqrt{2\pi}$.   (b) -1; $\sqrt{2}$.
9.4.3. (a) 1.000.   (b) .68.   **9.4.5.** (a) .117.   (b) .629.   **9.4.7.** 1.00.   **9.4.9.** .954.   **9.5.1.** (a) .383.   (b) .533.   (c) .309.   **9.5.3.** (a) Below .6 or above 59.4. (b) Below 5.33.   (c) Above 124.68.   **9.5.5.** $\phi(\mu_x + \mu_y, 13)$.   **9.5.7.** -7.8 to 12.8.   **9.5.9.** (a) .265, .001, .000.   (b) .265, .378, .000.   (c) 1.000, .000, .164. **9.5.11.** 166.   **9.7.1.** (a) Cannot reject.   (b) 49.16 to 50.84.   **9.7.3.** They would not be independent; therefore, one of the assumptions of random sampling would be violated.   Even if we define the population sampled as the population of this one subject's reaction times, it would be difficult to devise an experimental procedure justifying the assumption of independence.   **9.7.5.** The 36 scores are not independent, as two were obtained from each patient. **9.7.7.** (a) Reject at the .01 level of confidence.   (b) .52 to .76.   **9.7.9.** As the proportion is unknown, we maximize the error estimate by taking $p = .5$; then $n \geq 4{,}144$.   **9.8.1.** (a) .29.   (b) .14.   **9.8.3.** (a) Reject at the .001 level of confidence.   (b) -13.516 to -7.484.   **9.8.5.** (a) $p > .13$.   (b) $p > .31$.   (c) $-.21$ to .03.   (d) .27 to .45.   **9.8.7.** (a) Yes, as far as the statistical test is concerned.   (b) .000277 and .000545.   (c) That the 225 products produced by each model have been produced in such a way that there is no trend in the magnitudes of errors from the first member of the sample to the last.   Also, as only one model of each is built, it is assumed that any differences in precision between different models of the same design would be negligible in comparison with differences between designs.   **9.8.9.** (a) .74 to .85.   (b) That whatever factors are responsible for volunteering are unrelated to susceptibility to the vaccine.   **9.8.11.** The test based on the mean and variance of the 100 differences, yielding a critical ratio of 7.5.   This test is based upon the central-limit theorem, not Theorem 9.8.2.   The population

is the class of pairs $\{B - A$ for subject X, subject $X\}$. The other test assumes the two samples to be drawn independently.

CHAPTER 10

10.2.1. By combining the three extreme class intervals in each tail of the distribution, a χ_8^2 of 13.8 is obtained; thus the hypothesis cannot be rejected. **10.2.3.** $\chi_5^2 = 6.86$; thus the hypothesis cannot be rejected. **10.2.5.** Combining 0 and 1 we obtain $\chi_4^2 = 9.19$, just failing of significance at the .05 level. **10.2.7.** $\chi_4^2 = 20.65$; reject at the .005 level of confidence. Note that the largest discrepancy between theoretical and observed frequencies occurs for the class of values 4, 5, ... **10.2.9.** (a) No, as $\chi_1^2 = 4$ is significant at the .05 level. (b) That the 100 packages were sold independently, that is, that the sale of one package had no effect on the sale of another package, as far as color is concerned, and that no selective factor entered in which tended to make these 100 customers systematically different from customers of this store in general (or customers of other stores, if a generalization to the customers of other stores is to be made). **10.3.1.** (a) $\chi_9^2 = 27$; reject at the .005 level. (b) $\chi_9^2 = 275$; reject at the .005 level. **10.3.3.** $\chi_6^2 = 16$; reject at the .03 level. **10.3.5.** $\chi_6^2 = 16$; reject at the .03 level. **10.4.1.** (a) $\chi_1^2 = .4$; do not reject. (b) $\chi_3^2 = 7.3$; $.10 > p > .05$. (c) $\chi_2^2 = 7.4$; reject at the .03 level. **10.4.3.** $\chi_6^2 = 10.6$; do not reject. **10.4.5.** About 3,160. **10.5.1.** $\chi_{12}^2 = 15$; do not reject. **10.5.3.** The entries in the table are not frequencies. There is no way of modifying this table so as to justify a chi-square test of independence, as there is no way of obtaining frequencies from sums of scores. **10.5.5.** $\chi_5^2 = 13.7$; reject at the .03 level. Cells containing large theoretical frequencies contribute relatively little to the value of chi square, as the squared discrepancies are the same as for the low-frequency cells. **10.6.1.** (a) $\chi_9^2 = 10$; the hypothesis cannot be rejected. (b) 2.63 to 18.52.

CHAPTER 11

11.1.1. $t_{20} = 3.0$; thus the hypothesis can be rejected at the .01 level of confidence. Although this test is valid in that the probability of a type I error is given by the t tables, it would ordinarily have a very low power because ordinarily the parameters which would tend to make the critical ratio large would also tend to make chi square large. **11.2.1.** $t_9 = 2.33$; reject at the .05 level of confidence. The test assumes that the 10 differences can be considered a random sample from a normally distributed population. As the samples cannot be considered independent, only one t test can be made. **11.2.3.** $t_{17} = 3.5$; reject at the .01 level of confidence. The test assumes that the two populations of mileages are normal and have equal variance. The data could be paired at random, discarding one observation, and t_9 computed. The .05 confidence interval for the first make is 15.5 to 24.5.

CHAPTER 12

12.1.1. (*a*)

White		Red		
2	.05	.15	0	0
1	0	.30	.30	0
0	0	0	.15	.05
	0	1	2	3

(*b*) Red: (.05,0), (.45,1), (.45,2), (.05,3). White: (.20,0), (.60,1), (.20,2).
(*c*) $-.30$. **12.1.3.** (*a*) $\frac{1}{8}$. (*b*) $\frac{5}{8}$; $\frac{11}{24}$. (*c*) $\frac{13}{192}$; $\frac{95}{576}$. (*d*) $\frac{3}{64}$. **12.2.1.**
(*a*) $(3x^2 + 1)/2$; $(3y^2 + 1)/2$. (*b*) $3(x^2 + y^2)/(3x^2 + 1)$. (*c*) $(6x^2 + 3)/(12x^2 + 4)$. **12.2.3.** (*a*) $(5y + 1)/18$. (*b*) $(x + 3xy + y)/(12x + 3)$. (*c*)
$(18x + 5)/(12x + 3)$. **12.3.1.** $m_{y|0} = 4.40$, $m_{y|1} = 4.17$, $m_{y|2} = 3.57$, No.
12.3.3. $m_{y|x} = e - 1$. The regression is linear, but as X and Y are independent the regression line is parallel to the x axis. **12.3.5.** $ns_{x+y}^2 \equiv \Sigma(x + y - m_{x+y})^2 = \Sigma(x + y - m_x - m_y)^2 = \Sigma[(x - m_x) + (y - m_y)]^2 = \Sigma(x - m_x)^2 + \Sigma(y - m_y)^2 + 2\Sigma(x - m_x)(y - m_y) = ns_x^2 + ns_y^2 + 2rs_x s_y$. **12.4.1.** $\rho = 0$;
$\eta_{yx} = .452$. Lack of linearity of regression accounts for the discrepancy.
12.4.3. No, for example in Exercise 12.4.1, $\eta_{xy} = .368$. **12.7.1.** (*a*) Yes, a
scatter plot shows that the regression of Y on X is approximately linear.
(*b*) Grouping into intervals of length 5, with a multiples of 5 as mid-points,
yields $r = .70$. (*c*) $y_p = .594x + 27.8$. (*d*) $x_p = .815y - .7$. (*e*) 53.3.
(*f*) Combining extreme class intervals and testing the hypothesis that the
marginal distribution of X is normal, we obtain $\chi_7^2 = 2.91$, a quite good fit.
Similarly, for the marginal distribution of Y, $\chi_5^2 = 1.18$, an unusually close fit.
As each marginal sample distribution is approximately normal and as the
regression is linear, the assumption that the bivariate distribution is normal is
reasonable; therefore, we can test hypotheses about ρ. (*g*) Reject at the .001
level. (*h*) .62 to .77. (*i*) Zero. Within the interval -4.6 to 4.6. In the
sample, errors are slightly smaller for the intervals $x = 40$ and $x = 45$, but if
the bivariate distribution is normal the errors will not vary systematically
with x. (*j*) Zero; 9.5. (*k*) .07, assuming that errors are distributed normally
about the prediction line and that our estimate of the standard error is accurate. **12.7.3.** Higher for the heterogeneous group. As σ_e^2 is constant,
$\rho^2(= 1 - \sigma_e^2/\sigma_y^2)$ is higher the larger the value of σ_y^2. As $\rho \neq 0$ and the regression is linear, σ_y^2 is larger the greater the range of X. **12.7.5.** Psychologist B.
For example, even if a maze has zero reliability, the probability of being able
to reject, at the p level of confidence, the hypothesis that mean performance
scores of two groups of animals differ only by random sampling is p, if the
usual assumptions for the test are satisfied. Low reliabilities of measuring
instruments increase the probabilities of type II errors but do not affect the
probabilities of type I errors.

CHAPTER 13

13.4.1. (a) $F_{9,16} = 1.31$ (*not* 1.49). (b) Yes. (c) No, unless we wish to make this test of randomness of sampling; we already know the ratio of the two parameters. **13.4.3.** (a) $F_{24,48} = 2.72$; reject at the $2(.005) = .01$ level of confidence. (b) $F_{24,48} = 5.44$; reject at the .01 level of confidence. (c) $F_{24,48} = 2.72$; reject at the .005 level of confidence (by interpolation in the F tables). **13.4.5.** Random samples can be taken of the products produced by the two methods and the F ratio $n_1 s_1^2 (n_2 - 1)/n_2 s_2^2 (n_1 - 1)$ computed. It is assumed that each of the two distributions sampled is normal. The assumption of randomness of samples would in some cases be difficult to satisfy. **13.5.1.** (a) $F_{1,16} = 2.13$. (b) Not significant. (c) $t_{16} = 1.46 = \sqrt{F_{1,16}}$. (d) As we sampled the same population each time, our only conclusion would be that our method of sampling was not random or that a rare event had occurred. **13.5.3.** It would be assumed that the cephalic indices in each group (population) were normally distributed with the same variance, and that the two samples could be considered random. Then F could be used. **13.6.1.** (a) $F_{5,9} = 2.39$. (b) Yes. (c) That our method of sampling the population is not random (or that a rare event has occurred). **13.6.3.** $H = 12.9$; reject the hypothesis of homogeneity of variance at the .025 level. The F test cannot be used. The population sampled in each case is, strictly speaking, the increases or decreases during this period for all the stocks which would have been selected by the particular method. Obviously, this is not the population about which the investor would most like to draw an inference; it is the gains or losses from the future use of the method which are most important. As in many cases, it is impossible to secure a random sample from the population one is most interested in; the assumption that populations in the future will have about the same parameters as ones in the past may in this and other situations be fairly plausible, but there is no way of drawing a purely statistical inference about populations whose members are in the future. **13.9.1.** (a) $F_{3,12} = 7.17$. Using a one-tailed test, reject at the .01 level of confidence. The partition into varieties cannot be considered equivalent (statistically) to an arbitrary partition of samples drawn from a normal population, nor can the four columns of data be considered as four samples drawn at random from four populations having the same distributions. By assuming that the four populations have the same variance, we can infer that their means differ. In making this test, we have eliminated variation attributable to row (block) differences; the populations sampled can be considered as having been "corrected" by adjusting the value of each member according to the block it lies in, so that all blocks would have the same (estimated) mean. Strictly speaking, our conclusion concerning variety differences is valid only for the five blocks we selected randomly; in practice, there might be no reason for doubting that similar results would hold for the large area from which we selected the blocks at random. If there were only two varieties, a significant F would enable us to generalize to the whole area. (b) $F_{4,12} = 22.71$. Using a one-tailed test, reject at the .005 level. (A two-tailed test would also permit rejection at the .005 level.) The same remarks made in a apply, except that in this case it is obvious that we should limit our generalization about block differences to the four varieties (which were not selected randomly); of course, there may be some reason in terms of nutrition theory to generalize to other varieties. (c) $F_{3,16} = 1.16$. The enormous block differences make the value of F low, showing the advantage of the double partition design. (d) F would be difficult to interpret if the interaction estimate were used, as the methods are not randomly selected; the difficulties involved and the proper method of interpretation are beyond the scope of this text.

CHAPTER 14

14.7.1. 473. **14.7.3.** Yes; $p = .05$. **14.7.5.** Passes all three tests.

INDEX

Alternating harmonic series, 221
Analysis of variance, complex, 194–201
  computation of, 201–202
  degrees of freedom in, 193, 195, 199–201
  simple, 183–194
Arbitrary origin, 60
Arithmetic mean (*see* Mean)
Average, 50–52

Bernoulli's theorem, 40
Biased estimate, 110n.
Binomial distributions, definition of, 67
  derivation of, 65–67
  fitted to sample data, 73–74
  as limit of hypergeometric, 70–72
  moments of, 67–69
  normal approximation to, 96–98, 103–104
  Poisson approximation to, 75–77
Binomial expansion, 67
Bivariate distributions, 152–179
  definition of, 152
  marginal distributions of, 155–156
  moments of, 156
  normal, 170–175, 252–254
    ellipses of, 170–171, 254
    homoscedasticity of, 253

Central-limit theorem, 110
  in statistical inference, 110–115

Central tendency, measures of, 50–52
Change of variable, 236–237
Chi square, 123–142
  definition of, 123, 249
  degrees of freedom for, 123, 131, 135–136, 139
  proof of properties of, 249–250
  sum of two, 123, 250
  table for, 280
  tests, of goodness of fit, 124–133
    of homogeneity, 138–139
    of independence, 133–137
Combinations, 14
Computation, of a Poisson, 78
  of r, 175–176
  of sample moments, 57–63
  of sums of squares, 201–202
  of variance, 53
Conditional distributions, 157–162
Conditional probability, 25–26, 157–159
Confidence interval, 36–37
  for difference, between means, 117–118, 147–148
    between proportions, 119
  for mean, 107–109, 113–114, 145
  with one bound only, 47–49
  for percentile point, 208–209
  for proportion, 114–115
  for variance, 141–142
Confidence level (*see* Level of confidence)
Consistent estimate, 110n., 244

Contingency table, tests of independence in, 133–137
Continuous distributions, definition of, 88
  model, 94
  moments of, 95
Continuous functions, 222–223
Convergence, of a series, 220
  stochastic, 244
Correlation, product-moment, 163–167, 170–176
Correlation ratio, 168–169
Courant, R., 213, 222
Covariance, 162–166
Cramér, H., 213
Critical ratio, 110–113
Cumulative distribution functions, of continuous populations, 85, 232–233
  of finite populations, 6–7

Definite integral, 90–92, 223–224
Degrees of freedom, in analysis of variance, 193, 195, 199–201
  for chi square, 123, 131, 135–136, 139
  for t, 144, 200–201
Density function, 88–94, 232–233
Derivative, definition of, 86, 224–225
  in finding maxima and minima, 227–230, 252
  interpretation of, 227
  as proportion or probability density, 86, 88, 232–233
  second, 226–227, 230
  as slope, 227–228
  table of, 274
  theorems, 226
  as velocity, 227
Descriptive statistics, 1
Dichotomous population, 113, 118
Difference, among several means, 185–201

Difference, between two independent normally distributed variates, 116, 248–249
  between two means, 116–118, 146–149, 183–184
  between two proportions, 118–119
Discrete distributions, definition of, 82
  logic of inference for, 83
Distribution-free methods, 204–210
Distribution functions (*see* Cumulative distribution functions; Frequency functions)
Distributions, conditional, 157–162
  continuous, 88
  discrete, 82–83
  finite, 7
  graphic methods of showing, 8
  joint, 240–242
  probability, 22
  (*See also* other specific types of distributions)
Dixon, W. J., 213, 284

Edwards, A. L., 200, 214
Eisenhart, C., 285
Ellipses of bivariate normal distributions, 170–171, 254
Error, types of, 45–47
  (*See also* Standard error)
Estimate, biased, 110n.
  consistent, 110n., 244
  error of, 167, 173–175
  of a percentile, 209
  of a proportion, 118–119
  unbiased, 110, 146, 181–183, 185–186, 243, 245
  of variance, 110–112, 146, 181–183, 185–186, 190, 193–197
Eta, 168–169
Expectation, mathematical, 51–52, 233–234, 241–242
  of sample moments about origin, 242–243
  of sample variance, 245

Expected sampling distribution (*see* Sampling distribution)

F, definition of, 180
  distribution of, 180–181, 251
  table for, 282–283
Factorial, 13
Feller, W., 213
Finite population defined, 3–4
Fischer, R. A., 131, 143, 200, 213, 273, 281
Fitting to sample data, of binomial, 73–74
  of normal, 121–122, 131
  of Poisson, 79, 131–132
Frequency functions, continuous, 88, 232–233
  discrete, 82
  finite, 5
  model, 94
Frequency polygon, 8
Frequency table, 58
Fry, T. C., 213
Fundamental theorem of the calculus, 93, 231–232

Gamma function, 123, 144, 180, 249
Gaussian distributions (*see* Normal distributions)
Geometric mean, 52
Goodness-of-fit tests, 124–133
Gosset, W. S., 143
Graphic methods of showing distributions, 8
Grouping into class intervals, 61–63
Groups, sampling of several, 185–190
Guilford, J. P., 214

Harmonic series, 220–221
  alternating, 221
Histogram, 8
Hoel, P. G., 213

Homogeneity, tests of, 138–139
  of variance, 147, 185–186
Homoscedasticity, 175
  of normal bivariate distributions, 253
Hypergeometric distributions, binomial approximation to, 70–72
  definition of, 64
  moments of, 64–65
Hypothesis testing, logic of, 41–43, 83

Indefinite integral, 92–93, 231
Independence, 27, 159, 241–242
  tests of, 133–137
Independent variables, 116, 240–242
Inference, statistical, 1–2
  logic of, 41–43, 83
Infinite sequence, 219–220
Infinite series, 220–222
Inflection, point of, 230
Integrals, definite, 90–92, 223–224
  indefinite, 92–93, 231
  multiple, 237–240
  table of, 275
Interaction, 195–201
Intervals, class, 61–63

Joint distributions, 240–242

Law of large numbers, 243–244
Level, of confidence, 35–37, 46–48
  in using F, 181, 186–187
  of significance (*see* confidence, *above*)
Limit, of a sequence, 219–220
  of a series, 220–222
Lindquist, E. F., 200, 214
Linear regression, 162–167, 252
Linear transformation, in computation of r, 176
  of normal distributions, 102–103, 248
  (*See also* Transformations)

Logarithms, common, table of, 269–270

natural, table of, 271

Logic of statistical inference, 41–43, 83

McNemar, Q., 200, 214

Marginal distributions, 155–156, 174–175, 240–241

Massey, F. J., Jr., 213

Matched-pairs signed-ranks test, 209–210

table for, 288

Mean, 51–52

of conditional distributions, 159–161

confidence interval for, 107–109, 113–114, 145

of continuous distributions, 95

of finite distributions, 51–52

sampling distribution of, 17–18, 110–112

of several groups, 185–201

standard error of, 112

of subsample, 151

of sum of independent random variables, 106–107, 243

of two groups, 181–184

(*See also* Expectation)

Median, confidence interval for, 209

of finite population, 51

Merrington, M., 283

Mode, of chi-square distribution, 124

of finite distribution, 50

of normal distribution, 99

of *t* distribution, 144

Moment-generating functions, of chi-square distributions, 249

definition of, 235–236

of normal distributions, 247

Moments, computation of, 57–63

definition of, 57, 95, 156, 235

(*See also* Expectation)

Mood, A. M., 200, 213, 284

Multiple integral, 237–240

Nonparametric methods, 204–210

Normal bivariate distributions, 170–175

proof of properties of, 252–254

Normal distributions, as approximation to binomial, 96–98, 103–104

bivariate, 170–175, 252–254

cumulative, table of, 279

definition of, 98–99

density function of, table of, 278

fitted to sample data, 121–122, 127–128, 130–131

linear transformation of, 102–103, 248

mean of, 100, 247

mode of, 99

moment-generating function of, 247

moments of, 100–101, 247

proof of properties of, 245–249

use of, in finding confidence intervals, 107–109, 116–117

in hypothesis testing, 105–107, 116–117

variance of, 101, 247

with zero mean, unit variance, 102–104

One-tailed vs. two-tailed tests, 47–49, 106, 184, 210

in using F, 181

Operator, linear, 52, 95, 234, 240, 242

Order statistics, 207–208

Ordered pairs, class of, 4

Paired t test (*see t*)

Parameter, 47–48, 50, 83, 204

Partition of a sample, 191–202

Pearson, Karl, 125

Percentile points, confidence intervals for, 208–209

estimates of, 209

Permutations, 13

Peters, C. C., 213
Poisson distributions, computation of, 78
  definition of, 78
  as exact, 80–81
  fitted to sample, 79, 131–132
  as limit of binomial, 75–77
  moments of, 78–79
Population, continuous, 84
  discrete, 82
  finite, 3–4
Power of a test, 37–40, 106
Power series, 234
Prediction equation, 166–167
Primitive functions, 88, 93, 230–231
  table of, 275
Probability, calculus, 25–28
  conditional, 25–26, 157–159
  definition of, 21–22
Probability density, 86, 88, 157–159, 232–233
Probability distribution, 22
  (*See also* Probability density)
Product moment, 162–163
Product-moment correlation coefficient, assumption of linearity in, 163–166, 168–169
  computation of, 175–176
  confidence interval for, 171–173
  definition of, 163
  in regression equation, 166–167
  sampling distribution of, 170–171
  testing hypotheses about, 171–173
  transformation to z, 171–173
  table of, 273
Proportion density, 86, 88
Proportions, confidence intervals for, 114–115, 119
  difference between, 118–119
  testing hypotheses about, 113, 118

Random sampling, 18–20, 41, 241
Random variables, 51, 108, 240–243

Range, 53
Ranks, values as, 51
Regression, 157–167
  linear, 162–167, 252
Rider, P., 200, 214
Robbins, H., 213
Run test, 205–206
  table for, 285–287

Sample, 17
  size of, 112–113, 143
Sampling distribution, definition of, 17–18
  nonparametric, 204
  on various hypotheses, 30–31, 33, 38–41
Scatter plot, 173–174
Sets, 2
Sign test, 204–205
  table for, 284
Significance (*see* Level of confidence)
Size of sample, 112–113, 143
Small samples, 143, 146
Snedecor, G. W., 200, 214
Squares and square roots, table of, 256–268
Standard deviation, of a finite distribution, 53
  of a normal distribution, 101, 103, 105, 112
  (*See also* Variance)
Standard error, of a difference, 117
  of estimate, 167, 173–175
  of mean, 112
Statistic, 17, 50
Stochastic convergence, 244
"Student," 143
Subsample mean, test for, 151
Sum, of normal variates, 106–107
  of random variables, 242–244
  of squares, computation of, 192–196
Swed, F., 285

t, definition of, 143, 250
  degrees of freedom for, 144, 200–201
  distribution of, 143–145, 250–251
    mode of, 144
  after F, 186–187
  paired, 147–149, 198–201
  table of, 281
  tests, 145–151, 198–201
Taylor, Brook, 234
Taylor series, 234
Tchebysheff's inequality, 244–245
Thompson, C. M., 280, 283
Tolerance limits, 206–207
Transformations, for computational
    purposes, 59–60, 176
  of normal distributions, 102–103,
    121–122, 248
  r to z, 171–172
    table of, 273
  (*See also* Linear transformation)
Trigonometric functions, table of, 272
Tukey, John W., 187, 288
Two-tailed tests, 35, 105–106, 110–111, 181, 184
Type I error, 45–47
Type II error, 45–47

Unbiased estimate, 110, 146, 181–183,
    185–186, 243, 245
Universe (*see* Population)
Uspensky, J. V., 213

Van Voorhis, W. R., 213
Variability, measures of, 52–53
Variance, confidence interval for,
    141–142
  of a continuous distribution, 95
  estimate of, 110–112, 146, 181–183,
    185–186, 190, 193–197
  expectation of, 245
  of a finite distribution, 53
  (*See also* Analysis of variance)

Wilcoxon, Frank, 209, 288
Wilks, S. S., 213

Yates, F., 281

z transformation for r, 171–173
  table of, 273